Experiments in
ELECTRONICS

by   W. H. Evans

Professor of Electrical Engineering
University of Arizona

PRENTICE-HALL, INC.

Englewood Cliffs, N. J.

1959

PRENTICE-HALL ELECTRICAL ENGINEERING SERIES

W. L. Everitt, Ph. D., *Editor*

Library of Congress Catalog Card Number: 59-14245

PRINTED IN THE UNITED STATES OF AMERICA

29529

Preface

This manual provides the basis for laboratory exercises for introductory electronic courses. It consists of one hundred experiments on fifty different subjects, most of which are in the "circuits" area. Due to the extreme diversity of available equipment, no experiments in the microwave field have been included.

In order that a wide range of subjects be covered in a reasonable time, many of the experiments require a rigid minimum of work to be done and results to be obtained. Although the experiments can be used without modification, they can also be used creatively in accordance with the ideas of individual teachers, who may wish to alter the depth and objectives of selected experiments.

Several experiments are presented in each area in addition to the duplication on each subject. This is done to allow for equipment availability and instrument choice. Since it is thought that no one experiment is vital to the student's education, it should be possible to use the manual for many classes without repetition of experiments.

Many of the experiments contain a theoretical sketch to aid the student, in the event that adequate lecture preparation has not been possible. In addition, equipment and component lists have been provided to aid the instructor in preparing for the experiment. Modifications and substitutions will often be necessary.

Most of the experiments in this manual have been adapted from ones written by present and former staff members of the Electrical Engineering Department of Iowa State College. In view of this, the author wishes to express his thanks to all those staff members, in particular to Dean M. S. Coover and Dr. W. B. Boast, Head of the Electrical Engineering Department of Iowa State College, both of whom have been very encouraging and helpful.

W. H. EVANS

University of Arizona

List of Experiments

DEMODULATION OF FREQUENCY-MODULATED WAVES

NOISE IN VACUUM-TUBE AMPLIFIERS

FREQUENCY CONVERSION

VACUUM-TUBE VOLTMETERS

R-C TRANSIENTS

RINGING CIRCUITS

CLIPPING CIRCUITS

CLAMPING CIRCUITS

TRIGGER CIRCUITS

MULTIVIBRATORS

BLOCKING OSCILLATORS

ELECTROSTATIC SWEEP CIRCUITS

TRANSISTOR MULTIVIBRATORS

TRANSISTOR FLIP-FLOPS

TRANSISTOR BLOCKING OSCILLATORS

**TRANSISTOR RADIO FREQUENCY AND INTERMEDIATE
FREQUENCY AMPLIFIERS**

**TRANSISTOR CLIPPING, CLAMPING, AND WAVESHAPING
CIRCUITS**

TRANSISTOR AND VACUUM-TUBE CHARACTERISTICS

Cathode-Ray Oscillographs

Purpose

Oscillographs are basic tools in electronic experimentation. Familiarization with their uses is the primary objective of this experiment. A secondary purpose is the use of the ballistic equations to predict deflections.

Preliminary

1. Describe briefly how a cathode-ray oscillograph works. Illustrate your discussion with a block diagram showing the essential elements.

2. Explain how a sawtooth wave applied to the horizontal deflecting plates provides a linear time base.

Suppose the decay time of the sawtooth wave is not small in comparison to the build-up time. What effect will this have on the waveform seen on the screen? How can this effect be eliminated without altering the sawtooth waveform?

3. How can the phase angle between two voltages be measured on a cathode-ray oscillograph? Illustrate with a diagram and give the formula from which calculations of phase angle can be made.

4. Describe how to use a cathode-ray oscillograph for the measurement of frequency using Lissajous' patterns.

5. Plot the resultant pattern on the screen of an oscillograph when the following voltages are applied to the deflecting plates:

(a) $e_h = 100 \sin \ (\omega t + 0°)$ volts
$e_v = 100 \sin \ (\omega t + 30°)$ volts

(b) $e_h = 6000t$ volts $\quad 0 \le t \le 1/60$
$e_v = 100 \sin \ (2\pi 60t)$ volts

(c) $e_h = 100 \sin \ (2\pi 120t + \pi/4)$ volts
$e_v = 100 \sin \ (2\pi 60t)$ volts

Note: The *horizontal* deflecting plates cause the electron beam to deflect horizontally. The *vertical* plates cause the beam to deflect vertically.

6. (a)   Develop approximate equations for electric and magnetic deflection and illustrate.   (b)   Why is electric deflection preferred for oscilloscopes?

Performance

7. Sketch the front panel of a cathode-ray oscillograph.   Number each switch, knob, and terminal.   On a separate sheet of paper describe the purpose or function of each numbered element.

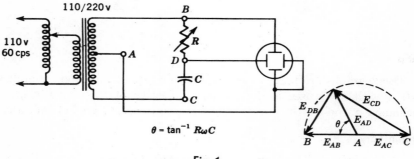

Fig. 1

8. Using a resistance-capacitance phase-shifter in the circuit of Fig. 1, connected directly to the oscillograph deflection plates, produce a picture for 30°, 45°, 60°, 90°, and 150° phase shift.   Record the values of R and C required to produce each picture.   If the deflection plate terminals are not available, the amplifiers may be used; however, these should be checked for equal phase shifts.

9. Apply 60 cycles to the horizontal input terminals of the oscillograph, and the output of an audio oscillator to the vertical terminals.   By the means of Lissajous' patterns, calibrate the oscillator from 30 cps to approximately 500 cps.

Calculations and conclusions

10. Compute the phase shift for the tests of part 8 from the formula in Fig. 1.   Compare with the measured values in tabular form and show differences.   From the results, determine what sort of accuracy is obtained by this method.   Does the accuracy depend on the amount of phase shift being measured?   Why?

11. Plot the calibration curve (frequency dial reading versus correction) for the oscillator as a broken-line curve.   Label carefully and indicate position of decade frequency switch of the oscillator.

12. Discuss briefly the general results of the test and any difficulties encountered.

References

Ryder, J. D., *Electronic Fundamentals and Applications*, 2d ed. (Englewood Cliffs, N. J.: Prentice-Hall, Inc., 1959).

Henney, K., and Richardson, G. A., *Principles of Radio*, 6th ed. (New York: John Wiley & Sons, Inc., 1952).

Oscillograph instruction manuals.

Materials required

Components	*Equipment*
1 variable voltage transformer	1 cathode-ray oscillograph (with instruction manual)
1 110–220 volt transformer	
1 0–100 K decade resistor (note that the maximum current approaches 100 ma)	1 audio frequency generator
1 0.1 μf capacitor, 400–600 volt	

EXPERIMENT

1-B

Cathode-Ray Oscillographs

Purpose

Familiarization with this valuable electronic instrument is the primary purpose of this experiment. A secondary purpose is the presentation of an elementary ballistic problem.

Preliminary

1. (a)   Name two methods of deflecting a beam of electrons. Define deflection sensitivity as applied to cathode-ray oscillographs utilizing both types of deflection.

(b)   Calculate the deflection sensitivity of an electrostatically deflected cathode-ray tube. The accelerating potential is 1250 volts, the deflection plates are 2.5 cm long, the separation of the deflection plates is 0.5 cm, and the distance to the screen is 25 cm.

(c)   A 100-volt rms 60-cycle signal is applied to the deflecting plates of part (b). Calculate the total deflection of the beam.

2. A voltage $e = 100 \sin (2\pi 60t)$ is applied to the vertical deflecting plates, and a voltage $e = 6000t$ is applied to the horizontal deflecting plates. Plot the trace, point by point, which will be obtained on the screen values of time from zero to 1/60 second.

Note: The vertical deflecting plates are the plates which cause vertical deflection of the electron beam. Similarly, the horizontal deflecting plates cause horizontal deflection.

3. If $e = 100 \sin (2\pi 60t)$ is on the horizontal deflecting plates, and $e = 100 \sin (2\pi 60t + \pi/3)$ is on the vertical deflecting plates, plot the trace obtained on the screen.

4. If $e = 100 \sin (2\pi 60t)$ is on both horizontal and vertical plates, plot the trace obtained on the screen.

5. How can phase angles be measured on a cathode-ray tube if the two signals to be compared are applied to the two pairs of deflecting plates? Show diagrams and develop equations.

4

6. If $e = 100 \sin (2\pi 60t)$ is on the horizontal plates, and $e = 100 \sin (2\pi 80t + \pi/3)$ is on the vertical plates, plot the trace obtained on the screen.

7. How can the frequency of two signals be compared by use of a cathode-ray oscillograph? Give diagrams of typical traces and explain the method.

8. What is a "linear sweep voltage?" What is it used for in a cathode-ray oscillograph?

9. Explain the operation of the phase-shifter in part 12. Give equations which can be used to compute the phase shift between voltage G-H and G-V.

Performance

Turn on the oscillator so that it may warm up and stabilize before it is used.

10. Make a sketch of the control panel of a cathode-ray oscillograph, showing all knobs, switches, and terminals. Give a word explanation of the purpose or function of each knob, switch, and terminal.

11. Using the external plate connections at the rear of the case, and an a-c voltage, measure the deflection sensitivity of each pair of deflecting plates. Record data for several voltages. Replace connections at the rear of the case.

12. Using a resistance-capacitance phase-shifter in the circuit of Fig. 1, connected through the oscillograph amplifiers, produce the pictures plotted in parts 3 and 4. Produce also pictures for phase shifts of 30°, 45°, and 90°. Record the value of R and C required to produce each picture.

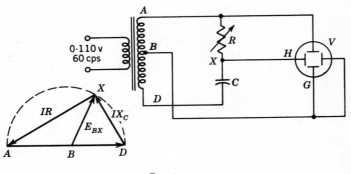

Fig. 1

13. Apply 60 cycles to the horizontal plates of the oscillograph, and the output of the audio oscillator to the vertical plates. By the use of Lissajous patterns, calibrate the oscillator at every possible point up to about 1000 cycles. Record the data.

Calculations and conclusions

14. Why should differences in horizontal and vertical sensitivities be expected in part 11? How could these be equalized?

15. Compare the noted phase shifts in part 12 with values calculated from R, W, and C. Discuss possible errors in this experimental method.

16. Plot the oscillator calibration data.

References

Ryder, J. D., *Electronic Fundamentals and Applications*, 2d ed. (Englewood Cliffs, N. J.: Prentice-Hall, Inc., 1959).

Henney, K., and Richardson, G. A., *Principles of Radio*, 6th ed. (New York: John Wiley & Sons, Inc., 1952).

Cathode-Ray Oscillograph Instruction Manual

Materials required

Components	*Equipment*
1 variable voltage transformer	1 cathode-ray oscillograph (with instruction manual)
1 110–220 volt transformer	
1 0–100 K decade resistor (note that the maximum current is approximately 100 ma for low resistance)	1 audio frequency generator
1 0.1 μf capacitor, 400–600 volt	

EXPERIMENT

2-A

Thermionic Emission and Space Charge

Purpose

The purpose of this experiment is to illustrate the effects of emission and space-charge phenomena with a tungsten filament tube of special construction.

Preliminary

1. Draw a complete diagram for a circuit to measure the volt-ampere characteristic of a diode high vacuum tube. Include meters and a means of varying filament current.

2. (a) Identify the symbols and a set of proper units in Dushman's equation. What is meant by "temperature saturation?"

(b) Identify the symbols and units for the Langmuir-Child law for parallel-plane and cylindrical diodes. What is meant by "space-charge-limited current?"

3. The FP-400 is a cylindrical electrode vacuum diode having:

anode diameter.....0.620 in.	filament diameter.....0.005 in.
anode length.......1.25 in.	filament length.......1.25 in.

filament volts....................4.0 volts
filament current................2.25 amperes
operating temperature...........2470° K
filament material................tungsten

Plot the volt-ampere curve for the FP-400 diode for a filament voltage of 4.0 volts. The portion of the curve in which the current is temperature-limited and the portion in which the current is space-charge-limited should be clearly indicated.

4. If the temperature varies with voltage as

$$T_0/T_1 = (V_0/V_1)^{0.336}$$

plot on the same curve sheet as for part 3 the curves for the same tube if the filament voltage is 3.5 volts.

5. (a)   Repeat part 4 for a filament voltage of 3.0 volts.

(b)   Explain the similarities and differences of the three volt-ampere curves.

Performance

6. Maintaining the filament voltage at 4 volts, vary the plate current from zero to not more than 50 ma, as the plate voltage is varied from zero to 125 volts, or less, if the 50 ma current is attained at less than 125 volts. Take 5 volt increments from zero to 30 volts.

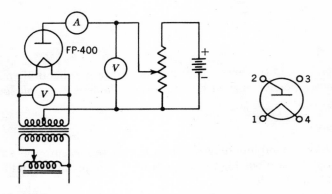

Fig. 1

7. Reduce the filament temperature by reducing the voltage to 3.5 volts, and repeat part 6.

8. Reduce the filament voltage to 3.0 volts and repeat part 6.

Calculations and conclusions

9. (a)   Plot the curves for which the data were taken.

(b)   Explain the difference in the curves of parts 6, 7, and 8. Compare with results obtained in parts 3, 4, and 5. Explain differences. Explain rounding of curve at the "knee."

(c)   What is the emission current corresponding to 3.0 volts filament voltage?

10. By plotting the data of part 6 on 3×3 cycle log-log paper, determine the true value of the voltage exponent a for use with your particular tube. Compare the experimental value of a with the theoretical value.

11. (a)   From the curve obtained in part 10 determine the value of K in the Langmuir-Child equation:

$$i = KE_b^a \text{(ma)}$$

(b) Calculate at least three values of current for different values of plate voltage and compare to results of parts 3 and 6. Explain differences.

References

Ryder, J. D., *Electronic Fundamentals and Applications*, 2d ed. (Englewood Cliffs, N. J.: Prentice-Hall, Inc., 1959).

Gray, T. S., *Applied Electronics* (New York: John Wiley & Sons, Inc., 1954).

Millman, J., and Seeley, S., *Electronics* (New York: McGraw-Hill Book Co., Inc., 1941).

Materials required

Components
1 FP-400 tube and socket
1 5 volt filament transformer, CT (approximately 2.5 amperes)
1 variable voltage transformer
1 approximately 5 K voltage divider, 100 ma (to adjust plate voltage)

Equipment
1 d-c power supply (approximately 150–200 volts at 100 ma)
1 200 volt d-c meter
1 50 ma d-c meter
1 5 volt a-c meter

2-B

Thermionic Emission and Space Charge

Purpose

Many vacuum-tube phenomena are related to peculiarities of cathode emission and the resulting space charge. A familiarity with these phenomena is the object of this experiment.

Information

The references at the end of this experiment give an excellent account of the theory of these two subjects. Concerning thermionic emission, some notable variations with respect to the presently used simple theory are noted in oxide-coated cathodes. Hence, pure metal (tungsten) filaments are usually used for laboratory experiments. Unfortunately, at least 99 per cent of receiving tubes have oxide-coated cathodes and are very unpredictable verifiers of emission equations.

Such a tube (6AL5) will be tested in this experiment because of its widespread use. The common complaint that these oxide-coated cathodes are unpredictable should not be misunderstood. Through research, knowledge of their behavior is increasing steadily. Many advanced articles on the subject have appeared in recent years.

Preliminary

1. (a) Identify the terms and units of Dushman's equation. Explain "temperature saturation."

(b) Identify the terms and units in the Langmuir-Child law for both parallel-plate and cylindrical diodes. What is meant by "space-charge-limited" current?

(c) What factors might be expected to modify experimental results in addition to those included in the equations of (a) and (b)?

(d) Do expressions similar to those above hold for tubes with different geometry?

2. Assuming the geometry for the cathode of a particular diode to be as shown in Fig. 1(a), calculate the temperature-limited current at 1000° C.

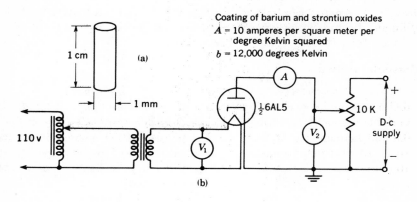

Coating of barium and strontium oxides
A = 10 amperes per square meter per degree Kelvin squared
b = 12,000 degrees Kelvin

Fig. 1

Performance

3. Connect the circuit of Fig. 1(b). With the filament set at 6.3 volts, adjust the plate voltage for 10 ma.

Note: The rating on this tube is only 9 ma per plate, therefore current flow above this value should be only momentary. Decrease the filament voltage and take data until the plate current is no longer detectable on a 100 microampere meter.

4. With the filament voltage at 2.0, 3.0, 4.0, 5.0, and 6.0 volts, increase the plate voltage until one of the 10 ma or 50 volt ratings is reached. Record the data.

Note: Forward voltages above 20 volts should be only momentary.

5. With the filament at its rated value, replace the plate circuit by means of a pulse generator and 10 ohm resistor for observing the plate current pulses on a CRO. Increase the voltage of 1 microsecond pulses, and record the voltage amplitude versus pulse current amplitude until saturation occurs or 500 ma is reached.

Calculations and conclusions

6. Plot the results of part 3.

7. Plot the results of part 4 on 3 × 3 log-log paper. Obtain approximate values for a in the Langmuir-Child equation, assuming an equation of the form $I = KE^a$.

8. What is the significance of the results obtained in part 5?

9. Discuss briefly any unusual results.

References

Ryder, J. D., *Electronic Fundamentals and Applications*, 2d ed. (Englewood Cliffs, N. J.: Prentice-Hall, Inc., 1959).

Gray, T. S., *Applied Electronics* (New York: John Wiley & Sons, Inc., 1954).

Millman, J., and Seeley, S., *Electronics* (New York: McGraw-Hill Book Co., Inc., 1941).

Materials required

Components	*Equipment*
1 6AL5 tube and socket	1 power supply (300 volts at 20 ma)
1 variable voltage transformer	1 pulse generator (50–100 volt 1 μsec
1 6.3 volt filament transformer	pulses at 1000 cps repetition rate)
1 10 K, 10 watt potentiometer	1 cathode-ray oscilloscope (high-frequency response and voltage calibrated)
1 10 ohm resistor	1 100 μa d-c meter
	1 5 ma d-c meter
	1 25 ma d-c meter
	1 1 volt d-c meter
	1 25 volt d-c meter
	1 300 volt d-c meter
	1 10 volt a-c meter

3-A

The High-Vacuum Diode Rectifier

Purpose

The purpose of this experiment is to study diode rectifiers. In particular, the influence of the volt-ampere characteristic on the average and rms output current will be studied.

Information

Diodes are important in many electronic circuits owing to their unilateral conductivity characteristic (see Fig. 1). In the case of thermionic diodes this unilateral conduction is due to electron emission from the cathode. The "static" volt-ampere characteristic is shown as the E_b vs I_b curve, and this curve is combined with R_L to give the E_{bb} vs I_b curve or "dynamic" characteristic.

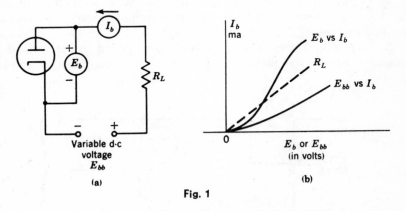

Fig. 1

Static plate resistance is given by E_b/I_b for any point on the static characteristic, while $\Delta E_b/\Delta I_b$ is defined as the dynamic plate resistance. The distinction between the meanings attached to "static" and "dynamic" in the two preceding sentences should be carefully noted.

13

In application, with a-c voltages applied, the most important output quantities are the average and rms values of the currents and voltages. If a current is known as a function of time, or ωt, the average and rms values are found as follows:

$$I_{\text{ave}} = \frac{1}{2\pi} \int_0^{2\pi} i_b \, d\omega t \, . \tag{1}$$

$$I_{\text{rms}} = \sqrt{\frac{1}{2\pi} \int_0^{2\pi} i_b^2 \, d\omega t} \tag{2}$$

These quantities may also be found from the curves of Fig. 1 by graphical integration, when the applied voltage waveshape is arbitrary.

Preliminary

1. Draw and label a typical diode volt-ampere characteristic. Show dynamic and static plate resistance at a point and illustrate how the dynamic volt-ampere curve is obtained.

2. Assume the volt-ampere curve for a particular diode is given by (3):

$$i_b = 0.28e_b^{1.5} \quad \text{ma} \tag{3}$$

Plot this curve on a rather large scale and determine graphically the waveform and the average current for $e_b = 50 \sin 377t$ volts.

3. If a d-c milliammeter is connected in series with the plate of the tube of part 2 with the given applied voltage, what is the maximum meter current? What component of the pulsating current is indicated by the d-c meter?

4. The maximum direct current is 100 ma. What is the minimum fuse size for a d-c meter indicating this value if the current is a half-wave rectified sine wave?

5. From Fig. 2 determine the waveshapes applied to the vertical and horizontal oscilloscope plates and determine the screen trace by graphical means.

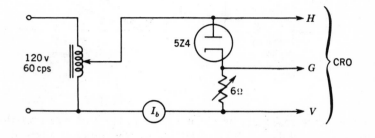

Fig. 2

Performance

6. Connect up the circuit of Fig. 2 and sketch the trace obtained. What is this curve? With a 50 volt peak applied signal, record the current waveshape as shown by the voltage across the 6 ohm resistor. Record I_b.

7. Connect up a circuit and plot a volt-ampere curve for one plate of a 5Z4. $(I_{b(max)} = 100$ ma)

Calculations and conclusions

8. From the curve plotted in part 7, graphically find the current waveshape for 50 volts (peak) applied and compare with that observed in part 6. Graphically compute the average plate current and compare with that measured in part 6.

9. List and explain, if possible, any unexpected occurrences during the experiment.

References

Ryder, J. D., *Electronic Fundamentals and Applications*, 2d ed. (Englewood Cliffs, N. J.: Prentice-Hall, Inc., 1959).

Gray, T. S., *Applied Electronics* (New York: John Wiley & Sons, Inc., 1954).

Materials required

Components	Equipment
1 5Z4 tube and socket	1 oscilloscope
1 6 ohm rheostat	1 power supply (0–150 volts and
1 variable voltage transformer	100 ma)
1 5 volt filament transformer	1 100 volt a-c meter
	1 100 ma d-c meter
	1 100 volt d-c meter

EXPERIMENT

3-B

The High-Vacuum Diode Rectifier

Purpose

The purpose of this experiment is to acquaint the student with rectifier action and the more common rectifier circuits. In particular the following items will be studied:

A. Rectifier voltage and current
B. Rectifier efficiency and peak inverse voltage
C. Half-wave, full-wave, and bridge circuits

Information

In Fig. 1 is shown a simple half-wave rectifier with a resistive load. The tube volt-ampere curve (e_b, i_b) and the load volt-ampere curve (R_L) are combined into the dynamic characteristic (e, i_b).

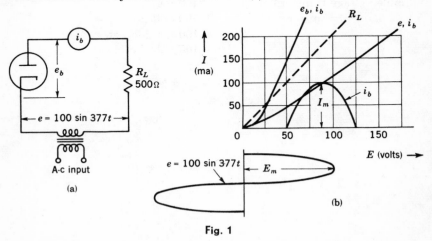

Fig. 1

An a-c input voltage is drawn and projected onto the dynamic characteristic to give the plate current pulse shape and magnitude. Time scales are not indicated. Average (d-c) and effective (rms) values are found from known functions of time (or ωt) as follows:

$$I_{\text{ave}} = \frac{1}{2\pi} \int_0^{2\pi} i_b \, d\omega t$$

$$I_{\text{rms}} = \sqrt{\frac{1}{2\pi} \int_0^{2\pi} i_b^2 \, d\omega t}$$

These values may also be found graphically by counting squares and ordinates.

$$I_{\text{ave}} = \frac{\text{no. of squares under curve} \times \text{value of each square}}{\text{length of baseline (full cycle)}}$$

$$\cong \frac{3.8 \times 1250}{150} \cong 36.6 \quad \text{ma}$$

$$I_{\text{rms}} = \sqrt{\frac{\text{sum of ordinates squared} \times \text{base for each rectangle}}{\text{full-cycle baseline}}}$$

$$\cong \sqrt{\frac{50^2 \times 25 + 100^2 \times 25 + 50^2 \times 25}{150}}$$

$$\cong \sqrt{\frac{62,500 + 250,000 + 62,500}{150}} \cong \sqrt{\frac{375,000}{150}} = 50 \quad \text{ma}$$

If the dynamic characteristic were straight, the true values would be 31.8 ma and 50.0 ma. The closeness of the roughly calculated answers is accidental.

The rectification efficiency is defined as

$$\eta_R = \frac{P_{\text{d-c output}}}{P_{\text{a-c input}}} \times 100\%$$

and in this case,

$$\eta_R = \frac{(I_{\text{ave}})^2 \times R \times 100\%}{(I_{\text{rms}})^2 (R + r_p)} = \frac{4}{\pi^2}\left(\frac{R}{r_p + R}\right) \times 100\%$$

$$= \frac{40.6\%}{1 + r_p/R} \cong 23\%$$

The "peak inverse voltage" in a rectifier circuit is defined as the maximum instantaneous voltage across the rectifier during the nonconduction period. In this circuit the peak inverse voltage is E_m or 100 volts.

The half-wave rectifier has a peak efficiency of only 40.6%. The circuits of Fig. 2 have limiting efficiencies of 81.2%. The peak inverse voltages for these circuits are equal to twice the rectified peak voltage plus the conducting tube drop.

The simple rectifiers of Figs. 1 and 2 are seldom used without filters to remove the a-c output components. A common type of rectifier filter is shown in Fig. 2(c). This low-pass filter is interposed between rectifier and load. It stores energy on voltage and current peaks and releases it when voltage and current tend to decrease. In this way, practically ripple-free output may be obtained.

Preliminary

Note: To avoid using the three filament transformers necessary for Fig. 2(b) where filamentary tubes are used, cathode type tubes (6AL5) will be employed for this experiment. These are not designed for power rectifier service, but are convenient for illustrating principles.

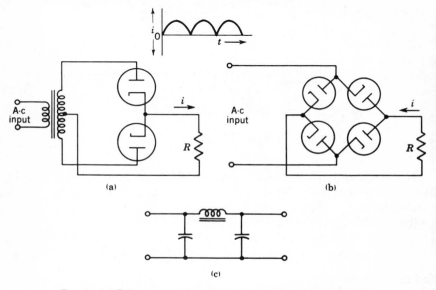

Fig. 2   (a) Full-wave rectifier; **(b)** bridge rectifier; **(c)** rectifier filter.

1. Assuming the plate resistance of a 6AL5 to be 500 ohms and constant, graphically find the average and rms values of voltage and current when operated into a 10,000 ohm load from a source of $150 \sin 377t$ volts.

2. Draw circuits, using 6AL5 rectifiers, of the half-wave, full-wave, and bridge types with 10,000 ohm loads. Determine the maximum input voltage to attain rated plate current of 9 ma. A 1/1 transformer with center-tapped secondary will be assumed for the full-wave circuit. Calculate rms current, η_R, and PIV for each circuit.

Performance

3. Set up and operate each of the circuits of part 2. Record waveshapes and readings obtained.

4. To each circuit set up in part 3 apply each of the following filters. Record output waveshapes and magnitude of ripple.
   (a) single capacitor, 10 μf
   (b) capacitor plus inductor, 10 henry
   (c) capacitor plus inductor plus capacitor, 10 μf

Calculations and conclusions

5. Briefly compare the three rectifiers tested as to advantages and possible uses.

6. List and explain if possible any unexpected experimental results and occurrences.

References

R.C.A. Receiving Tube Manual.

Gray, T. S., *Applied Electronics* (New York: John Wiley & Sons, Inc., 1954).

Materials required

Components	*Equipment*
2 6AL5 tubes and sockets	1 variable ratio auto-transformer
1 1/1 isolating transformer with center-tapped secondary	1 oscillograph
2 10 μf capacitors, 300 volt	1 10 ma d-c meter
1 10 henry choke, 10 ma	1 25 ma a-c meter
1 10 K resistor, 2 watt	1 200 volt d-c meter
2 6.3 volt filament transformers	1 100 volt a-c meter

EXPERIMENT

4-A

Vacuum-Tube Characteristics

Purpose

The purpose of this experiment is to investigate the terminal characteristics of a triode vacuum tube. In particular the following items will be studied:

A. Triode plate characteristics
B. Measurement of plate resistance
C. Measurement of amplification factor

Information

The theoretical reasoning behind the behavior of vacuum tubes is difficult in proportion to the thoroughness of the investigation. Experimentally, however, the vacuum tube has only three terminals (plate, grid, and cathode). If the current versus voltage relationship for each possible pair of these terminals is known (as a function of the third terminal potential), it is not necessary to know the internal tube phenomena to design

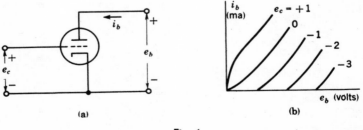

(a)   (b)

Fig. 1

circuits using existing tubes. On the other hand, internal phenomena must be understood to design tubes to have specified characteristics. In this experiment, attention will be restricted to tube behavior as seen from its external terminals.

The most used vacuum-tube operation consists essentially in connecting a signal between grid and cathode and obtaining an amplified copy of this signal between plate and cathode. As viewed between plate and cathode, the tube has a volt-ampere characteristic such as any nonlinear resistor except that this characteristic can be changed by the voltage between grid and cathode. Such a plate circuit volt-ampere family of curves is shown in Fig. 1(b).

In Fig. 1, grid current is not shown since the usual operation is with the grid negative with respect to the cathode; however, for the characteristic shown for $e_c = +1$ volt, grid current will flow. If grid current is neglected, Fig. 1(b) will completely describe the external tube behavior. Other families (grid voltage versus plate voltage as a function of plate current, and grid voltage versus plate current as a function of plate voltage) can be plotted or derived from the plate family and will also completely describe tube behavior. By selecting uniformly spaced ordinates (plate current values), the constant-current tube characteristics can be drawn. Their general appearance is shown in Fig. 2(a). By taking uniformly spaced values of plate voltage, the transfer characteristics can be drawn as in Fig. 2(b).

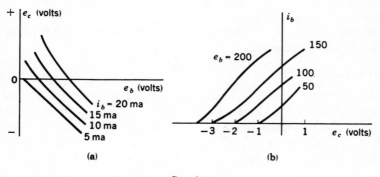

Fig. 2

In all these families of curves, for any particular set of applied potentials, each of the quantities such as static plate resistance, dynamic plate resistance (r_p), amplification factor (μ), and mutual conductance (g_m) can be found from the graph.

It is sometimes desirable to measure these quantities directly, and this can be done by several methods. Figure 3 illustrates typical circuits for measurement of r_p and μ. The measurement of r_p is an ordinary a-c resistance measurement, and an a-c bridge is ideal for the purpose. To measure μ, the ratio R_1 to R_2 of Fig. 3(b) is adjusted to null. Since no a-c plate current is then flowing, the amplification factor is R_1/R_2.

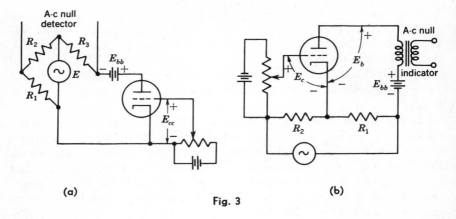

(a)   (b)

Fig. 3

Preliminary

1. Why are the volt-ampere characteristics of vacuum tubes necessary for complete analysis of electronic circuits while the volt-ampere characteristics for resistors, capacitors, and inductors are not?

2. Illustrate how μ, r_p, and g_m are found from the plate characteristics.

3. Illustrate the derivation of the "constant-current" and "transfer" characteristics from the plate family.

4. What is the significance of the terms "dynamic" and "static" when applied to plate resistance?

Performance

5. Set up the circuit of Fig. 4 to take data and plot a family of plate characteristics. Use grid voltages of $+1$, 0, -1, -5, -10, and -15 volts. Do not exceed ratings of the plate dissipation of 5 watts, plate voltage 300 volts, plate current 40 ma. (To obtain results with fewer readings, plot points on graph as observations are made.)

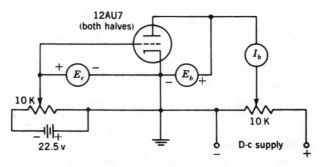

Fig. 4

6. Set up a circuit similar to that of Fig. 3(a) and measure r_p at 1000 cps with $E_b = 100$ volts, for values of plate current from zero to 40 ma. A 1:1 isolation transformer will be advisable if a commercial a-c impedance bridge is used to keep d-c current out of the bridge elements. Do not exceed rating of part 5.

7. Set up a circuit similar to that of Fig. 3(b) and measure μ at 1000 cps over the same range as in part 6.

Calculations and conclusions

8. Compare values of r_p and μ as obtained in parts 6 and 7 with values at $E_s = 0$, $E_b = 100$ volts, as taken from the graph of part 5.

9. In per cent, does μ or r_p change more over the range measured? Why is this reasonable?

10. Discuss, and explain, if possible, any unexpected phenomena observed.

References

Terman, F. E., and Pettit, J. M., *Electronic Measurements* (New York: McGraw-Hill Book Co., Inc., 1952).

Ryder, J. D., *Electronic Fundamentals and Applications*, 2d ed. (Englewood Cliffs, N. J.: Prentice-Hall, Inc., 1959).

Materials required

Components	*Equipment*
1 12AU7 tube and socket	1 audio oscillator
2 10 K potentiometers, 10 watt	1 d-c vacuum-tube voltmeter (to
3 1000 ohm decade boxes (40 ma maximum)	measure plate voltage, sensitive d-c d'Arsonval meter can be used)
1 1:1 isolation transformer	1 0–25 volt d-c meter
	1 0–50 ma d-c meter
	1 null detector (scope, headphones, sensitive VTVM, etc.)
	1 300 volt d-c power supply, 40 ma
	1 22.5 volt d-c supply or battery

EXPERIMENT

4-B

Vacuum-Tube Characteristics

Purpose

This experiment will illustrate how vacuum-tube terminal characteristics are obtained and give some indications as to their use. In particular, the following factors concerning pentodes will be studied:

A.   Their nonlinear volt-ampere characteristics
B.   Qualitative action of screen and suppressor grids
C.   Vacuum-tube parameters

Information

As illustrated in Fig. 1(a), a pentode, tetrode, or triode is similar to any other nonlinear resistor when viewed from the plate-cathode terminals. In the case of tubes, however, the volt-ampere characteristic can be changed

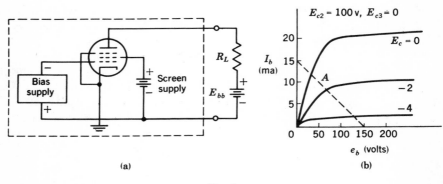

(a)   (b)

Fig. 1

within limits by varying the potential applied to the control grid, and to a lesser extent by varying screen and suppressor voltages.

Figure 1(b) illustrates the way in which the volt-ampere relationship may be changed by different values of E_c. (All tube voltages are specified as potential rises with respect to cathode.) Point A of this figure is the graphic solution for $E_{bb} = 150$ volts, $E_c = -2$ volts, $R_L = 10$ K, and E_{c2} and E_{c3} as given.

The set of volt-ampere characteristics given in Fig. 1(b) is called the plate characteristics. Two other sets of curves are sometimes used. The "constant-current" characteristics give plate voltage as a function of grid voltage with plate current as a parameter — Fig. 2(a). The "transfer" characteristics give plate current as a function of grid voltage with plate voltage as a parameter — Fig. 2(b). Any two of these curve families can be derived from any one of the others.

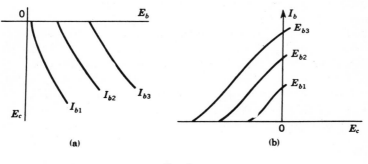

(a)   (b)

Fig. 2

In these sets of characteristic curves, positive grid values are not shown, since this is not a common type of operation for pentodes.

Since the suppressor grid and screen grid potentials are ordinarily d-c, pentodes are treated as triodes with respect to their plate, grid, and cathode

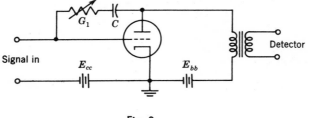

Fig. 3

terminals. However, owing to the screen grid, very little capacitance exists between grid and plate, in contrast to the triode. Because of secondary emission from the plate, tetrode traits are eliminated by the suppressor grid. These extra grids occasionally are used to vary the electron stream in the same way as the control grid is used.

The tube parameters r_p, μ, and g_m for any set of conditions can be found from any of the given curves. For example, at the point A in Fig. 1, the approximate values are: $\mu = 25$, $r_p = 9$ K, $g_m = 2800$ μmhos. Since point A is below the knee of the curve, the given values are not representative of usual pentode operation. Ordinary a-c impedance bridges may be used to measure r_p if provision for the d-c plate current is made. A circuit of the type of Fig. 3 can be used to measure g_m. A detector null occurs when $G_1 = g_m$.

Preliminary

1. Why are volt-ampere characteristics important in the solution of vacuum-tube circuits? Why is the plate family more commonly used than the others?

2. From a complete 6AU6 plate family, derive the constant-current characteristic for $I_b = 5$ ma ($E_{g2} = 100$ volts, $E_{g3} = 0$). Under the same conditions, derive the transfer characteristic for $E_b = 200$ volts.

3. Graphically find the plate current of a 6AU6, if $E_{bb} = 300$ volts, $E_{c2} = 100$ volts, $E_{c3} = 0$, $E_{c1} = -1$ volt, and $R_L = 30$ K (see Fig. 1).

4. From the 6AU6 plate characteristics, find the value of μ, r_p, and g_m for $E_b = 200$ volts, $E_{c1} = -1$ volt, $E_{c2} = 100$ volts, and $E_{c3} = 0$.

Performance

5. Set up a circuit similar to that of Fig. 4, and plot a family of plate characteristics for the 6AU6 for $E_{c1} = 0$, -1, -2, and -3 volts. Keep

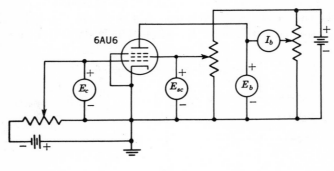

Fig. 4

$E_{c2} = 100$ volts and do not exceed plate and screen ratings of 3 and 0.6 watts, respectively. This will necessitate monitoring the screen grid current.

6. Set up a circuit and check the result of part 3. In the same circuit, change E_{c1} by one volt and note the change in plate voltage. Also change E_{c2} by 5 volts and note plate voltage change.

7. Set up a circuit similar to Fig. 3 and measure g_m under the conditions of part 2.

Calculations and conclusions

8. Why are the experimentally derived plate characteristics different from those used in the preliminary?

9. Compare the values of g_m obtained from the preliminary with the measured value.

10. List and explain, if possible, any unexpected results or occurrences noticed.

References

Ryder, J. D., *Electronic Fundamentals and Applications*, 2d ed. (Englewood Cliffs, N. J.: Prentice-Hall, Inc., 1959).

Gray, T. S., *Applied Electronics* (New York: John Wiley & Sons, Inc., 1954).

Materials required

Components	*Equipment*
1 6AU6 and socket	1 audio oscillator
3 10 K potentiometers, 10 watt	1 null detector (oscilloscope, etc.)
1 100 K decade resistor	1 power supply, 300 volt, 15 ma
1 10 μf capacitor, 400 volt	1 300 volt d-c meter (VTVM preferable)
1 7.5 volt battery	1 100 volt d-c meter
	1 10 volt d-c meter
	1 20 ma d-c meter
	1 10 ma d-c meter

5-A

Vacuum-Tube Voltage Amplifiers

Purpose

The purpose of this experiment is to study small-signal vacuum-tube amplifiers. This will be restricted to resistance-capacitance coupled triode amplifiers. Specifically the following points will be studied:

A. The effects of plate supply and bias voltages
B. The effects of load resistance
C. The gain as a function of frequency

Information

As viewed from the plate and cathode terminals, the vacuum tube is a nonlinear resistance whose value, for positive plate voltage, may be controlled by the potential of the grid with respect to the cathode.

A typical set of volt-ampere characteristics for a triode is illustrated in Fig. 1. The current values for negative E_b are zero.

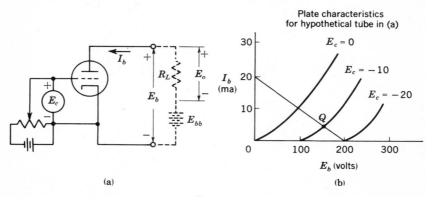

(a)   (b)

Fig. 1

Obviously, the plate current is some function of the plate voltage and grid voltage. If a unit change of plate voltage produces ΔI_b change in I_b

(E_c fixed), and $1/\mu$ volts change in E_c produces the same ΔI_b (E_b fixed), then the grid is said to be μ times as effective as the plate in determining plate current. Since μ is almost constant over a large range of tube operation, equation (1) can be written

$$i_b = f(\mu e_c + e_b) \tag{1}$$

If the f of (1) can be represented by a power series, it can be roughly approximated by the linear term

$$i_b = g_p(\mu e_c + e_b) \tag{2}$$

$$g_p = \frac{\partial i_b}{\partial e_b} = \frac{1}{r_p}, \quad g_m = \mu g_p = \frac{\partial i_b}{\partial e_c}, \quad \mu = -\frac{\partial e_b}{\partial e_c}$$

The terms given below equation (2) are: dynamic plate conductance (reciprocal of dynamic plate resistance), mutual conductance, and amplification factor. All can be found from the graph of Fig. 1. If all potentials and currents are considered as d-c plus a-c, equation (3) can be written and considered as representing the equivalent circuits of Fig. 2.

$$i_b = I_p + i_p, \quad e_c = E_c + e_c, \quad e_b = E_b + i_p$$

$$i_p = g_p(\mu e_g + e_p) = \frac{\mu e_g + e_p}{r_p} \tag{3}$$

In Fig. 2(c) rms values have been substituted for instantaneous ones, and the load voltage for e_p. The gain A of Fig. 2(c) is given by $A = E_o/E_g = -\mu R_L/(r_p + R_L) = -g_m/(g_p + G_L)$ with $G_L = 1/R_L$. This gain is for small signals and does not indicate the influence of coupling capacitors, tube capacitances, and wiring capacitance.

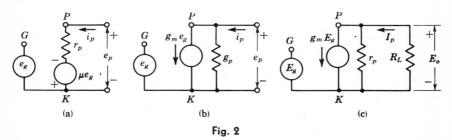

Fig. 2

If a 200 volt d-c supply in series with $R_L = 10$ K is connected as in Fig. 1(a), the graphical solution for voltage and current including the non-linear resistor (tube) is shown in Fig. 1(b) assuming $E_c = -10$ volts. The dotted line representing the battery plus R_L is called the "load line," and the intersection is the Q-point or quiescent (no signal) operating point. The dynamic plate resistance (r_p), the amplification factor (μ), and the mutual conductance can be evaluated at the Q-point from the plate characteristics. Clearly, these factors will change with grid bias, plate supply, and load resistance since each of these affects the Q-point. Of the three factors (μ, r_p, and g_m), μ is much more constant than the other two. This seems reasonable since tube geometry should be the main contributing factor of the ratio of the plate's and grid's effectiveness in controlling the plate current. It should be noted that equation (2) is perfectly general if g_m and μ are given correctly as functions of e_c and e_b, instead of being considered as constants.

Preliminary

1. Calculate and tabulate the voltage gain of the circuit of Fig. 3 for $R_L = 2$ K, 4 K, 8 K, 16 K, and 32 K. $C_1 = 0.1$ μf, $f = 1000$ cps, $r_p = 7700$, and $\mu = 17$. Repeat for $C_1 = 0.01$ and 0.001 μf. Plot the three curves on the same graph. (Neglect tube capacitances.)

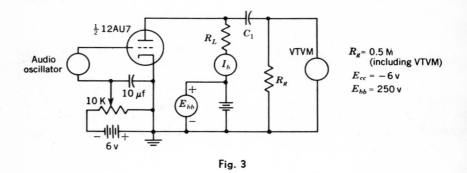

Fig. 3

2. Calculate and plot on three-cycle, semi-log paper the gain versus frequency for the circuit of Fig. 3 from 20 cps to 10 kc. $C_1 = 0.001$ and $R_L = 32$ K.

3. Referring to the plate characteristics of the 12AU7, what general trends would be expected as E_{bb} and E_{cc} are varied?

Performance

4. Measure the quantities calculated in part 1, and compare on the same graph. Use signals as small as can be conveniently measured.

5. Measure and compare the quantities calculated in part 2 (small signals).

6. Separately vary E_{bb} and E_{cc} to note changes caused. Maximum value of usable signal is also of interest here, so an oscillograph across the output will be of value. Use $R_L = 8$ K, $C_1 = 0.1$ μf, and $f = 1000$ cps. (Tube ratings should not be exceeded.)

Calculations and conclusions

7. Discuss the results of part 6.
8. Discuss and explain, if possible, any unexpected or unusual results.

References

Ryder, J. D., *Electronic Fundamentals and Applications*, 2d ed. (Englewood Cliffs, N. J.: Prentice-Hall, Inc., 1959).

Corcoran, G. F., and Price, H. W., *Electronics* (New York: John Wiley & Sons, Inc., 1954).

Materials required

Components	*Equipment*
1 12AU7 tube and socket	1 audio oscillator
1 10 K potentiometer, 5 watt	2 vacuum-tube voltmeters (to measure input and output)
1 each 2 K, 4 K, 8 K, 16 K, and 32 K resistors, 1 watt (or 1 decade for R_L)	1 300 volt d-c voltmeter
	1 25 ma d-c meter
1 1 megohm resistor (to parallel with VTVM for 0.5 megohm R_g)	1 10 volt d-c voltmeter
1 10 μf capacitor, 50 volt	1 cathode-ray oscillograph
1 0.1 μf capacitor, 300 volt	1 d-c power supply (300 volts d-c at 25 ma and 6.3 volts a-c)
1 0.01 μf capacitor, 300 volt	
1 0.001 μf capacitor, 300 volt	
1 22.5 volt battery	

5-B

Vacuum-Tube Voltage Amplifiers

Purpose

The purpose of this experiment is to study small-signal vacuum-tube amplifiers. To illustrate one type, pentode resistance-capacitive audio amplifiers will be considered. Specifically the following points will be studied:

A. The effects of supply voltages
B. The effect of load resistance
C. The effect of frequency on gain

Information

While this experiment is not directly concerned with the graphical method, it is useful as a starting point. As seen from the external terminals

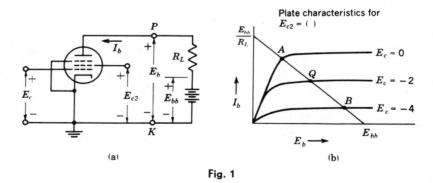

Fig. 1

(plate and cathode), the pentode (or triode or tetrode) is a nonlinear resistor whose characteristics may be controlled by applied screen and control grid voltages. If E_c, E_{c2}, E_{bb}, and the load resistance are specified for a circuit such as Fig. 1(a), the quiescent operating point (Q-point) may be found by ordinary graphical means as in Fig. 1(b). If E_c were changed to 0 volt, the point of operation would be A, while $E_c = -4$ volts would give point B.

In general, at any Q-point the plate current is some function of the plate and control grid voltage. (E_{c2} is constant and $E_{c3} = 0$, i.e., connected to cathode.) The effect of the control grid can be satisfactorily included by saying that E_c is μ times more effective in controlling the plate current than the plate voltage. Equation (1) results when the plate current is considered to be a function of e_b and e_c, directly from the mathematical definition of the differential.

$$i_b = i_b(e_c, e_b)$$

$$di_b = \frac{\partial i_b}{\partial e_c} de_c + \frac{\partial i_b}{\partial e_b} de_b \tag{1}$$

If now the differentials are replaced by the rms values of a sinusoidal change, and the partial derivatives by their definitions, equation (2) results.

$$\frac{\partial i_b}{\partial e_b} = g_p = \frac{1}{r_p}, \quad \frac{\partial i_b}{\partial e_c} = g_m, \quad \frac{g_m}{g_p} = \mu$$

Equation (3) is a more common statement of equation (2). From another approach equations (2) and (3) can be written for instantaneous currents

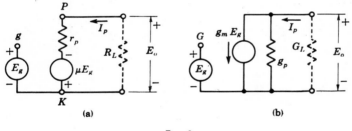

Fig. 2

and made perfectly general if the coefficients are made functions of e_p and e_g.

$$I_p = g_m E_g + g_p E_p \tag{2}$$

$$I_p = \frac{1}{r_p}(E_p + \mu E_g) \tag{3}$$

The equivalent circuits of Fig. 2 can be used to represent equation (3), where E_o replaces E_p. The gain of the circuits of Fig. 2 are given by either form of equation (4).

$$A = \frac{E_o}{E_g} = \frac{\mu R_L}{r_p + R_L} = \frac{-g_m}{g_p + G_L} \tag{4}$$

The equivalent circuits for triodes and pentodes are the same. The general tube functions are similar; i.e., the portion of the emitted cathode electrons going to the plate is varied by varying the potential applied between the cathode and a control grid in the path of these electrons. In the triode, however, a capacitance exists between the grid and plate, making complete isolation between these circuits difficult. In the pentode, grid number 2 is at a-c ground (by-passed to cathode) but positive with respect to the cathode. This effectively isolates plate and grid circuits. Secondary emission problems would ordinarily arise, but these are effectively avoided by the suppressor grid (grid number 3) which is normally at cathode potential.

Preliminary

1. Calculate the gain of the circuit of Fig. 3 at 1000 cps. (For a screen grid voltage of 100 volts and $E_{cc} = -2$ volts, the following values are typical: $r_p = 100$ K, $g_m = 2200$ μmhos.)

2. Find the high and low frequencies at which the gain has dropped to 0.707 times the 1000 cps gain — the upper and lower half-power frequencies.

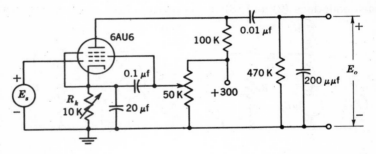

Fig. 3

3. Calculate the gain for load resistances of 5 K, 10 K, 25 K, 50 K, and 100 K, under the conditions of part 1. Plot gain versus load resistance.

4. What effect would a change in grid, screen, and plate voltages have on the voltage gain?

Performance

5. Check the results calculated in part 3.

6. Take data to plot a gain frequency curve and plot on 5-cycle semi-log paper. The shunt capacitance of 200 $\mu\mu$f is intended to include tube, wiring, and measuring instrument capacitances.

7. Take data and plot voltage gain versus plate, screen, and grid voltages. Both plate and screen current should be metered and not allowed

to exceed 10 and 5 ma, respectively. Maintain the values of part 1 for the voltages not being varied.

Calculations and conclusions

8. Briefly summarize your observations of pentode voltage amplifiers.
9. Discuss any deviation from expected results.

References

Ryder, J. D., *Electronic Fundamentals and Applications*, 2d ed. (Englewood Cliffs, N. J.: Prentice-Hall, Inc., 1959).

Corcoran, G. F., and Price, H. W., *Electronics* (New York: John Wiley & Sons, Inc., 1954).

Materials required

Components	*Equipment*
1 6AU6 tube and socket	1 audio oscillator
1 10 K potentiometer, 5 watt	2 a-c vacuum-tube voltmeters (to measure input and output)
1 50 K potentiometer, 5 watt	
1 100 K decade resistor	1 oscilloscope (to observe output)
1 470 K resistor, $\frac{1}{2}$ watt	2 0–300 volt d-c meter
1 20 μf capacitor, 10 volt	1 0–10 volt d-c meter
1 0.1 μf capacitor, 400 volt	1 0–5 ma d-c meter
1 0.01 μf capacitor, 400 volt	1 0–10 ma d-c meter
1 variable capacitor (to make up shunt capacitance to 200 $\mu\mu$f total shunt capacitance)	1 power supply (300 volts at 20 ma and 6.3 volts, a-c)

EXPERIMENT

6-A

The Cathode Follower

Purpose

The purpose of this experiment is to study the operation and design of cathode followers.

Information

Figures 1, 2, and 3 show several versions of the cathode follower circuit. By normal methods of circuit analysis the equations (1), (2), and (3) may be derived from Fig. 1.

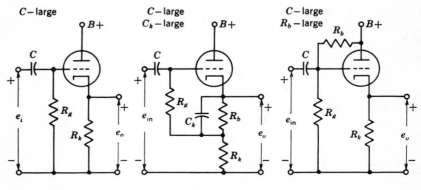

Fig. 1   Fig. 2   Fig. 3

$$Y_{in} = \frac{1}{R_g} + j\omega[C_{gp} + C_{gk}(1 - A)] \tag{1}$$

$$A = \frac{\mu R_k}{r_p + R_k(1 + \mu)} = \frac{g_m R_k}{g_m R_k + g_p R_k + 1} \tag{2}$$

$$Y_{out} = \frac{1}{R_k} + g_p + g_m \tag{3}$$

With the bias arrangement of Fig. 2, a very high input resistance may
be obtained, while Fig. 3 illustrates a very simple bias arrangement with
lower input resistance.

Graphical analysis of the cathode follower is somewhat complicated
when the plate characteristics for the grounded-cathode connection are
used. What is normally desired for any active four-terminal network is
output voltage versus output current for constant input voltage or current.
In this case the input is more conveniently taken with respect to the plate,

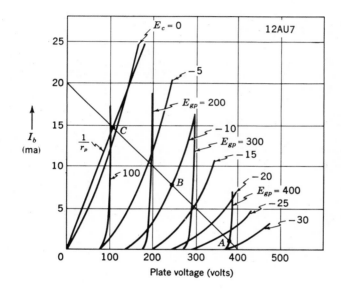

Fig. 4

since its potential is fixed, while the cathode potential follows that of the
grid. A set of characteristics of this type is shown in Fig. 4. For example, to
find the $E_{gp} = 200$ volt characteristic,

$$E_{gp} = E_b - E_{kg}$$

so that this line may be found by noting a succession of points where plate
voltage plus the magnitude of the cathode to grid voltage equals 200 volts.
Since the lines are almost exactly straight, except for low plate currents,
few points are needed and the characteristics are easily drawn.

Figure 4 also shows a 20 K (cathode to ground) load line for a 400 volt
supply. Point A represents a good quiescent point for amplifying positive
pulses, point B for a-c operation, and point C for negative pulses and the

limit of zero grid current operation. The following voltages apply for the three points:

Point A	Point B	Point C
E_b = 373 volts	E_b = 245 volts	E_b = 115 volts
E_{kg} = −27 volts	E_{kg} = −10 volts	E_{kg} = 0 volts
E_{gp} = 400 volts	E_{gp} = 255 volts	E_{gp} = 115 volts
E_{in} = 0 volts	E_{in} = 145 volts	E_{in} = 285 volts
E_{out} = 27 volts	E_{out} = 155 volts	E_{out} = 285 volts

An important phenomenon occurs when the cathode follower is used for very fast pulses. As the pulse goes positive, the tube will conduct and charge the cathode to ground (filament) capacitance, giving a good rise time. As the pulse now starts negative, the cathode potential cannot change instantaneously, so the tube may be cut off and an exponential decay caused, with R_k and the cathode capacitance controlling the time constant.

An approximate method is often used for cathode follower design. If the tube were linear, the following equation would hold:

$$i_b = I_b + i_p = \frac{E_{bb} + \mu e_c}{R_L + r_p} \tag{4}$$

To keep the grid current zero, e_c must be zero or negative. The approximation for $e_c = 0$ gives equation (5).

$$\frac{I_b}{E_b} = \frac{1}{r_p} \qquad \text{(as shown in Fig. 4)} \tag{5}$$

If $e_c = 0$,

$$E_{pk} = \frac{E_{bb}}{r_p + R_L} r_p \qquad \text{(point } B \text{ in Fig. 4)} \tag{6}$$

$$\text{Peak to peak output} = E_{p-p} = E_{bb} - \frac{E_{bb} r_p}{r_p + R_L} \tag{7}$$

Quiescent plate voltage (for linear operation) is E_Q, and

$$E_Q = E_{bb} - \frac{E_{p-p}}{2} = \frac{E_{bb}}{2}\left(\frac{2r_p + R_L}{r_p + R_L}\right) \tag{8}$$

To find the grid bias, equations (9) and (10) are used.

$$I_b r_p = E_Q + \mu E_c \tag{9}$$

$$\therefore E_c = -\frac{E_{bb}}{2\mu} \tag{10}$$

since
$$\frac{E_{bb} + \mu E_c}{r_p + R_L} r_p = \frac{E_{bb}}{2}\left(\frac{2r_p + R_L}{r_p + R_L}\right) + \mu E_c\left(\frac{r_p + R_L}{r_p + R_L}\right) \tag{11}$$

Since the cathode follower has 100 per cent feedback, these equations are sufficiently accurate for many purposes.

Preliminary

1. (a) Why is the cathode follower generally classed as a "voltage feedback" device?

(b) Give the advantages and disadvantages of negative feedback in amplifiers.

(c) What are the particular advantages and uses of cathode followers?

2. Derive equations (1), (2), and (3).

3. Construct a set of characteristics similar to those in Fig. 4 for the 12AU7. Take E_{gp} steps of 50 volts, $E_{bb} = 200$ volts, with $R_L = 1$ K and 10 K. Determine the gain, grid bias, and maximum voltage output for a sine-wave input. Show suitable bias schemes using the circuit of Fig. 2 — do not use resistor sizes greater than 1 megohm. Neglect the effects of R_b.

4. From equation (2), what factors prevent unity gain and interfere with linearity of the output?

Performance

5. Set up and check the circuits of part 3. Use an E_{bb} slightly higher than 200 volts to make up for the drop in R_b.

6. Set up the circuit of Fig. 3 with $R_L = 10$ K and a 2 megohm potentiometer for $R_b + R_g$. Adjust the bias for operation at points A, B, and C (of Fig. 4) and record the output waveform for a maximum sine-wave input.

Calculations and conclusions

7. Compare computed and measured results.

8. List and explain, if possible, any unusual phenomena.

References

Ryder, J. D., *Electronic Fundamentals and Applications*, 2d ed. (Englewood Cliffs, N. J.: Prentice-Hall, Inc., 1959).

Whittle, R. L., "*Design of Cathode Followers*," *Tele-Tech*, July, 1948.

Materials required

Components

1 12AU7 tube and socket
1 1 μf coupling capacitor
1 8 μf by-pass capacitor
1 2 megohm potentiometer

1 5 K potentiometer
1 1 K resistor
1 10 K resistor

Equipment

1 cathode-ray oscillograph (to view waveforms)

2 a-c voltmeters to measure input and output voltage

1 d-c milliameter to measure plate current (25 ma)

1 audio oscillator to provide 120 volts of signal (lower output and a step-up transformer are satisfactory)

1 d-c power supply (200–250 volts at 25 ma and 6.3 volts, a-c)

1 multimeter or one 300 volt and one 25 volt voltmeter to set d-c potentials

6-B

The Cathode Follower

Purpose

The purpose of this experiment is to study the effects of negative feedback on the gain, distortion, and output impedance of amplifiers, particularly as applied to the cathode follower circuit.

Information

Many variations of cathode follower circuits are used, but the major differences are in the bias arrangements. With the switch in position A,

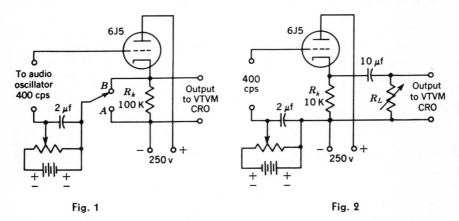

Fig. 1   Fig. 2

Fig. 1 represents one of the more simple arrangements for analytical purposes since the bias circuit does not enter the mathematical expressions. For the switch in position A equations (1) and (2) hold, while for switch position B, equations (3) and (4) give the gain and output impedance. Position B is a normal amplifier except that the plate is at a-c ground.

$$A' = \frac{\mu R_k}{r_p + R_k(1 + \mu)} = \frac{\mu/(\mu + 1)}{1 + r_p/R_k(1 + \mu)} \tag{1}$$

$$R'_{out} = \frac{1}{g_m + g_p + G_k} = \frac{r_p R_k}{r_p + R_k(1 + \mu)} \tag{2}$$

$$A = \frac{\mu R_k}{r_p + R_k} \tag{3}$$

$$R_{out} = \frac{r_p R_k}{r_p + R_k} \tag{4}$$

If distortion is present in an amplifier at some particular instant, this means that the gain is in error at that instant. By taking the ratio of A' to A, the distortion reduction factor is obtained, assuming the same output voltage, and this is, of course, the same as the gain reduction factor.

$$\frac{A'}{A} = \frac{\mu R_k}{r_p + R_k(1 + \mu)} \div \frac{\mu R_k}{r_p + R_k} = \frac{r_p + R_k}{r_p + R_k(1 + \mu)} = \frac{1}{1 + \mu R_k/(r_p + R_k)} \tag{5}$$

From equation (1) it is seen that if $R_k(1 + \mu) \gg r_p$, the gain is $\mu/(\mu + 1)$, which is essentially unity if μ is large and almost constant (since the μ of most tubes does not vary as much as g_m and r_p).

In solving for output versus input voltage, a convenient method is to work from a load line. The grid voltage, plate voltage, and output voltage for a point on the load line can be found and the input voltage determined from the relation $e_o - e_i + e_c = 0$.

Preliminary

Note: Capacitor reactances may be neglected.

1. (a)   List several advantages of negative feedback. Which of these apply to the cathode follower?

    (b)   What are the two general types of negative feedback? Under what classification would the cathode follower fall? Why?

    (c)   Derive equations (1) and (2).

2. By the use of a load line for the cathode follower of Fig. 1, compute the table of values of E_c (actual grid voltage), E_b (plate voltage), E_o (output voltage), and E_i (input voltage). Plot a curve of E_o vs E_i. What positive voltage must be placed in series with the a-c signal voltage to place the quiescent point in the middle of the linear operating range?

3. On a separate sheet, plot output versus signal voltage for Fig. 1 as an ordinary amplifier (grid return to B, $E_{cc} = -9$ volts). What are the obvious differences between this characteristic and that for the cathode follower?

Performance

4. With grid return to B, $E_c = -8$ volts in Fig. 1, increase the signal voltage until just noticeable distortion appears on the CRO connected to

the output. Measure appropriate circuit voltages, plate current, input voltage, and output voltage. Reduce input and measure gain.

5. With grid return to A, repeat part 4. With signal removed, make a d-c input versus d-c output record and plot on the same graph as the curve calculated in part 2.

6. With the connection of Fig. 2, apply a sinusoidal input signal to give a reasonable output with no visible distortion. Vary R_L and calculate power in R_L by $P = E^2/R_L$ to find maximum power output. R_L at this time is equal to the internal resistance of the cathode follower.

Calculations and conclusions

7. Discuss and justify, if possible, any discrepancies between calculated and measured results.

8. Calculate the output impedance of Fig. 2 and compare with a graph of P_{out} vs R_L data taken in part 6.

9. (a)   Why is the cathode follower especially good when a large linear output range is needed?

(b)   If the gain of a cathode follower were measured, would this gain be stable from day to day? Explain.

References

Ryder, J. D., *Electronic Fundamentals and Applications*, 2d ed. (Englewood Cliffs, N. J.: Prentice-Hall, Inc., 1959).

Millman, J., and Seeley, S., *Electronics* (New York: McGraw-Hill Book Co., Inc., 1941).

Materials required

Components	*Equipment*
1 6J5 tube and socket	1 cathode-ray oscillograph (to view waveforms)
1 2 μf by-pass capacitor	
1 10 μf coupling capacitor	2 a-c voltmeters (to measure input and output voltages)
1 10 K bias adjustment potentiometer	
1 10 K resistor, 5 watt	1 multimeter or one 300 volt and one 25 volt voltmeter to set d-c potentials
1 100 K resistor	
1 10 K (total) decade resistor	
	1 25 ma d-c meter to measure plate current
	1 audio oscillator to provide 60 volts of signal (lower output and a step-up transformer are satisfactory)
	1 d-c power supply (250 volts at 25 ma and 6.3 volts, a-c)

EXPERIMENT

7-A

Negative Feedback

Purpose

The purpose of this experiment is to demonstrate some of the major features of negative feedback in amplifiers. The features receiving particular attention are as follows:

A. Distortion reduction (equal to gain reduction)
B. Gain stability with respect to component variation
C. Output impedance

Information

The major advantages of the negative feedback type of amplifier are mentioned under "Purpose." These will be demonstrated in terms of Figs. 1 and 2.

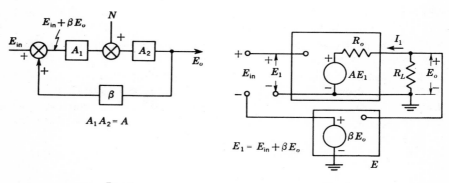

Fig. 1   Fig. 2

In Fig. 1 the following equations hold:

$$[A_1(E_{in} + \beta E_o) + N]A_2 = E_o \tag{1}$$

$$\therefore E_o = E_{in}\frac{A}{1 - A\beta} + N\frac{A_2}{1 - A\beta} \tag{2}$$

From equation (2) it can be concluded that a distortion or noise signal (N) can be reduced by applying a fraction (β) of the output signal back into the input of the amplifier. The reduction of distortion or noise voltage is accompanied by an equal reduction of the overall gain (E_o/E_{in}). Further consideration will indicate that the advantages are very real for distortion voltages (for they arise in the high-level or output stages) but are difficult to realize for noise (which almost invariably occurs in the low-level input stages).

Stability of gain in this experiment will be described in terms of "sensitivity," a quantity defined in equation (3).

$$S = \left| \frac{\text{per cent change in a circuit parameter } (W)}{\text{per cent change in gain due to change in } W} \right| = \left| \frac{(dW/W) \quad 100\%}{(dA/A) \quad 100\%} \right| \quad (3)$$

For example, in a common resistance coupled amplifier with a gain $-\mu R_L/(r_p + R_L)$, the sensitivity with respect to μ is one, while that with respect to r_p is $(r_p + R_L)/r_p$. The effect of feedback on S will be demonstrated later in this experiment.

In Fig. 2, with $\beta = 0$, R_L should equal R_o for maximum power transfer. If a generator (E_o) is substituted for R_L and the ratio of E_o/I_1 evaluated, this will be the output resistance in any case. E_{in} is zero.

$$E_o - AE_1 = I_1 R_o$$
$$E_o - A\beta E_o = I_1 R_o$$
$$\text{Output resistance} = \frac{E_o}{I_1} = \frac{R_o}{1 - A\beta} \quad (4)$$

Equation (4) illustrates the modified output impedance due to negative feedback.

Negative feedback amplifiers are usually classified as "voltage" or

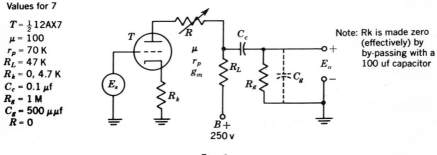

Values for 7

$T = \frac{1}{2}$ 12AX7
$\mu = 100$
$r_p = 70$ K
$R_L = 47$ K
$R_k = 0, 4.7$ K
$C_c = 0.1 \, \mu f$
$R_g = 1$ M
$C_g = 500 \, \mu\mu f$
$R = 0$

Note: Rk is made zero (effectively) by by-passing with a 100 uf capacitor

B+
250 v

Fig. 3

"current" feedback amplifiers. The voltage feedback amplifier tends to maintain constant output voltage; therefore its apparent internal impedance is decreased. In current feedback, the voltage feedback is proportional to the output current. This tends to maintain constant output current and therefore represents increased internal impedance. In many amplifiers the type of feedback is difficult to determine, so that the change of internal impedance is probably the best criterion for deciding the type — voltage or current.

Many other facts about and uses for feedback amplifiers are available. Essentially, all servomechanism theory is feedback theory (if mechanical devices are allowed). For further information see "References" at the end of the experiment and "Information" in Experiment 7-B.

Preliminary

1. Give some advantages and disadvantages of negative feedback in amplifiers.

2. Give some circuit applications or design advantages for negative feedback amplifiers.

3. Give circuit diagrams for four negative feedback arrangements and a sentence or two on the operation of each.

4. Derive the gain and output impedance expressions for the circuit of Fig. 3 ($R = 0$). When deriving output impedance, assume C_c, R_g, and C_g can all be neglected. Is voltage or current feedback present?

5. The factor $(1 - A\beta)$ gives the gain reduction factor and, hence, the distortion reduction factor for an amplifier. When defined as in (5) it is called the "return difference" with respect to the element in question, R_k in this case.

$$F = 1 - A\beta = \frac{A}{A'} = \frac{\text{gain without feedback } (R_k = \text{max. gain value})}{\text{gain with feedback } (R_k \text{ unequal to zero})} \quad (5)$$

Note that the quantity β can also be determined from (5). Determine the return difference F for Fig. 3 (neglecting C_c, R_g, and C_g) with respect to R_k.

6. (a) Determine the sensitivity of Fig. 3 with respect to r_p ($R_k = 0$); neglect C_c, R_g, and C_g).

(b) Repeat with $R_k = 4.7$ K.

7. Plot on 4-cycle semi-log graph paper the gain of Fig. 3 from 20 cps to 20,000 cps. Use values of R_k of zero and 4.7 K ($R = 0$).

Performance

8. Check experimentally and plot on the same graph the curves taken in part 7. Note that R_g and C_g should include input impedance of all measuring instruments.

9. (a) With the circuit of Fig. 3 and $R_k = 0$, note the change in gain at 1000 cps as R is changed from zero to 27,000 ohms. This is used to represent the tendency of vacuum tubes to have increasing r_p with age.

(b)   Repeat (a) with R_k = 4.7 K.

10. (a)   With the circuit of Fig. 3 and R_k = 0, increase the input signal until very noticeable distortion is observed on an oscilloscope connected across the output terminals. Record the output voltage and waveshape.

(b)   Repeat (a) with R_k = 4.7 K. In this case increase the input until an output voltage equal to that in part (a) is obtained. Record the waveshape.

Calculations and conclusions

11. Did feedback improve the frequency response? Why? Under what conditions would this circuit improve frequency response?

12. Discuss briefly the following points:

(a)   comparison of calculated and experimental results

(b)   fulfillment of expected advantages (including reduction of frequency distortion)

(c)   a method of determining output impedance of the amplifier

(d)   any unexpected results observed.

References

Ryder, J. D., *Electronic Fundamentals and Applications*, 2d ed. (Englewood Cliffs, N. J.: Prentice-Hall, Inc., 1959).

Bode, H. W., *Circuit Analysis and Feedback Amplifiers* (Princeton, N. J.: D. Van Nostrand Co., Inc., 1945).

Materials required

Components	*Test Equipment*
1 12AX7 tube and socket	1 cathode-ray oscilloscope
1 0.1 μf 300 volt capacitor	(to view waveforms)
1 100 μf 10 volt capacitor	1 a-c vacuum-tube voltmeter
1 variable or decade capacitor	(to measure output voltage)
(to adjust C_g to 500 μμf)	1 a-c vacuum-tube voltmeter or
1 47 K, 1 watt resistor	rectifier type meter
1 4.7 K, 1 watt resistor	(to measure input voltage)
1 variable or decade resistor	1 300 volt d-c meter
(to adjust R_g to 1 megohm)	(to set operating potentials)
1 27 K, 1 watt resistor	1 audio oscillator (0–10,000 cps,
(NOTE: Decade components of	0–10 volts)
proper rating are suitable	1 d-c power supply (250 volts, 5 ma
for the above compo-	with 6.3 volts, a-c)
nents.)	

7-B

Negative Feedback

Purpose

The purpose of this experiment is further study of the effects of negative feedback on amplifier performance.

Information

Amplifiers have many characteristics which determine their suitability for particular applications. Voltage gain, power gain, power output, frequency response, phase shift, distortion, noise, input impedance, output impedance, drift, and stability are all important in particular applications.

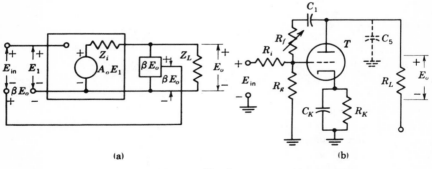

(a)   (b)

Fig. 1

Many of these characteristics can be modified by the use of negative feedback. In most cases the improvement of some qualities must be done at the expense of others. For example, negative feedback can improve distortion, stability, and frequency response — but at the expense of voltage gain. Voltage gain, however, is easy to obtain.

This experiment is on an elementary level and deals only with vacuum-tube amplifiers. However, the same principles apply to transistor amplifiers and to several other types. The whole theory of feedback amplifiers has been adapted to servomechanism problems and extended to the point that most new theory is coming from the latter field. Mathematically, servomechanism and feedback theory are the same.

The distortion reduction, due to negative feedback, can be shown to be proportional to the gain reduction (feedback) causing such an improvement. The improvement of gain stability is described by a function called "sensitivity," which is defined here by equation (1).

$$S = \frac{\text{per unit change in a circuit parameter } (w)}{\text{per unit change in gain due to change in } w} = \lim_{\Delta w \to 0} \frac{\Delta w / w}{\Delta A / A} \qquad (1)$$

The w in equation (1) might be g_m, r_p, R_L, E_{bb}, or any other parameter.

The above and other effects of negative feedback will be calculated for the simple circuits of Fig. 1 and then investigated experimentally.

Preliminary

1. Derive the gain with feedback A_f in terms of A_o and β for the circuit of Fig. 1(a).

2. (a) Derive the gain expression for the circuit of Fig. 1(b), with R_L in parallel with C_s taken as Z_L. Neglect C_1 and the cathode bias components.

   (b) The tube is a 12AX7 ($\mu = 100$, $r_p = 70$ K), $R_i = 100$ K, $R_g = 1$ megohm, $R_L = 47$ K, $C_s = 500$ $\mu\mu$f, and other components have negligible effect. Find R_f to reduce the mid-frequency gain to 10. Plot gain versus frequency to 20 kc, with R_f equal to infinity and also for R_f equal to the value found.

3. How could the circuit of Fig. 1(b) be used to measure mutual conductance?

4. Solve for the input impedance (exclude R_i) and output impedance (exclude R_L) for the circuit of Fig. 1(b). What effect does feedback have on these expressions?

5. Find the sensitivity of the circuit in Fig. 1(b) with respect to r_p, without feedback and with R_f set to give a gain of 10.

6. In general, what effect does negative feedback have on the noise generated by an amplifier?

Performance

7. Set up the circuit of Fig. 1(b) and take frequency response data from 20 to 20,000 cps. C_5 should be 500 $\mu\mu$f including the input capacitance of any measuring equipment (oscilloscope and vacuum-tube voltmeter). R_f = infinity, R_i = 100 K, R_g = 1 megohm, R_L = 47 K, R_K = 1.5 K, C_K = 10 μf, and B^+ = 250 volts. Input voltage should be about 0.1 volt. Vary E_{bb} by plus and minus 100 volts and note change in gain at 1000 cps.

8. Repeat part 7 with R_f as calculated in part 2(b).

9. Substitute a decade resistor for R_f and use this to measure the mutual conductance of the tube.

Calculations and conclusions

10. Plot the data obtained in parts 7 and 8 along with the calculated values.

11. Comment on any significant points observed in the experimental work and the data obtained.

References

Ryder, J. D., *Electronic Fundamentals and Applications*, 2d ed. (Englewood Cliffs, N. J.: Prentice-Hall, Inc., 1959).

Martin, T. L., *Electronic Circuits* (Englewood Cliffs, N. J.: Prentice-Hall, Inc., 1955).

Seeley, S., *Electron-Tube Circuits* (New York: McGraw-Hill Book Co., Inc., 1950).

Materials required

Components	*Equipment*
1 12AX7 tube and socket	1 150–350 volt power supply with 6.3 volts a-c
1 1 megohm decade resistor	1 cathode-ray oscilloscope
1 1 megohm resistor	1 20–20 kc generator
1 100 K resistor	2 a-c vacuum-tube voltmeters
1 47 K resistor	1 multimeter, 20,000 ohms per volt
1 1.5 K resistor	
2 10 μf capacitors, 600 volts	
1 450 μμf capacitor	

8-A

Q-Measurements

Purpose

The major objective of this experiment is to study the Q of coils and capacitors and its influence on their applications. Incidental notice will be taken of distributed capacitance and of dielectrics.

Information

The most common definition for Q or quality factor as associated with a coil is $Q = \omega L/R$. Other definitions are occasionally used. Its importance stems from the fact that "high-Q" is synonymous with "low loss." High-Q tuned circuits then are very selective (see "Preliminary") and only lightly damped. A shock-excited high-Q tuned circuit will "ring" or oscillate for longer periods than low-Q circuits.

Since Q has been applied to excellence of coils (losslessness), it has also been applied to capacitors to indicate the ratio of their reactance to re-

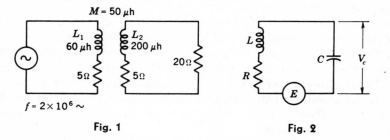

Fig. 1   Fig. 2

sistance. The reciprocal of Q is termed D or dissipation factor. When Q is one or less, D-measurements are commonly made.

Preliminary

1. List the factors that determine the Q of a coil.
2. Determine the Q of the primary circuit alone. Determine the effect

on the Q of the primary circuit produced by coupling the secondary circuit as shown in Fig. 1.

3. If the Q of a series RLC circuit is defined by the relation $Q = \left| \dfrac{V_c}{E} \right|$ at resonance,

(a) In the given circuit (Fig. 2) prove that this is equivalent to $Q = \omega_r L/R$.

(b) If a resistance R_{sh} is now placed across the capacitor, prove that the new Q of the circuit is

$$Q' = Q \left[\frac{1}{1 + Q^2(R/R_{sh})} \right]$$

if $R_{sh} \gg R$. (However, R_{sh} may not be large compared to Q^2R. R_{sh} represents the input resistance of a measuring instrument.)

Note: The method suggested by Fig. 2 is used in the most commonly used Q-meter.

4. What is meant by the "power factor" of a dielectric? Define "dielectric loss factor."

5. What effect does the use of a dielectric-coil form of high-loss factor have on the Q of a coil?

6. List the following dielectrics in order of excellence at 10 megacycle: Teflon, black Bakelite, polystyrene, hard rubber, fibre, wood. (Excellence here refers only to their losses and does not indicate other desirable features such as breakdown strength and mechanical properties.)

Performance

7. Study the instructions for operating the Q-meter.

8. Measure the Q of three coils: coil No. 1, 28 turns of copper wire supported by low-loss material measured at 7.5×10^6 cps; coil No. 2, cotton-covered close-wound coil measured at 1000 kc; coil No. 3, a 2.5 millihenry choke. Determine R and L of the three coils.

9. Couple a 1000 ohm resistance to coil No. 2 using a few turns of wire for a secondary, and determine Q, R, and L. What has caused the change?

10. Insert a copper disk in coil No. 2 and again determine Q, R, and L.

11. Insert in coil No. 1 the various materials supplied and determine the effect of each on Q and R of the coil at 7.5×10^6 cycles. List the materials in order of increasing losses.

12. Using coil No. 2 take data necessary to determine its distributed capacity.

Calculations and conclusions

13. From the data taken in part 12 make a plot of C_T vs $1/f^2$, and from this determine the distributed capacity. Give the theory behind this

method. What is the natural resonant frequency of coil No. 2? Can it be used as an inductance above this frequency? In plotting this curve, a scale large enough to insure accuracy *must* be used.

14. Did Q, L, and R change in part 10? Why?

References

Q-meter instruction book.

Materials required

Components

1 coil of number 12 bare copper wire, 28 turns, about 1 inch in diameter and 3 inches long, and mounted (Q of at least 250 at 7.5 mc)

1 coil of about 50 turns of cotton-covered wire on a 2 inch Bakelite form with a 10-turn secondary closely coupled and a removable copper disk.

1 2.5 millihenry choke

1 assortment of dielectrics of equal volume to fit into coil No. 1

1 1000 ohm resistor

1 100 ohm resistor

1 10 ohm resistor

Equipment

1 Q-meter (Boonton Radio Corp. type 160A)

8-B

Q-Measurements

Purpose

The losses in reactive circuits, especially if tuned, are of primary importance in determining frequency and transient responses. A study of these losses as related to Q is the purpose of this experiment.

Information

Q of a coil is defined by $Q = \omega L/R$. For a capacitor, $Q = \omega CR$. Since coils are almost always more lossy than capacitors, they will receive particular attention. The most convenient and easily understood instrument for the study is the Boonton Radio Corporation type 160A Q-meter. First its operation and uses will be outlined.

Figure 1 shows the fundamental schematic diagram of the Q-meter. The oscillator furnishes a current I, measured by the ammeter, to the special

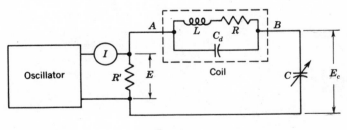

Fig. 1

resistance R' (0.04 ohm). R' is usually small compared to the other resistances in the circuit, and can be neglected. A known voltage E is thus introduced into the series circuit comprising the calibrated variable condenser C and the coil under test. The variable condenser is then tuned to resonance and the ratio of E_c to I used to find Q.

The Q-meter measures directly equivalent inductance, resistance, and Q, called L_e, R_e, and Q_e, respectively. Figure 2(a) shows the approximate equivalent circuit of a coil. It is approximate because the distributed capacitance is assumed to be lumped. Figure 2(b) shows the effective inductance and resistance of the equivalent circuit. If C_d is small, L_e and R_e are very nearly L and R, respectively. If the coil of Fig. 2 is series-resonated in the Q-meter, the Q read by the Q-meter will be the equivalent Q which may be written as $Q_e = \omega L_e / R_e$.

By writing the impedance of the coil of Fig. 2(a) and comparing it to the circuit of Fig. 2(b) several useful relationships can be obtained. Assuming that $R \ll \omega L$ and using the relationship $\omega^2 = 1/L_e C$ (at resonance), the following relationships can be found:

$$L = L_e \left(\frac{C}{C + C_d} \right) \qquad L \equiv \text{true inductance}$$

$$R = R_e \left(\frac{C}{C + C_d} \right)^2 \qquad R = \text{true resistance}$$

$$Q = Q_e \left(\frac{C + C_d}{C} \right) \qquad Q = \frac{\omega L}{R} \equiv \text{true } Q$$

Note: The distributed capacitance must be known. This is the topic of the next section.

To show the theory behind this distributed capacitance measurement, it

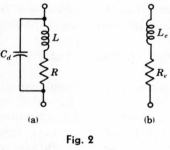

must first be shown that the distributed capacitance of the coil may be placed in parallel with the tuning capacitance of the Q-meter provided $C_d \ll C$. Redrawing Fig. 1 as shown in Fig. 3(a) and assuming C_d apart from the coil, Thevenin's theorem can be applied to terminals A and B. The resulting circuit is shown in (b). The circuit will resonate at $L \cong 1/\omega(C + C_d)$. As a first approximation, the variation of E' with C can be disregarded.

(a)   (b)

Fig. 2

Rearranging the last relationship and solving for C gives $C = (1/\omega^2)$ $(1/L) - C_d$. Thus, if the Q-meter is tuned to resonance at several different frequencies and the Q-meter tuning capacitor setting C is plotted against $1/\omega^2$, a straight line will result. The slope of this line will be $1/L$ and the C-axis intercept will be $-C_d$.

The method of this Q-meter lends itself to convenient measurement of inductance, capacitance, and even dielectric constant in terms of the calibrated capacitor and radio frequency generator.

Preliminary

1. (a) List the factors that determine the Q of a coil. (b) What factors influence the distributed capacitance of a coil?

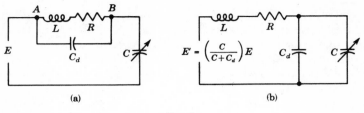

Fig. 3

2. Define capacitor power factor and D dissipation factor.

3. Neglecting C_d, show that $Q = E_c/E = \omega L/R$ at resonance for Fig. 1.

4. Discuss the relation between Q and frequency response and between Q and transient response.

Performance

5. Study the instructions for operating the Q-meter.

6. Measure Q_e of an 80-meter output coil. Vary the secondary load from 100 ohms to open circuit, and take data to plot Q_e, L_e, and R_e versus secondary load resistance.

7. Using one half of a 20-meter coil, take data to determine the distributed capacitance C_d. Include data such that Q, L, and R can be computed. Vary the frequency over the greatest possible range (3–10 mc). Take about six readings.

8. Using one coil from a 465 kc i-f transformer, take data of Q versus frequency over the widest possible range.

9. Measure, by substitution, the capacitance of several small capacitors. Record data such that C, R, and Q may be determined. Record all information printed on the capacitor for the purpose of identification.

10. Using the 20-meter coil at 10 mc, insert equal volumes of the following dielectrics into the coil and determine their effect on the Q. Be sure to retune the circuit each time.

Teflon	Hard rubber
Polystyrene	Fibre
Lucite	Wood
Black Bakelite	

Calculations and conclusions

11. Plot the data taken in parts 7 and 8.

12. Record and explain any unexpected experimental phenomena.

References

Instruction manual for Q-meter.

Materials required

Components

1 80-meter coil (two coils of about 50 turns of enameled wire, 2 to 3 inches in diameter, wound side by side, air-wound.)

1 465 kc i-f transformer coil

1 set of resistors for part 6 (100, 300, 1000, 3000, and 10,000 ohms)

1 set of equal volume dielectrics (see part 10)

Equipment

1 Q-meter

9-A

Singly Tuned Radio Frequency Amplifiers

Purpose

The general objective is the understanding of radio frequency amplifiers. In particular, two types of amplifiers containing one resonant circuit each will be studied.

Information

Two circuits (and their equivalents) frequently used for radio frequency amplification are shown in Fig. 1. Beside each schematic diagram the a-c equivalent circuit is given. For the circuit of Fig. 1(a), equation (1) may be written. g_p is neglected.

$$E_o\left[\left(\frac{1}{R_g} + \frac{R}{R^2\omega^2L^2}\right) + j\left(\omega C - \frac{\omega L}{R^2\omega^2L^2}\right)\right] = -g_m E_g \tag{1}$$

$$A = \frac{E_o}{E_g} = \frac{-g_m}{\left(\frac{1}{R_g} + \frac{R}{R^2 + \omega^2L^2}\right) + j\left(\omega C - \frac{\omega L}{R^2 + \omega^2L^2}\right)} \tag{2}$$

If in equation (2) C is the only adjustable element, it is quite obvious that A is a maximum when the reactive term is zero — or the parallel circuit is in resonance.

$$A = \frac{-g_m}{\frac{1}{R_g} + \frac{1}{R + \omega_{ar}^2L^2/R}} \cong \frac{-g_m}{\frac{1}{R_g} + \frac{RC}{L}} = \frac{-g_m}{\frac{1}{R_g} + \frac{1}{R_{ar}}} = -g_m R_{eg} \tag{3}$$

$$R_{eQ} = \frac{R_g R_{ar}}{R_g + R_{ar}}$$

Note: Since the pentode is normally used, and $R_g \gg R_{ar}$, the bandpass characteristics are almost entirely controlled by the tuned circuit.

For the circuit of Fig. 1(b), equations (4) may be written. The mutually induced voltage is arbitrarily picked as positive.

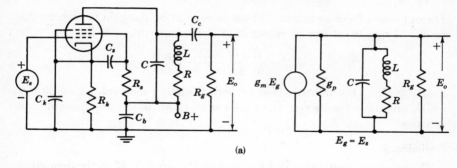

(a)

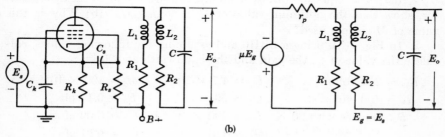

(b)

Fig. 1

$$I_1(r_p + R_1 + j\omega L_1) + I_2(j\omega M) = -\mu E_g$$

$$I_1(j\omega M) + I_2\left[R_2 + j\left(\omega L_2 - \frac{1}{\omega c}\right)\right] = 0 \tag{4}$$

In equation (5), I_2 is found. Both numerator and denominator have been divided by r_p.

$$I_2 = \frac{\begin{vmatrix} \left(\dfrac{r_p + R_1 + j\omega L_1}{r_p}\right) & \left(\dfrac{-\mu E_g}{r_p}\right) \\ (j\omega M) & (0) \end{vmatrix}}{\begin{vmatrix} \left(\dfrac{r_p + R_1 + j\omega L_1}{r_p}\right) & \left(\dfrac{-j\omega M}{r_p}\right) \\ (j\omega M) & \left(R_2 + j\omega L_2 - \dfrac{j}{\omega c}\right) \end{vmatrix}} \cong -\frac{g_m E_g(j\omega M)}{R_2 + j\left(\omega L_2 - \dfrac{1}{\omega c}\right)} \tag{5}$$

r_p is very large.

$$E_2 = \frac{I_2}{j\omega c} = \frac{-g_m E_g(M/C)}{R_2 + j\left(\omega L_2 - \dfrac{1}{\omega c}\right)} \tag{6}$$

E_2 will be maximum (with ω as the variable) when the imaginary part of the denominator is zero (easily checked by taking $\partial|E_2|^2/\partial\omega = 0$).

$$A_{max} = \frac{E_{2(max)}}{E_g} = -g_m\frac{M}{R_2 C} = -g_m\frac{M}{L_2}\frac{L_2}{R_2 C} = -g_m\left(\frac{M}{L_2}\right)R_{ar} \tag{7}$$

It can be seen from equation (7) that at resonance, the gain is proportional to R_{ar}. From (6) it can be shown that A is proportional to Z_{ar},

$$Z_{ar} = \frac{(R_2 + j\omega L)(1/j\omega c)}{R_2 + j(\omega L - 1/\omega c)}$$

if $\omega L_2 \gg R_2$. This indicates that for high-Q singly tuned voltage amplifiers, which are almost universal, the tank circuits control the bandpass characteristics.

Preliminary

1. (a) From equation (5), by including the effect of M in the denominator, show that the optimum value of M is $\sqrt{r_p R_2 L_2 C_2}$. (b) Why is this value of M seldom used?

2. In Fig. 1(b), using a 6BH6 and assuming the following values, calculate the value of C, the gain and the bandwidth at 800 kc.

$E_{bb} = 250$ volts	$L_1 = 4.7 \times 10^{-3}$ h	$M = 100 \times 10^{-6}$ h
$R_k = 100$ ohms	$Q_1 = 50$	$E_s \cong 0.1$ volt
R_s: replace with 20 K voltage divider to give $E_{sg} = 150$ volts	$L_2 = 200 \times 10^{-6}$ h $Q_2 = 120$	$C_k = 0.02 \ \mu$f $C_s = 0.01 \ \mu$f

3. In what applications are the amplifiers of the type of Fig. 1 generally used?

Performance

4. Set up the circuit of Fig. 1(b) with the values as in part 2. Test for maximum gain. Plot a response curve over the range of ±20 kc.

5. To check the given circuit for non-critical operation, make the following changes and record results:

$$E_{bb} \pm 25 \text{ volts}$$
$$E_{sg} \pm 20 \text{ volts}$$
$$R_k \pm 20 \text{ ohms}$$

Calculations and conclusions

6. Discuss any features of the circuit operation that were not expected.

References

Gray, T. S., *Applied Electronics* (New York: John Wiley & Sons, Inc., 1954).

Ryder, J. D., *Electronic Fundamentals and Applications*, 2d ed. (Englewood Cliffs, N. J.: Prentice-Hall, Inc., 1959).

Seeley, S., *Electron-Tube Circuits* (New York: McGraw-Hill Book Co., Inc., 1950).

Materials required

Components

1 6BH6 and socket

1 200 ohm potentiometer (for R_k)

1 approximately 20 K potentiometer (for R_s)

2 approximately 0.02 μf capacitors (by-pass)

1 14-7558 Meissner r-f coil (typical measured parameters given — these may be changed by slugs)

Test Equipment

1 250 volt d-c power supply with 6.3 volt filament output

1 radio frequency generator

2 r-f vacuum-tube voltmeters (1 if r-f generator has output meter)

1 20,000 ohms per volt multimeter (to set potentials)

1 oscilloscope (optional)

9-B

Singly Tuned Radio Frequency Amplifiers

Purpose

The general objective of this experiment is the understanding of tuning amplifiers. Two types of radio frequency amplifiers, each containing one resonant circuit, will be studied.

Information

Tuned amplifiers are widely used. They could be classified as follows:
1. Amplifiers with a single-tuned circuit
2. Amplifiers with multiple-tuned circuits
3. Amplifiers with stagger-tuned circuits
4. Amplifiers with filter coupling networks (includes crystal and mechanical filters)
5. Distributed amplifiers
6. Traveling wave amplifiers

Amplifiers of type 1 are cascaded amplifiers of the type to be studied here (singly tuned).

In general, radio frequency amplifiers may operate Class A, B, or C. The highest gain (voltage or power) is realized in Class A operation, while the greatest power output from a tube is realized in Class C operation, Class B being intermediate in both respects. Only Class A or B may be used for amplifying modulated signals. The singly tuned amplifiers of this experiment are classified as Class A voltage amplifiers.

In Fig. 1, two examples of singly tuned radio frequency amplifiers are shown, along with simplified schematic diagrams. In Fig. 1(a), the total effect of circuit losses are approximated by a single parallel resistance R. Since, for $Q > 1$, the impedance of the tuned circuit at resonance is resistive and equal to $L/R_L C$, the R is defined in equation (1). C_c is assumed an a-c short circuit.

$$\frac{1}{R} = \frac{1}{R_g} + \frac{1}{r_p} + \frac{R_L C}{L} \tag{1}$$

This parallel resistance is a good approximation only near the resonant frequency; notice that $\omega L = 1/\omega c$ does not exactly define the resonant frequency f_{ar}.

$$-g_m E_g = E_o\left[\frac{1}{R} + j\left(\omega c - \frac{1}{\omega L}\right)\right] \tag{2}$$

Let

$$\omega_o^2 = 1/LC, \ \omega = \omega_o(1 + \delta),$$

and

$$R = \frac{L}{CR_{eQ}} = \frac{\omega_o L}{R_{eQ}}\frac{1}{\omega_o C} = \frac{Q_o}{\omega_o C}$$

R_{eq} is a fictitious resistance in series with L that would account for total circuit loss and give correct resistance at resonance.

$$|A| = \left|\frac{-g_m R}{1 + j2\delta Q_o}\right| = \frac{A_{\max}}{\sqrt{1 + 4\delta^2 Q_o^2}} \tag{3}$$

In Fig. 1(b), E_o is found from the product of secondary current and capacitive reactance. The secondary current is found from the two loop equations.

$$A = \frac{E_o}{E_s} = \frac{I_2}{j\omega c E_g} = \frac{1}{E_g j\omega c}\begin{vmatrix}(r_p + R_1 + j\omega L_1) & (-\mu E_g) \\ (j\omega M) & (0) \\ (r_p + R_1 + j\omega L_1) & (j\omega M) \\ (j\omega M) & \left[R_2 + j\left(\omega L_2 - \frac{1}{\omega c_2}\right)\right]\end{vmatrix}$$

$$r_p \gg |R_1 + j\omega L_1|$$

$$A \cong \frac{g_m M/C}{R_2 + j\left(\omega L_2 - \frac{1}{\omega c_2}\right) + \frac{\omega^2 M^2}{r_p}} = \frac{g_m M/R_2 C}{1 + \frac{\omega^2 M^2}{R_2 r_p} + j\frac{\omega L_2}{R_2}\left(1 - \frac{1}{\omega^2 L_2 C}\right)} \tag{4}$$

If Q is high, maximum gain occurs when the imaginary term disappears, or when

$$A_{\max} \cong \frac{g_m M/C}{R_2 + \omega_0^2 M^2/r_p} \tag{5}$$

By taking $\partial A_{\max}/\partial M$ an optimum value of M may be found, but this value,

$$M_{opt} = \sqrt{r_p R_2/\omega_o^2} \tag{6}$$

is difficult to realize. From equation (4), if $R_2 r_p \gg \omega^2 M^2$, the gain [equation (6)] is

$$|A| \cong A_{\max}\frac{1}{\sqrt{1 + 4Q_o^2\delta^2}} \tag{7}$$

identical to that of equation (3).

Preliminary

1. Show that the bandwidth in cps (frequency difference between half power points) is f_o/Q_o, for the circuit of Fig. 1(a).

2. If, in the actual circuit of Fig. 1(a), $f_{ar} = 10^6$ cps, $L = 250$ μh, $Q = 50$ (at resonance), calculate the magnitude of the impedance over three bandwidths centered around 10^6 cps. Repeat for the approximate equivalent circuit; plot both on the same graph.

3. Why is the value of M_{opt} [equation (6)] hard to realize?

4. What factors that may affect the gain of the amplifiers have been neglected under "Information?" How would each factor show up?

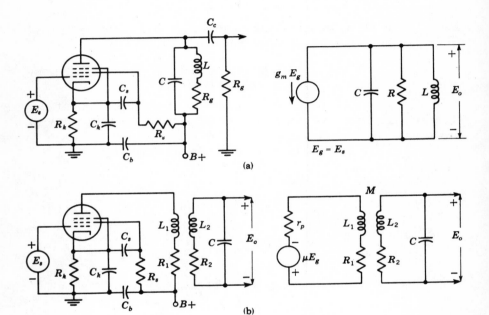

Fig. 1

Performance

5. Connect the circuit of Fig. 1(a) with the following components:

Tube 6BH6
$E_{bb} = 250$ volts
$R_k = 100$ ohms
R_s = replace with 20 K voltage divider to give $E_{sg} = 150$ volts

$C_k = C_s = 0.02$ μf
$C_c = 100$ μf
R_q = made up to 100 K including measuring equipment
$L = 250$ μh
$Q = 50$ (at resonance)
$f_{ar} = 10^6$ cps

Measure the gain at frequencies calculated in part 2.

6. Take data to indicate the effects of varying R_k, E_{sg}, and E_{bb}.

Calculations and conclusions

7. Since the magnitude of the gain is $g_m Z_L$, how do the measurements of part 5 compare to the calculations of part 2?

8. List and explain, if possible, any unexpected experimental results.

References

Gray, T. S., *Applied Electronics* (New York: John Wiley & Sons, Inc., 1954).

Ryder, J. D., *Electronic Fundamentals and Applications*, 2d ed. (Englewood Cliffs, N. J.: Prentice-Hall, Inc., 1959).

Seeley, S., *Electron-Tube Circuits* (New York: McGraw-Hill Book Co., Inc., 1950).

Materials required

Components	*Equipment*
1 6BH6 and socket	1 250 volt d-c power supply with 6.3 volt filament output
1 200 ohm potentiometer for R_k	
1 approximately 20 K potentiometer for setting E_{sq}	1 radio frequency generator
	2 r-f vacuum-tube voltmeters (1 if r-f generator has output meter)
2 approximately 0.02 μf capacitors	
1 approximately 1000 μμf capacitors	1 20,000 ohms per volt multimeter to set potentials
1 250 μh coil (see part 5 for requirements)	
	1 oscilloscope (optional)
1 approximately 100 μμf variable capacitor to tune L to 1 mc	

10-A

Doubly Tuned Radio Frequency Amplifiers

Purpose

To give a flat bandpass and greater skirt rejection, multiple-tuned circuit amplifiers are used. In this experiment the most commonly used amplifiers employing two tuned circuits will be studied.

Information

The doubly tuned transformer-coupled amplifier is very widely used for intermediate frequency amplifiers. Figure 1 gives a representative circuit and approximate equivalent circuits. Since pentodes are used, $g_p \ll \omega C_1$. The generator simplifies to $g_m E_g / j\omega C_1$ and the series impedance is approximated by $1/j\omega C$. Solving the two-loop circuit of Fig. 1(c) for the gain A gives equation (1).

$$A = \frac{E_2}{E_g} = \frac{I_2(1/j\omega C_2)}{E_g} =$$

$$\frac{-jg_m M/\omega C_1 C_2}{\left[R_1 + j\left(\omega L_1 - \frac{1}{\omega C_2}\right)\right]\left[R_2 + j\left(\omega L_2 - \frac{1}{\omega C_2}\right)\right] + \omega^2 M^2} \tag{1}$$

Assume circuit of high Q factors (10 or higher).

$$\omega_r^2 \cong \omega_o^2 = \frac{1}{L_1 C_1} \cong \frac{1}{L_2 C_2} \qquad R_1 + j(\omega L_1 - 1/\omega C_1) \cong R_1(1 + j2Q_1\delta)$$

$$\omega = \omega_o(1 + \delta) \qquad R_2 + j(\omega L_2 - 1/\omega C_2) \cong R_2(1 + j2Q_2\delta)$$

$$Q_1 = \frac{\omega_o L_1}{R_1} \qquad \omega^2 M^2 = \omega_o^2(1 + \delta)^2 k^2 L_1 L_2 \cong \omega_o^2 k^2 L_1 L_2 \tag{2}$$

$$Q_2 = \frac{\omega_o L_2}{R_2} \qquad \frac{1}{\omega C_1 C_2} = \frac{1}{\omega_o(1 + \delta)C_1 C_2} \cong \frac{1}{\omega_o C_1 C_2}$$

all based on $\delta \ll 1$

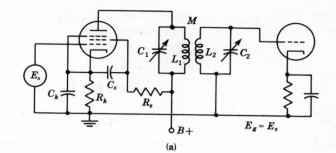

(a)

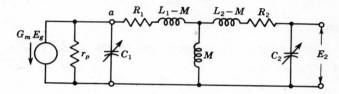

(b)

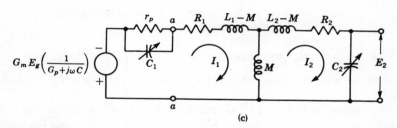

(c)

Fig. 1

$$A = \frac{-jg_mk\sqrt{L_1L_2}/\omega_oC_1C_2}{R_1R_2(1+j2Q_1\delta)(1+j2Q_2\delta)+\omega_o^2k^2L_1L_2} =$$

$$\frac{-jg_mk\sqrt{Q_1Q_2}\sqrt{R_1R_2}}{\left(\dfrac{1}{Q_1Q_2}-4\delta^2+k^2\right)+j2\delta\dfrac{Q_1+Q_2}{Q_1Q_2}} \quad (3)$$

By taking the $\partial|A^2|/\partial\delta = 0$, two values of δ to maximize $|A|$ are found.

$$\delta = \pm\frac{1}{2}\sqrt{k^2+\frac{1}{Q_1Q_2}-\frac{(Q_1+Q_2)^2}{2Q_1^2Q_2^2}} \cong \pm\frac{1}{2}\sqrt{k^2-\frac{1}{Q_1Q_2}} \quad (4)$$

This latter approximation assumes that either $Q_1 = Q_2$ or $\sqrt{Q_1Q_2} = 1/2(Q_1+Q_2)$. Equation (4) assumes $k^2 \geq 1/Q_1Q_2$. Critical coupling, k_c, is that value of k which will make the radical equal to zero. Its value is given in equation (5).

$$k_c = \frac{1}{\sqrt{Q_1Q_2}} \quad (5)$$

In terms of k_c, equation (3) may be rewritten as (6). The imaginary term in the denominator of (3) has been approximated by $4\delta/\sqrt{Q_1Q_2}$.

$$A = \frac{-jg_m\sqrt{R_1R_2}\,k/k_c}{(k_c^2 - 4\delta^2 + k^2) + j4\delta k_c} \tag{6}$$

$$|A_{max}| = \frac{g_m\sqrt{R_1R_2}}{2k_c^2} \begin{cases} \text{if } \delta = 0 \text{ and } k = k_c \\[2mm] \text{if } \delta = \pm\frac{1}{2}\sqrt{k^2 - \frac{1}{Q_1Q_2}} \text{ and } k \geq k_c \end{cases} \tag{7}$$

$|A_{max}|$ in equation (7) may be checked by taking the absolute value in (6) and substituting δ from (4). A set of universal curves is given in Fig. 2.

Preliminary

1. Assume the following conditions for the circuit of Fig. 1(a):

Tube 6BH6	$L_1 = L_2 = 1.70$ mh
$E_{bb} = 250$ volts	$Q_1 = Q_2 = 50$
$E_{sg} = 150$ volts	$\omega_o = 465$ kc
(obtained by replacing R_s with 20 K potentiometer for voltage division)	$C_s = C_k \cong 0.05$ μf
$E_{cc} = -1$ volt (100 ohm R_k)	

Calculate the gain at resonance and the maximum gain for $k/k_c = 0.5$, 1.0 and 2.0.

2. Referring to Fig. 2, a good definition for "bandwidth" in the over-coupled case would seem to be the frequency difference between the points where the gain decreases to its value at $\delta = 0$. Starting with equation (5) show that at these points

$$\delta = \pm\frac{1}{\sqrt{2}}\sqrt{k^2 - k_c^2}$$

Performance

3. Set up the circuit of Fig. 1(a) with the values as in part 1. Tune C_1 and C_2 to a maximum E_2 with a signal input of 465 kc. By tuning slowly through resonance and observing a VTVM across C_2, determine if the transformer is overcoupled. If so, adjust C_1 and C_2 to equal peaks on either side of 465 kc. Take data and plot a response curve of the circuit.

Calculations and conclusions

4. From the plotted response curve, what is the "bandwidth" of the amplifier as proposed in part 2, or until the gain is down 3 db?

5. Discuss any irregularities observed during the performance of the experiment.

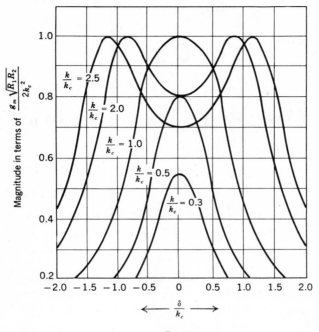

Fig. 2

References

Ryder, J. D., *Electronic Fundamentals and Applications*, 2d ed. (Englewood Cliffs, N. J.: Prentice-Hall, Inc., 1959).

Seeley, S., *Electron-Tube Circuits* (New York: McGraw-Hill Book Co., Inc., 1950).

Valley, G. E., and Wallman, H., *Vacuum Tube Amplifiers*, vol. 18, Rad. Lab. Series (New York: McGraw-Hill Book Co., Inc., 1948).

Materials required

Components	*Equipment*
1 6BH6 and socket	1 250 volt d-c power supply with 6.3 volt a-c filament output
1 200 ohm potentiometer for R_k	
2 approximately 0.05 μf capacitors	1 radio frequency generator
1 approximately 20 K potentiometer to set E_{sq}	2 r-f vacuum-tube voltmeters (1 if r-f generator has output meter)
1 approximately 465 kc i-f transformer	1 20,000 ohms per volt multimeter to set potentials

10-B

Doubly Tuned Radio Frequency Amplifiers

Purpose

The objective of this experiment is familiarization with the analysis and operation of the most commonly used bandpass amplifier.

Information

To obtain an amplifier with a wide, flat bandpass region with sharp rejection outside this bandwidth is not an easy problem. Single-tuned, double-tuned, multiple-tuned, and many varieties of stagger-tuned amplifiers have been used for this purpose. The one type to be analyzed here (Fig. 1) is the basic intermediate frequency amplifier type used in several hundreds of millions of radio and television receivers. To reduce the algebraic complexity in the solution of Fig. 1, identical primary and secondary circuits will be used. This loss of generality is not important in most practical cases, since the normal design is with identical circuits. In the few cases of widely different primary and secondary loading, a substitution of $Q = \sqrt{Q_1 Q_2}$ and $R = \sqrt{R_1 R_2}$ will usually give good results. A second approximation in Fig. 1 is the use of parallel coil resistance to simulate the series coil losses in R_1 and R_2.

Writing the nodal equations for Fig. 1(b) and solving for E_o/E_g, equation (1) is found.

$$A = \frac{E_o}{E_g} = \frac{g_m \Gamma_m / j\omega}{\left[G + j\left(\omega C - \frac{\Gamma}{\omega} \right) \right]^2 + \frac{\Gamma_m{}^2}{\omega^2}} \tag{1}$$

$$\Gamma = L/(L^2 - M^2) = L/(L^2 - K^2 L^2) = 1/L(1 - K^2),$$

$$\Gamma_m = \frac{K}{L(1 - K^2)}$$

Upon substitution for the inverse inductances, the conductance G, which is RC/L if we neglect r_p, letting $\omega = \omega_o(1 + \delta) = (1 + \delta)/\sqrt{LC}$, letting $Q_o = \omega_o L/R$, and rearranging, equation (2) may be written

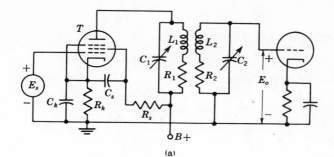

(a)

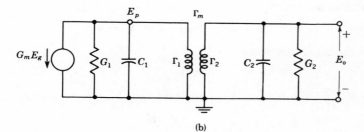

(b)

$$G_1 = G_p + \frac{R_1 C_1}{L_1}, \quad \Gamma_1 = L_2/(L_1 L_2 - M^2)$$

$$G_2 = \frac{R_2 C_2}{L_2} \Gamma_2 = L_1/(L_1 L_2 - M^2)$$

$$\Gamma_m = M/(L_1 L_2 - M^2)$$

Fig. 1

$$A = -jG_m K$$

$$\frac{\omega_o L(1 + \delta)(1 - K^2)}{\left\{ \frac{RC}{L} \omega_o L(1 + \delta)(1 - K^2) + j[(1 + \delta)^2(1 - K^2) - 1] \right\}^2 + K^2}$$

$$= \frac{-jg_m K(\omega_o L Q_o)(1 + \delta)(1 - K^2)Q_o}{\left\{ (1 - K^2)(1 + \delta) + jQ_o[(1 + \delta)^2(1 - K^2) - 1] \right\}^2 + K^2 Q_o^2} \tag{2}$$

Since $K^2 \ll 1$ (as will be seen later), and δ will ordinarily be small compared to unity, A may be approximated by equation (3):

$$A \cong \frac{-jg_m K Q_o R_{ar}}{(1 + j2Q_o \delta)^2 + K^2 Q_o^2} = \frac{-jg_m K Q_o R_{ar}}{(1 + K^2 Q_o^2 - 4Q_o^2 \delta^2) + j4Q_o \delta} \tag{3}$$

$$R_{ar} = L/RC = Q_o \omega_o L$$

If (3) is solved for maxima and minima (by taking $\partial |A|^2/\partial \delta = 0$), five values may be found. The value $K = K_c = 1/Q_o$ is termed "critical coupling."

Case I
$$K \geq \frac{1}{Q_o}$$

Three minima occur when

$$\delta = 0, \quad \delta = +\infty \quad \text{and} \quad \delta = -\infty$$

Two maxima occur when

$$\delta = \pm\frac{1}{2}\sqrt{K^2 - \frac{1}{Q_o^2}} \tag{4}$$

Case II
$$K \leq \frac{1}{Q_o}$$

Two minima occur when

$$\delta = +\infty \quad \text{and} \quad \delta = -\infty$$

One maximum occurs when

$$\delta = 0 \tag{5}$$

If $K = K_c$ and $\delta = 0$, then $A_{\max}$ may be found from equation (3).

$$A_{\max} = \frac{-jG_mR_{ar}}{2} \tag{6}$$

This is also the value of maximum gain if $K > K_c$ and δ is given by the values in equation (4). The values of gain when $\delta = 0$ and $K > K_c$ is given by (7):

$$A_{(\delta=0)} = \frac{-jG_mR_{ar}KQ_o}{1 + Q_o^2K^2} = A_{\max}\frac{2KQ_o}{1 + Q^2K^2} \tag{7}$$

Variation of gain with coupling is illustrated by Fig. 2.

Preliminary

1. In Fig. 1, the dissipation in both primary and secondary have been simulated by single shunt resistors. In what respects do the results of this approximate circuit match the original, and how do the two differ?

2. Why are triodes seldom used for intermediate frequency amplifiers? What modifications of the circuit of Fig. 1 would be desirable if a triode grounded-grid connection were to be used?

3. Assume the following values in Fig. 1:

> Tube 6BH6
> $G_m = 4000 \ \mu$ mhos $F_o = 465$ kc
> $L_1 = L_2 = 1.3$ mh $E_{bb} = 250$ volts
> $E_{cc} = 1$ volt $E_{sg} = 150$ volts

A bandwidth of 20 kc is desired with only 10% variation (notice that this

bandwidth extends beyond the deviations at which maximum gain occurs).
As a preliminary calculation, show that $A_{(\delta=0)}$ also occurs when

$$\delta = \pm \frac{1}{\sqrt{2}} \sqrt{k^2 - \frac{1}{Q_0^2}}$$

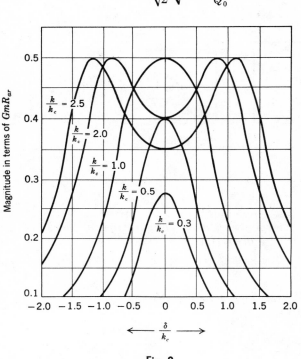

Fig. 2

Find A_{max}, Q_o, and M.

4. In what respect would slug tuned coils change the analysis given under "Information?"

Performance

5. Set up the circuit of Fig. 1 and by means of an AM signal adjust the transformer to maximum output. By means of a swept frequency generator, obtain the response curve on an oscillograph — Fig. 3. Use potentials of part 3. Observe and record the response curve as the coefficient of coupling is varied. (If a transformer with a variable M is not available, take the response curves of the several transformers provided.)

6. With the same circuit as in part 5, measure the gain of a calibrated transformer and compare with calculated results for same transformer. (See tube characteristics in appendix for necessary parameters.)

Calculations and conclusions

7. Were any discrepancies noted between calculated and experimental results? Explain if possible.

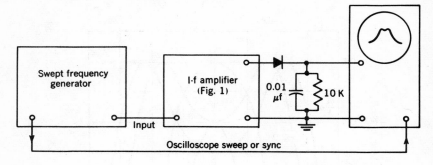

Fig. 3

References

Ryder, J. D., *Electronic Fundamentals and Applications*, 2d ed. (Englewood Cliffs, N. J.: Prentice-Hall, Inc., 1959).

Martin, T. L., *Electronic Circuits* (Englewood Cliffs, N. J.: Prentice-Hall, Inc., 1955).

Seeley, S., *Electron-Tube Circuits* (New York: McGraw-Hill Book Co., Inc., 1950).

Materials required

Components

1 6BH6 and socket
1 200 ohm potentiometer for R_k
1 approximately 20 K potentiometer to set E_{sg}
2 approximately 0.05 μf capacitors
1 calibrated, variable coupling i-f amplifier (or several fixed calibrated transformers with different coupling coefficients)

Test Equipment

1 250 volt d-c supply with filament output
1 swept frequency r-f generator (if this is not available the work must be shortened and point by point plotting used)
2 radio frequency vacuum-tube voltmeters (one if generator has metered output)
1 20,000 ohms per volt multimeter

EXPERIMENT

11-A

Frequency-Compensated Amplifiers

Purpose

A better understanding of the methods for broadening the frequency response of resistance-capacitance coupled amplifiers is the object of this experiment.

Information

The gain of R-C coupled amplifiers decreases both at low and at high frequencies. The low-frequency "roll-off" is due to the coupling capacitor and perhaps to cathode by-passing. The high-frequency roll-off is due to shunt capacitance from the plate and grid circuits to ground.

Many methods are available for high-frequency compensation, and they range from simple to very complicated. In this experiment, only the most elementary (and most widely used) forms of compensation will be tested. Since the important circuit capacitances are very difficult to control without chassis type construction, the circuits to be tested will be made purposefully poor in both high- and low-frequency response. For best results, however, the circuit leads should be kept to a minimum length.

Preliminary

1. Calculate the input resistance of the output cathode follower, including the 100 K and 150 K resistors.

2. Using this value of input resistance and assuming the output resistance of the 6AK5 is small in comparison, calculate f_1, the low-frequency half-power frequency. (For no low-frequency compensation, $R_x = 0$.)

3. Assuming the output-plus-wiring capacitance of the 6AK5 is 5 $\mu\mu$f, $R_L = 10$ K, $R_x = 0$, and $C_x = 0$, calculate f_2, the upper half-power frequency.

4. What value of inductance must be added in series with R_L in part 3 to make the gain at f_2 equal to A_{mid} (mid-frequency gain)?

5. Neglecting cathode and screen degeneration, what time constant of $C_x R_x$ would be suitable for low-frequency compensation?

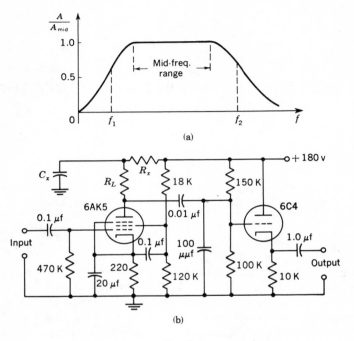

Fig. 1

Performance

6. Set up the circuit of Fig. 1 with $C_x = R_x = 0$ and $R_L = 10$ K. Take data for a frequency response curve, noting the half-power frequencies. Use both a vacuum-tube voltmeter and an oscilloscope on the output.

7. Under the conditions of part 6, vary R_L from 10 K to 1 K and note the change in f_1 and f_2.

8. Under the conditions of part 6, add inductance of 1 to 10 millihenries in series with R_L and take sufficient data points to determine the shape of the high-frequency response.

9. Under the conditions of part 6, except $R_x = 10$ K, vary C_x from zero to 1 µf and note the low-frequency response.

Calculations and conclusions

10. Plot the data taken under performance. Use six-cycle semi-log paper.

11. On the same sheet as used for the results of part 6, add the most favorable results found in parts 8 and 9 to show the improvement due to compensation.

12. Discuss briefly any unusual results observed.

References

Ryder, J. D., *Electronic Fundamentals and Applications*, 2d ed. (Englewood Cliffs, N. J.: Prentice-Hall, Inc., 1959).

Valley, G. E., and Wallman, H., *Vacuum Tube Amplifiers*, vol. 18, Rad. Lab. Series (New York: McGraw-Hill Book Co., Inc., 1948).

Anner, G. E., *Elements of Television Systems* (Englewood Cliffs, N. J.: Prentice-Hall, Inc., 1951).

Materials required

Components
1 6AK5 tube and socket
1 6C4 tube and socket
1 1–10 mh choke (or set of chokes 1, 2, 4, 7.5, and 10 mh)
1 220 ohm resistor
1 1 K resistor
1 2 K resistor
1 4 K, 1 watt resistor
1 7.5 K, 1 watt resistor
3 10 K, 2 watt resistors
1 18 K resistor
1 100 K resistor
1 120 K resistor
1 150 K resistor
1 470 K resistor
1 1 μf decade capacitor
1 100 $\mu\mu$f capacitor
1 0.01 μf capacitor
1 0.1 μf capacitor
1 1 μf, 200 volt capacitor
1 20 μf, 25 volt capacitor

Equipment
1 power supply (180 volts at 25 ma and 6.3 volts, a-c)
1 video generator (to 300kc)
1 d-c cathode-ray oscilloscope
2 a-c vacuum-tube voltmeters
1 multimeter

EXPERIMENT

11-B

Frequency-Compensated Amplifiers

Purpose

The purpose of this experiment is to study the methods of high- and low-frequency compensation of resistance-capacitance coupled amplifiers.

Information

Limits to low-frequency gain are imposed by the interstage coupling network, cathode degeneration, and screen degeneration. Methods are available to partially compensate for this low-frequency roll-off. By-passing part of the plate load resistor is the most common method. Actually, with present-day components it is seldom necessary to carry out low-frequency compensation. It will not be considered in this experiment, except in the preliminary.

High-frequency gain is limited by shunt capacitance in the plate circuit, of the wiring, of the coupling components, and in the input of the next stage. The most advanced approach to the problem of compensation is to consider these capacitances as part of a four-terminal coupling filter and design the filter for the highest possible cut-off frequency. This method is not used except in critical applications owing to extreme complications. The general analytical solution to the four-terminal coupling problem with arbitrary end capacitance is not known.

In this experiment, four of the most common and single compensation methods will be used. These are shunt, series, shunt and series, and cathode compensation.

Preliminary

1. Calculate the lower half-power frequency f_1 of the circuit of Fig. 1.
2. Calculate f_2, the upper half-power frequency of the circuit of Fig. 1, for $R_L = 1$ K, 2 K, 7.5 K, and 10 K. Note that the high frequency has been artificially limited by the addition of two capacitors. Assume 5 $\mu\mu$f additional capacitance in the plate circuit for tube and wiring.

3. If $R_L = 10$ K, find the value of L_1 to make the gain at f_2 equal to A_{mid} (the gain at mid-frequency).

4. Under the conditions of part 3 with $L_1 = 0$, find a value of L_2 to give suitable high-frequency compensation.

5. Find suitable values of L_1 and L_2 for compensation.

6. Explain how C_k may be used to increase f_2 and find a suitable value.

7. Show by means of sketches the effects of poor high- and low-frequency response when an amplifier is tested with square waves.

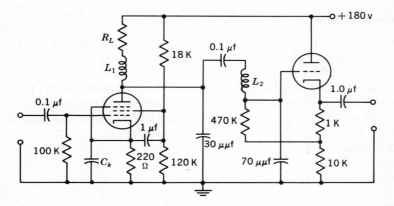

Note: Consider L_1, L_2 and C_k all zero unless specific values are given.

Fig. 1

Performance

8. Set up the circuit of Fig. 1 and check the values of f_1 and f_2.

9. Check both high- and low-frequency response of the circuit of Fig. 1 by means of a square-wave generator and an oscillograph under the following conditions. Adjust the compensating elements while testing for optimum results.

    (a) no compensation
    (b) shunt compensation
    (c) series compensation
    (d) series-shunt compensation
    (e) cathode compensation

Sketch the results in each case.

Calculations and conclusions

10. Sketch in tabular form the best results for each of the tests of part 9.

11. Discuss briefly the experimental results.

References

Ryder, J. D., *Electronic Fundamentals and Applications*, 2d ed. (Englewood Cliffs, N. J.: Prentice-Hall, Inc., 1959).

Valley, G. E., and Wallman, H., *Vacuum Tube Amplifiers*, vol. 18, Rad. Lab. Series (New York: McGraw-Hill Book Co., Inc., 1948).

Anner, G. E., *Elements of Television Systems* (Englewood Cliffs, N. J.: Prentice-Hall, Inc., 1952).

Materials required

Components	*Equipment*
1 6AK5 tube and socket	1 power supply (180 volts at 25 ma and 6.3 volts, a-c)
1 6C4 tube and socket	
1 0.5–5 mh variable inductor	1 video generator (to 300 kc)
1 1–10 mh variable inductor	1 square-wave generator
1 220 ohm resistor	2 a-c vacuum-tube voltmeters
2 10 K, 2 watt resistors	1 multimeter
1 18 K resistor	
1 100 K resistor	
1 120 K resistor	
1 150 K resistor	
1 470 K resistor	
1 0–0.1 μf decade capacitor	
1 30 $\mu\mu$f capacitor	
1 70 $\mu\mu$f capacitor	
2 0.1 μf capacitors	
2 1 μf, 250 volt capacitors	

12-A

Direct-Coupled Amplifiers

Purpose

The objective of this experiment is familiarization with the laboratory aspects of some direct-coupled amplifiers.

Information

Amplifiers capable of amplifying d-c voltages are being applied to many problems. Some uses are as voltage regulators, computers, servomechanisms, and a wide variety of measuring instruments. The one paramount problem in these direct-coupled amplifiers is "drift." When the input to the amplifier is held at a fixed d-c potential, the output is found to "drift" in a random manner. Since the stages are no longer d-c isolated, operation from a single power supply is impractical.

In Fig. 1(a) and (b), two of the many older types of direct-coupled amplifiers are shown. Figure 1(a) requires too many d-c supplies, and (b) requires a very high voltage supply. Power supply difficulties in cascaded amplifiers are perhaps best solved by a circuit such as Fig. 1(c). A positive and a negative supply, both well regulated, are required for as many cascaded amplifiers as desired.

The amplifier of Fig. 1(c) is termed a "difference" amplifier. It has many interesting features and advantages. If the output is taken plate-to-plate, it is proportional to the difference between e_1 and e_2. If the output is taken one plate to ground, it is still approximately proportional to $e_1 - e_2$ (exact if $R_k = \infty$). It is also an excellent direct-coupled amplifier if one grid is grounded. Plate supply variations tend to cancel as do the effects due to changes in cathode emission. The R_3 and R_4 divider arrangement is used to adjust the d-c potential for coupling.

Many other good d-c amplifier arrangements are possible. For example, mechanically modulated or "chopper" amplifiers are capable of much greater freedom from drift than even the difference amplifier. This experiment, however, will concern itself only with the difference amplifier.

Preliminary

1. From an equivalent circuit for Fig. 1(c) (and assuming it to be applicable at d-c) derive a gain expression

$$\left(\frac{e_{01} - e_{02}}{e_1 - e_2} \right)$$

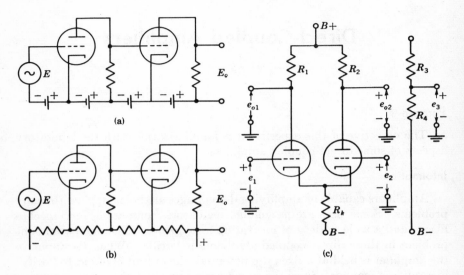

Fig. 1

2. If the output is e_{02} and R_1 is zero, derive an expression for e_{02} from the equivalent circuit.

3. If the output is e_{02}, e_2 is grounded, and R_1 is zero, derive a gain expression.

4. (a) Explain why power supply and filament temperature variations tend to be less important in the difference amplifier.

(b) Why are two triodes in a single envelope preferred for difference amplifiers?

Performance

5. Connect the circuit of Fig. 2(a). Ground E_{in} and record the drift of E_{out} as measured with a high-impedance d-c vacuum-tube voltmeter. Note the character of E_{out} — no change, slow drift, slow drift plus erratic change, etc.

6. With an input circuit such as Fig. 2(b), take data of E_{out} vs E_{in}.

7. Connect two 12AU7 as cascaded difference amplifiers as shown in Fig. 3. The input bias may be adjusted by the 50 K cathode potentiometer,

and the output bias by the coupling potentiometer. All biases should be between 5 and 10 volts when the input is grounded and the output is zero. Check the drift of this amplifier as in part 5.

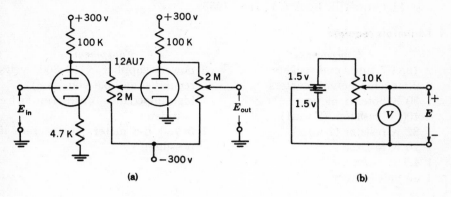

(a)   **(b)**

Fig. 2

8. Take data of E_{out} vs E_{in} for the amplifier of part 7.

9. Connect a single difference amplifier as in Fig. 1(c) with the second grid grounded. Take data of both e_{01} and e_{02} vs e_1.

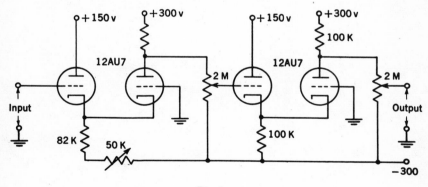

Fig. 3

Calculations and conclusions

10. Plot the data taken under "Performance."

11. Discuss any unusual features of the experimental results.

References

Seeley, S., *Electron-Tube Circuits* (New York: McGraw-Hill Book Co., Inc., 1950).

Valley, G. E., and Wallman, H., *Vacuum Tube Amplifiers*, vol. 18, Rad. Lab. Series (New York: McGraw-Hill Book Co., Inc., 1948).

Korn, G. A., and Korn, T. M., *Electronic Analog Computers* (New York: McGraw-Hill Book Co., Inc., 1953).

Materials required

Components

2 12AU7 tubes and sockets
2 2 megohm potentiometers
1 50 K potentiometer
4 100 K resistors (2 watt)
1 82 K resistor (2 watt)
1 10 K resistor
1 4.7 K resistor
1 45 volt battery

Equipment

3 power supplies (150–300 volts regulated and 6.3 volts, a-c)
1 high-impedance vacuum-tube voltmeter
1 5 volt d-c meter (center zero if possible)

12-B

Direct-Coupled Amplifiers

Purpose

The purpose of this experiment is to study a method of stabilizing direct-coupled amplifiers against drift.

Information

The experiment will be performed on a previously constructed computer-type direct-coupled amplifier, owing to the slight complexity of the circuit to be studied. The feedback network and the interconnections between the direct-coupled amplifier and the chopper amplifier are left out and will have to be connected externally.

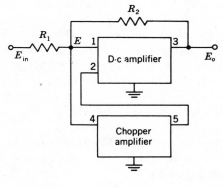

Fig. 1

The chopper-stabilized d-c amplifier to be used in this experiment is shown in block form by Fig. 1. It is necessary to understand the operation of each part before proceeding with the theoretical calculations.

With reference to Fig. 2, the direct-coupled amplifier to be used in this experiment is a Philbrick Model K2-W plug-in amplifier. The amplifier has two inputs which give gains of equal magnitude but opposite in sign. This is accomplished by driving the second stage on the grid and on the cathode, the latter through the input cathode follower as shown. After this combination is amplified by use of the third stage, the signal is taken out through

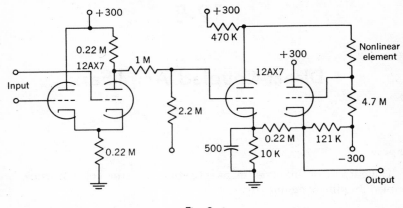

Fig. 2

an output cathode follower. Feedback between the last two stages is used to stabilize the amplifier against oscillation.

The direct-coupled amplifier gain is rated at 15,000 and the output is rated at +50 to −50 volts under loads to 50 K.

Figure 3 shows a schematic of the chopper amplifier. Only d-c and low frequencies reach the grid of the first stage. Higher frequencies are by-passed to ground. The voltages which do reach the grid are short circuited to ground at a 60-cycle rate by the chopper. This provides a square-wave signal to the grid. This square wave is amplified by the two stages and fed back to the opposite contact of the chopper which clamps the square wave to zero. Since the output square wave is clamped at zero, an average voltage is produced at the output. Thus the overall amplifier is a d-c (and low-frequency) amplifier whose gain depends upon the amplification of a 60-cycle square wave.

The twin balancing circuit is used to balance any 60-cycle alternating current picked up on the grid. It can also be used to zero-set the output of the complete amplifier shown by Fig. 1.

Preliminary

1. Calculate the d-c gain of the chopper amplifier of Fig. 3 from input to output. Assume that the a-c amplifier is sufficiently flat to amplify the square wave without distortion.

2. It will be noted that the combination of the 10 megohm resistor and 6 μf condenser constitutes an R-C filter which primarily determines the

frequency response. Using this and the results of part 1, sketch the expected frequency response.

3. Using the block diagram of Fig. 1, let

$$-A_1(f) = \text{voltage gain from terminal 1 to terminal 3}$$
$$A_2(f) = \text{voltage gain from terminal 2 to terminal 3}$$

and

$$-A_3(f) = \text{voltage gain from terminal 4 to terminal 5}$$

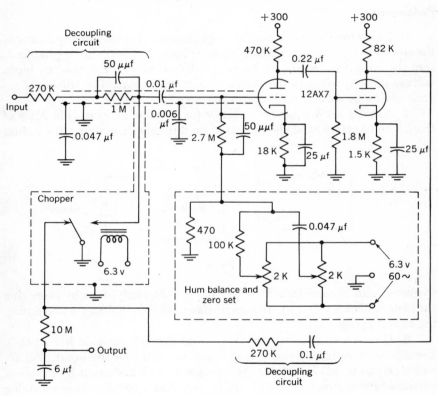

Fig. 3

Now assume that the voltage output of terminal 3 is due to signals on 1 and 2 plus a constant K which is due to a d-c (or slowly varying) drift in the d-c amplifier. Show that

$$E_2 = -E_1\left(\cfrac{1}{1 + \cfrac{2}{A_1 + A_2 A_3}}\right) + \frac{2K}{2 + (A_1 + A_2 A_3)}$$

where the assumption $R_1 = R_2$ has been made.

4. From the previous result, briefly explain how d-c drift is reduced. Why is an a-c amplifier used to stabilize the direct-coupled amplifier? Do small variations in A_1, A_2, or A_3 have much effect on the operation of the amplifier? By what factor is drift reduced owing to the presence of the chopper amplifier?

5. Sketch the expected gain of the amplifier from terminals 1 to 3 in db from d-c to 1000 cps.

Performance

6. Using the chopper amplifier alone, measure the d-c gain by means of the circuit of Fig. 4 and the following technique. With the input grounded, zero the output by means of the hum balance circuit. Increase the input voltage until 1 volt appears at the output. If considerable drifting is experienced, take several readings for improved accuracy.

7. Using a low-frequency oscillator (or function generator) in place of the 1.5 volt battery, find the gain at several frequencies so that the cut-off

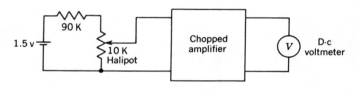

Fig. 4

frequency can be determined. This can be most easily done by observing the instantaneous voltage variation by means of a d-c voltmeter and noting the peak to peak value.

8. Connect up the circuit of Fig. 1 and measure the gain from 1 to 3. Use a helipot voltage dividing circuit and oscillator on the input. Set R_1 and R_2 equal to 500 K. Meter the voltages at 1, 3, and input by means of vacuum-tube voltmeters. Set 1 mv on terminal 1 to prevent overdriving the output. Measure the gain from 20 to 20 kc.

Calculations and conclusions

9. Tabulate all results and compare with predicted results.
10. Discuss any unusual or unexpected experimental results.

References

Seeley, S., *Electron-Tube Circuits* (New York: McGraw-Hill Book Co., Inc., 1950).

Valley, G. E., and Wallman, H., *Vacuum Tube Amplifiers*, vol. 18, Rad. Lab. Series (New York: McGraw-Hill Book Co., Inc., 1948).

Korn, G. A., and Korn, T. M., *Electronic Analog Computers* (New York: McGraw-Hill Book Co., Inc., 1952).

Materials required

Components

1 Philbrick Model K2-W amplifier with mounting
1 chopper amplifier as in Fig. 3
2 500 K resistors
1 90 K resistor
1 10 K helipot (or equivalent)

Equipment

2 power supplies (300 volts regulated 20 ma and 6.3 volts, a-c)
1 low-frequency oscillator (down to 10^{-2} cps)
1 d-c vacuum-tube voltmeter (a good quality, high-impedance instrument is required)
1 audio frequency oscillator
1 multimeter

13-A

Power Supply Regulators

Purpose

The object of this experiment is familiarization with power supply regulator circuits and components.

Information

This experiment limits itself to a few of the many available components and circuits. The wide usage and increasingly narrow specifications for such supplies, however, make it advisable for each student to become as proficient as possible in their application and design. The modern precise regulator with its high "loop-gain" is difficult to design and construct. The student may appreciate later the simple and well-behaved circuits of this experiment.

Preliminary

1. Show a characteristic volt-ampere curve for a voltage regulator tube. Indicate the useable operating range.

2. A OD3/VR150 voltage regulator tube has the following ratings:

d-c operating voltage............150 volts (approx.)
d-c operating current............5–40 ma
regulation (5 to 30 ma)..........2 volts
regulation (5 to 40 ma)..........4 volts

Design a circuit which may be used with the tube to furnish a constant voltage of 150 volts to a load from a 350 volt source. The variation of load voltage is to be held to 4 volts maximum. Specify power rating of the voltage-dropping resistor.

What maximum current may be furnished to the load?

3. Explain qualitatively the operation of the circuit of Fig. 2. Discuss both for changes of input voltage and changes in load resistance. How do the characteristic pentode volt-ampere curves help the current regulating action?

Performance

4. *Volt-ampere characteristic of a voltage regulator tube.* Take data for the volt-ampere characteristic curves for a type OD3/VR150 voltage regulator tube using the circuit of Fig. 1, within the current range of 5 to 40 ma. A set of data should be taken for increasing current, and another set

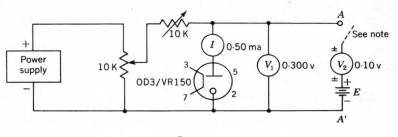

Fig. 1

for decreasing current. The purpose of the circuit of AA' is to provide a means of measuring small voltage differences.

Note: Leave circuit disconnected at point A until V_1 shows that the total voltage is approximately 150 volts. E should be either 145 or 155 volts, approximately.

5. *Pentode current stabilizer.* Connect the pentode current stabilizer shown in Fig. 2.

(a) Set V_1 at 300 volts and R_1 at its minimum value. Vary load resistance and record V_2 and I. Reduce load resistance to zero as the final step.

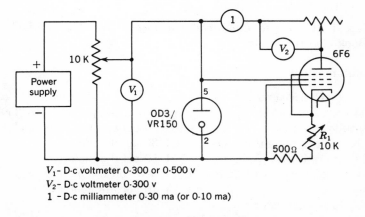

V_1 - D-c voltmeter 0-300 or 0-500 v
V_2 - D-c voltmeter 0-300 v
1 - D-c milliammeter 0-30 ma (or 0-10 ma)

Fig. 2 Pentode current stabilizer.

(b) Set R_1 so that about 5 ma is furnished to the load. Repeat the procedure of part (a).

(c) Set load resistance to its maximum value and R_1 at zero. Vary V_1 over its entire range down to zero starting from the highest value and record V_1, V_2, and I. Use a potentiometer to obtain voltages below the lowest range of the power supply. Observe and record qualitatively the change in the nature of the glow in the voltage regulator tube. Obtain enough points to define the curve in the region where the current starts to decrease rapidly.

(d) Repeat part (c) when R_1 is adjusted to furnish about 5 ma to the load when V_1 is 300 volts.

Calculations and conclusions

6. Plot the volt-ampere curve for the OD3/VR150 tube and an auxiliary curve showing the small variations in tube voltage. Discuss the general shape of the curves and the reasons for any peculiarities.

7. Discuss the purpose of V_2 and the battery E in Fig. 1.

8. For the pentode current stabilizer calculate and plot curves of (a) load current vs load resistance, constant input voltage; (b) load current vs input voltage, constant load resistance.

9. Discuss the curves of part 8. Explain any sudden "breaks" in the curves.

10. Discuss the qualitative characteristics of the glow in the tubes with changing current.

References

Millman, J., and Seeley, S., *Electronics* (New York: McGraw-Hill Book Co., Inc., 1941).

Terman, F. E., *Radio Engineers' Handbook* (New York: McGraw-Hill Book Co., Inc., 1943).

Materials required

Components	*Equipment*
1 OD3 tube and socket	1 power supply (170 to 350 volts,
1 6F6 tube and socket	50 ma and 6.3 volts, a-c)
3 10 K, 50 ma potentiometers (or	1 30 ma d-c meter
slide wire resistors)	1 50 ma d-c meter
4 45 volt batteries (with 22.5 volt	2 300 volt d-c meters
taps)	1 10 volt d-c meter
1 15 K, 10 watt resistor	
1 500 ohm, 2 watt resistor	

13-B

Power Supply Regulators

Purpose

The purpose of this experiment is the study of voltage regulators for power supplies.

Information

Many electronic circuits require well-regulated voltages for proper operation. Direct-coupled amplifiers, computer circuits, television circuits, and precision instruments are all examples of circuits often requiring well-regulated voltages.

The several general methods of voltage regulation involve: shunt regulators, electron tube regulators, magnetic amplifier regulators, and transistor regulators. Only the first two of these methods will be covered in this experiment. Several examples are shown in Fig. 1.

Good voltage regulators depend on a stable reference voltage and stable d-c amplifiers to amplify any error voltage. Reference voltage sources commonly used include batteries, regulator tubes, Zener diodes, and standard cells. All types of d-c amplifiers including chopper amplifiers are used.

Preliminary

1. From a knowledge of gaseous conduction, show the probable volt-ampere characteristics of gaseous regulator tubes on both sides of the usable region as shown in Fig. 1(a).

2. Simple shunt regulators of the Fig. 1(b) type are useful for regulating small loads (currents). Assume the OD3 regulator has a linear characteristic from 146 volts at 5 ma to 152 volts at 40 ma. A 15,000 ohm load is to be regulated from a 300 volt supply. Find the value of R_1, the maximum source voltage variation possible, and the per cent load voltage variation for a source variation of 5 per cent on either side of 300 volts.

3. By graphical means, determine the following for the circuit of Fig. 1(d).

(a) What is the load voltage variation with 450 volts input and R_a adjusted to 300 volts output at no load, when the load resistance is varied from infinity to 6000 ohms?

(b) What is the load voltage variation with 6000 ohms load resistance and R_a adjusted to 300 volts with 450 volts input, when the input is varied from 400 to 500 volts?

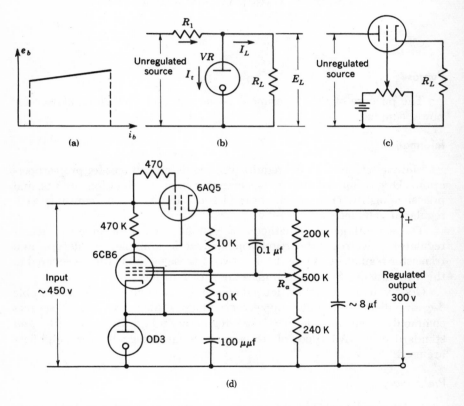

(d)

Fig. 1(a) Glow tube volt-ampere characteristic (normal glow region);
(b) gas-tube shunt regulator; (c) simple regulator with battery reference.

Performance

4. Take data for a volt-ampere curve of an OD3 regulator tube from zero to 50 ma plate current. *Caution:* Always keep as large a series resistance as possible to prevent tube damage.

5. Set up and check the circuit and calculations of part 2.

6. Set up and check the circuit and calculations of part 3. Keep an oscilloscope across the load to check for ripple, etc.

Calculations and conclusions

7. Plot the curve required under "Performance."

8. Discuss any unexpected experimental observations or deviations from calculated results.

References

Millman, J., and Seeley, S., *Electronics* (New York: McGraw-Hill Book Co., Inc., 1941).

Terman, F. E., *Radio Engineers' Handbook* (New York: McGraw-Hill Book Co., Inc., 1943).

Materials required

Components	*Equipment*
1 OD3 tube and socket	1 power supply (150 to 500 volts, 100 ma and 6.3 volts, a-c)
1 6CB6 tube and socket	
1 6AQ5 tube and socket	1 1 ma d-c meter
3 10 K, 50 ma potentiometers (or slide wire resistors)	1 10 ma d-c meter
1 470 ohm resistor	1 100 ma d-c meter
2 10 K, 2 watt resistors	1 300 volt d-c meter
1 200 K resistor	1 500 volt d-c meter
1 240 K resistor	1 cathode-ray oscillograph
1 100 $\mu\mu$f capacitor	1 multimeter
1 0.1 μf capacitor	
1 8 μf, 400 volt capacitor	

14-A

Audio Frequency Power Amplifiers

Purpose

The purpose of this experiment is to study the graphical analysis by which the power output, efficiency, and distortion of a Class A_1 audio frequency power amplifier may be calculated, and to experimentally compare these results with the actual values.

Information

The tube used in this experiment (the 2A3) is not modern, but it is still widely used and available. Characteristics are included in Appendix A.

Preliminary

1. On the curves supplied in Appendix A, plot the load characteristics for resistance loads of 1500, 2500, and 5000 ohms. The circuit to be used is shown in Fig. 1. The supply voltage will be 250 volts. All measurements and computations are made at 400 cycles. Do not exceed the rated plate dissipation of 15 watts. Neglect the resistance of the choke coil, and use a common Q-point. What value of grid bias should be used?

2. Assuming that the distortion will be small if the plate current is never less than 10 ma, find the effective signal voltage to produce maximum power output for each assigned value of load resistance while limited to Class A operation.

3. For conditions established in part 2, compute the d-c, fundamental, and second harmonic components of plate current produced by the signal. Compute the ratio of the effective value of the combined distortion components to that of the fundamental. This ratio multiplied by 100 is the per cent distortion.

4. Compute the power output and efficiency for each of the load resistances. Assume, as in a practical power amplifier, that the choke coil has a reactance large enough to be neglected.

Performance

5. Connect the circuit as shown, starting with the smallest assigned value of load resistance.

6. By means of bias and E_{bb} adjustment, set E_b to 250 volts and I_b to 60 ma. Apply a signal as large as possible without producing peak clipping. Record E_{bb}, E_{cc}, signal voltage, output voltage, and plate current, noting the change in plate current, if any, when the signal is applied. Repeat for each value of load resistance.

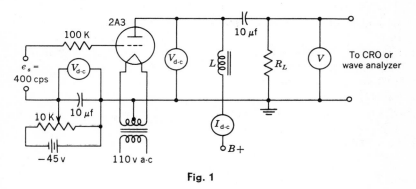

Fig. 1

7. Operate the 2A3 with rated load resistance and vary the input signal. Measure input and output voltages. Indicate the point where distortion becomes appreciable (as observed on the CRO), and the point where I_b begins to rise. Set E_{cc} and E_{bb} as in part 6.

8. Using the wave analyzer, measure the distortion components in the output, when using each of the three values of load resistance and the corresponding values of signal voltage used in part 6.

Calculations and conclusions

9. From the data of part 7, plot power and output voltage as functions of input voltage. Indicate the point where distortion became noticeable on the scope, and the point where I_b began to rise.

10. Did the increases in distortions and in the value of I_b occur at the same point? What is the reason for this sudden increase in distortion?

11. Compute the measured quantities corresponding to those obtained from calculations made under "Preliminary" and compare in tabular form any discrepancies observed.

References

Ryder, J. D., *Electronic Fundamentals and Applications*, 2d ed. (Englewood Cliffs, N. J.: Prentice-Hall, Inc., 1959).

Seeley, S., *Electron-Tube Circuits* (New York: McGraw-Hill Book Co., Inc., 1950).

Everitt, W. L., *Communications Engineering* (New York: McGraw-Hill Book Co., Inc., 1937).

Materials required

Components	*Equipment*
1 2A3 and socket	1 audio frequency generator
1 choke (8 henries or larger at 100 ma and less than 100 ohms resistance	1 cathode-ray oscillograph
	1 wave analyzer
	1 300 volt d-c voltmeter
1 1500 ohm, 10 watt resistor	1 a-c vacuum-tube voltmeter
1 2500 ohm, 10 watt resistor	1 50 volt d-c voltmeter
1 5000 ohm, 10 watt resistor	1 100 ma millammeter
1 100,000 ohm resistor	
1 10,000 ohm bias potentiometer	
2 10 μf, 600 volt capacitors	
1 2.5 volt filament transformer	

14-B

Audio Frequency Power Amplifier

Purpose

The purpose of this experiment is to become familiar with the design and problems of audio frequency power amplifiers. In particular, a beam power amplifier will be tested.

Information

Beam power amplifiers are very popular owing to their large power sensitivity — large power output for moderate grid voltages. (Characteristics for the 6AQ5 tube will be found in Appendix A.) In order to illustrate the use of the tube as a power amplifier and to show poor transformer effects at the same time, a filament transformer will be used as an output transformer.

Preliminary

1. In Fig. 1, using graphical methods, determine (a) the d-c power input with no signal, (b) the maximum fundamental power output with the restrictions that the plate current is never less than 5 ma and the grid is never positive, (c) the per cent second and third harmonic distortion, (d) the d-c power input with maximum signal, and (e) the plate dissipation under maximum signal conditions. Note: Assume no-signal bias is -12.5 volts and adjust R_k until this is achieved — screen grid current must be considered.

2. If the bias in Fig. 1 were fixed, would the Q-point shift as signal is applied? Note: This question is very sketchily covered by most textbooks. The correct question is: "Is the quiescent operating point a point on the dynamic path of operation?" A correct answer may be found by considering the d-c and a-c components of plate current versus grid voltage with the knowledge that the d-c component of plate current shifts.

Performance

3. Connect the circuit of Fig. 1. Set bias to -12.5 volts. With 100 cps

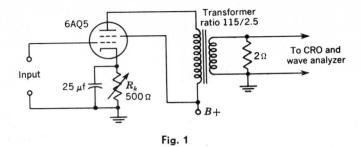

Fig. 1

input, check all of the values calculated in part 1. (The plate voltage, plate current, and screen current should be metered.)

4. With a 2 volt input signal, take data for a frequency curve 50 cps to 15,000 cps.

5. In place of the 2 ohm load insert 1, 5, 10, and 20 ohms and note the maximum undistorted power output for each value, as evidenced by the oscilloscope.

Calculations and conclusions

6. Tabulate experimental and calculated results and discuss differences. Plot the frequency response curve and the power output versus load resistance.

7. In what respects does the output transformer seem to be deficient?

References

Ryder, J. D., *Electronic Fundamentals and Applications*, 2d ed. (Englewood Cliffs, N. J.: Prentice-Hall, Inc., 1959).

Corcoran, G. F., and Price, H. W., *Electronics* (New York: John Wiley & Sons, Inc., 1954).

Everitt, W. L., *Communications Engineering* (New York: McGraw-Hill Book Co., Inc., 1937).

Materials required

Components	*Equipment*
1 6AQ5 tube and socket	1 power supply 250 volts at 100 ma and 6.3 volts, a-c
1 25 μf (or larger) capacitor, 25 volt rating	1 audio frequency generator
1 500 ohm rheostat for R_k	1 cathode-ray oscillograph
1 110 to 2.5 volt filament transformer	1 wave analyzer
1 set of 10 watt resistors, 1, 2, 5, 10, and 20 ohms	1 300 volt d-c meter
	1 100 ma d-c meter
	1 10 ma d-c meter
	1 multimeter for miscellaneous tests

15-A

The Class A Push-Pull Amplifier

Purpose

The purpose of this experiment is (1) to study the graphical method of securing operating characteristics of a Class A_1 push-pull amplifier from individual tube characteristics, and (2) to experimentally compare the actual characteristics with those predicted in the graphical analysis.

Preliminary

1. When a push-pull circuit is used, a higher plate voltage and bias are used, and a power output greater than twice that obtainable from one tube operating singly is possible, while still retaining Class A_1 operation. Explain why this does not result in a great increase in distortion.

2. Aside from greater power output and reduced distortion, give two other advantages of the push-pull circuit.

3. What is the underlying theory upon which the "composite tube" graphical analysis is based?

4. Two sets of plate characteristic curves for the Type 2A3 tubes are supplied in Appendix A. Using these, prepare a composite diagram of two tubes operating in push-pull. The plate supply voltage is 250 volts, the bias is −45 volts. Neglect the resistance of the transformer. Using the ratio of Δe_b to Δi_b of the zero-volt grid signal line, find the equivalent plate resistance of the composite tube. How does this compare with "typical values" given for the plate resistance of a single type 2A3 tube?

5. For loads per tube of 375, 625, 1250, 1875, and 3750 ohms, calculate the power output, efficiency, and percentage third harmonic distortion for maximum allowable grid swing with each load. Operation is to be Class A_1. Tabulate these values for comparison with the results to be determined in the actual circuit.

6. Plot these results as functions of load resistance. Use a separate sheet for each variable, P_{out}, etc.

Performance

7. Connect the circuit of Fig. 1. Adjust the bias so that, with no signal applied, the plate currents in the tubes are equal to the current corresponding to the bias given under "Preliminary," and the voltage across each tube is approximately 250 volts.

8. Apply a signal just large enough to avoid cutoff or peak clipping in either tube, as revealed by the CRO connected in turn across the 10 ohm resistor in the plate circuit of each tube. For values of R of 1500, 2500, 5000, 7500, and 15,000 ohms, corresponding to the loads per tube given in the "Preliminary," find power output, efficiency, and per cent third harmonic distortion. Compare these results by tabulation with those found in the "Preliminary." Check per cent second harmonic distortion in each case.

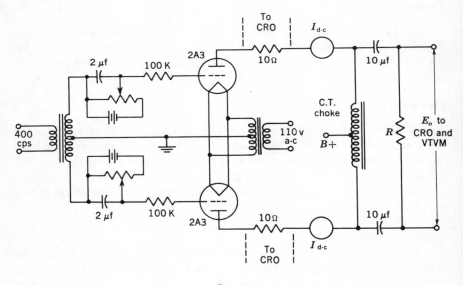

Fig. 1

9. For the value of R giving the largest power output in part 8, find power output, efficiency, and per cent third harmonic distortion for 25, 50, 75, and 100 per cent of the allowable grid signal found in part 8.

Calculations and conclusions

10. Plot the results of part 8 on the same sheets as those used in the "Preliminary." From the curves of power output, what value of R would give maximum power? How does this compare with the value of plate resistance found in part 4?

11. Plot the results of part 9 as a function of percentage allowable signal.

12. Explain why the circuit actually used gives the same results as if an output transformer were used.

13. Discuss in general the theory, results, and any discrepancies found.

References

Ryder, J. D., *Electronic Fundamentals and Applications*, 2d ed. (Englewood Cliffs, N. J.: Prentice-Hall, Inc., 1959).

Corcoran, G. F., and Price, H. W., *Electronics* (New York: John Wiley & Sons, Inc., 1954).

Everitt, W. L., *Communications Engineering* (New York: McGraw-Hill Book Co., Inc., 1937).

Materials required

Components

2 2A3 tubes and sockets
1 2.5 volt filament transformer
1 push-pull input transformer (to supply 50 volt signal from available audio frequency generator)
2 2 μf capacitors
2 10 μf capacitors (600 volt ratings)
2 10,000 ohm potentiometers
2 45 volt batteries
2 10 ohm resistors
2 100,000 ohm resistors
1 set of 20 watt resistors (1500, 2500, 5000, 7500, and 15,000 ohms)

Equipment

1 power supply 120 ma at 250 volts
1 cathode-ray oscillograph
1 wave analyzer
1 audio frequency generator
2 100 ma d-c meters
1 multimeter (20,000 ohms per volt)

15-B

Class A Push-Pull Amplifier

Purpose

The purpose of this experiment is to become familiar with push-pull amplifiers by checking analytical results with experimental results.

Preliminary

1. Explain carefully why more power output at a given amount of distortion can be obtained from two tubes operated in push-pull than can be obtained from the same two tubes operated in parallel. How are d-c transformer saturation problems reduced?

2. By the use of typical triode transfer characteristics (i_b vs.e_c) show the waveform of current for each tube in a push-pull amplifier and how the two waveforms combine to produce very little distortion in the resultant. Use Class AB bias so that the current waveforms for each tube will be seriously distorted.

3. Prepare a set of composite characteristics for the 6AQ5 tubes to be used. The plate supply and the grid bias voltages will be $E_{bb} = 250$ volts and $E_{cc} = -12.5$ volts.

4. Using incremental methods, determine the effective dynamic resistance of the composite tube. Compare with the "typical" dynamic plate resistance for one tube as given for the tube or as computed for one tube.

5. For the plate to plate load resistances of 5000, 10,000, 20,000, and 40,000, compute the following for a maximum grid signal in Class A_1 operation: (a) d-c power input; (b) a-c power output; (c) plate efficiency.

Performance

6. Connect the circuit as shown in Fig. 1. With zero signal adjust the plate voltage as measured from cathode to plate of one of the tubes to the value selected for your tubes. Adjust the bias voltages of each tube so that the plate currents are at values previously selected. Make a "trimming" adjustment of plate voltage and current. Record actual value of all d-c voltages and currents.

7. With a load of 10,000 ohms plate to plate, apply a grid signal of 12.5 volts (peak) at 1000 cps. Record the a-c input and output voltages and plate current of each tube, plate and plate supply voltages for each tube, bias voltages for each tube, and draw a sketch of the current waveforms. Repeat for loads of 5000, 20,000, and 40,000 ohms.

8. Determine the load resistance in part 7 which yields the greatest a-c power output. Using this resistance repeat the measurements of part 7 except with the signal voltage varied in at least 5 steps from a low value to a value large enough to cause serious grid clipping, as observed by an oscilloscope connected from the grid of one of the tubes to ground. For each step of grid voltage record all voltages and currents and measure second, third, and fourth harmonic distortion. For the last step measure the distortion up to the tenth harmonic if possible.

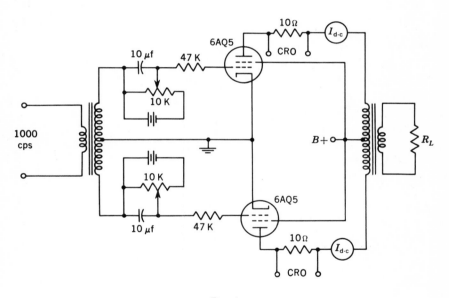

Fig. 1

9. With the optimum load and 2 volt grid signal, take data for an output versus frequency plot from 50 to 15,000 cps.

Calculations and conclusions

10. Compute, from the results of part 7, the d-c power input, a-c power output, and plate efficiency. Plot each as a function of load resistance on the same sheets as similar plots from part 5. Explain any significant differences between values from part 5 and part 7.

11. Plot second, third, and fourth harmonic distortion as a function of grid voltage from the tests of part 8.

12. Account for the second and fourth harmonic distortion found in part 8. Discuss the significance of the higher-order harmonics found in the last part of this test. How could even-harmonic distortion be minimized if a common bias were used for both tubes?

13. Discuss any unexpected experimental phenomena.

References

Ryder, J. D., *Electronic Fundamentals and Applications*, 2d ed. (Englewood Cliffs, N. J.: Prentice-Hall, Inc., 1959).

Corcoran, G. F., and Price, H. W., *Electronics* (New York: John Wiley & Sons, Inc., 1954).

Everitt, W. L., *Communications Engineering* (New York: McGraw-Hill Book Co., Inc., 1937).

Materials required

Components

2 6AQ5 tubes and sockets
2 10 μf capacitors
2 10,000 ohm potentiometers
2 47,000 ohm resistors
2 10 ohm resistors
2 22.5 volt batteries
1 push-pull input transformer (to supply 20 volts from available audio frequency)
1 push-pull output transformer of approximately 15 watts rating
1 set of load resistors, 20 watt to provide the plate to plate resistances of part 2

Equipment

1 power supply 125 ma at 250 volts
1 cathode-ray oscillograph
1 audio frequency generator
2 100 ma d-c meters
1 multimeter (20,000 ohms per volt)

EXPERIMENT

16-A

Class B Audio Frequency Amplifiers

Purpose

The objective of this experiment is to become familiar with push-pull amplifiers. In particular, a Class B amplifier will be analyzed and experimentally verified.

Information

The subject of Class B audio amplifiers is quite adequately covered in each of the listed references; however, a few additional comments may further clarify the experimental objectives.

In the strict sense, Class B means 180° of plate conduction; however, as an approximate "rule of thumb" 10 per cent of full signal plate current is allowed with no input signal. Low distortion in Class B operation requires tubes and transformers of excellent balance to cancel even harmonic distortion. These balance conditions are usually too costly for low power amplifiers and are used almost exclusively in high power modulators. In these applications, the added efficiency justifies the added component precision, which is more easily attained in the larger components. "Class B" implies B_2 because Class B_1 is practically never used.

This experiment will be done at "receiving tube" power levels, but the methods are identical to higher power applications.

Preliminary

1. Draw the composite characteristics for determining the operation of the two 6V6 beam power tetrodes. Use the following applied potentials: $E_{bb} = E_{c2} = 250$ volts, $E_{cc} = -25$ volts.

2. For the plate to plate load resistances of 2.5 K, 5 K, and 10 K, determine the following factors if the grid is driven to a maximum instantaneous potential of $+10$ volts.

    (a) Power output

    (b) Per cent third harmonic distortion

(c) Power input and plate efficiency (estimate screen grid current at 10 ma)

Performance

3. Connect the circuit of Fig. 1 with the potentials of part 1. Check all of the values calculated in part 2 plus the waveshapes in the grid and plate circuits.

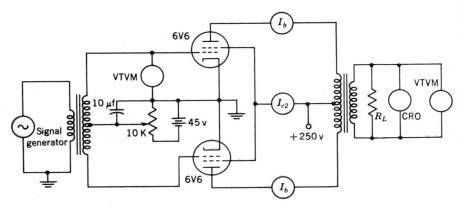

Fig. 1

Note: (1) Tubes must be selected for best possible d-c balance. (2) It may not be possible to drive grids to +10 volts unless the audio frequency oscillator has an adequate power output. If not, compromise to some attainable value with only small peak distortion.

4. Measure second and third harmonic distortion components at one grid and the load with a wave analyzer.

5. Take data for a frequency response curve of the amplifier.

Calculations and conclusions

6. Tabulate calculated and experimental results. Plot the frequency response.

7. Discuss experiment as applicable.

References

Ryder, J. D., *Electronic Fundamentals and Applications*, 2d ed. (Englewood Cliffs, N. J.: Prentice-Hall, Inc., 1959).

Corcoran, G. F., and Price, H. W., *Electronics* (New York: John Wiley & Sons, Inc., 1954).

Everitt, W. L., *Communications Engineering* (New York: McGraw-Hill Book Co., Inc., 1937).

Materials required

Components

2 6V6 tubes and sockets (selected for d-c balance)

2 transformers (input and output suitable to 6V6 and available audio frequency generator)

1 set of 25 watt resistors to produce plate to plate resistances listed in part 2

1 10 μf capacitor

1 10 K potentiometer

1 45 volt battery

Equipment

1 power supply 125 ma at 250 volts and 6.3 volts, a-c

1 cathode-ray oscillograph (d-c is preferable

1 wave analyzer

1 audio frequency generator

2 a-c vacuum-tube voltmeters

2 100 ma d-c meters

1 25 ma d-c meter

1 multimeter (20,000 ohms per volt)

16-B

Class B Audio Frequency Amplifiers

Purpose

The purpose of this experiment is familiarization with push-pull amplifiers, their analysis and testing.

Information

The Class B push-pull amplifier is mostly used for modulators where efficiency is very important. Balance between tubes is very important and receiving types must be carefully selected.

Preliminary

1. Draw the composite characteristics for determining the operation of two 2A3 triodes in push-pull. Use a plate voltage of 250 volts and a grid bias of −60 volts.

2. Draw 3000, 5000, and 10,000 ohm plate to plate load lines and determine the following by graphical means (drive the grids to +10 volts):
   (a) Power output
   (b) Per cent second and third harmonic distortion
   (c) Plate circuit efficiency and d-c power input

Performance

3. Connect the circuit of Fig. 1 and check the values calculated in part 2. Tubes should be selected as carefully as possible for the balance.

4. With a convenient constant input voltage, check the frequency response.

5. Connect the circuit of Fig. 2. With a bias of −20 volts, a plate to plate resistance of 4000 ohms, and grids driven 10 volts positive, measure the same quantities as were measured in part 3.

Calculations and conclusions

6. Tabulate the results of parts 2, 3, and 5. Plot the results of part 4.

7. Compare triodes and pentodes as Class B amplifiers.
8. Discuss any unusual experimental phenomena.

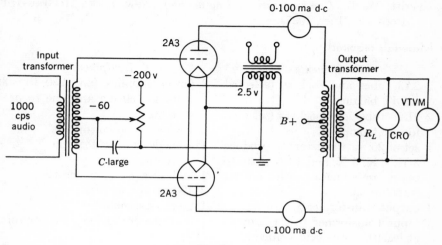

Fig. 1

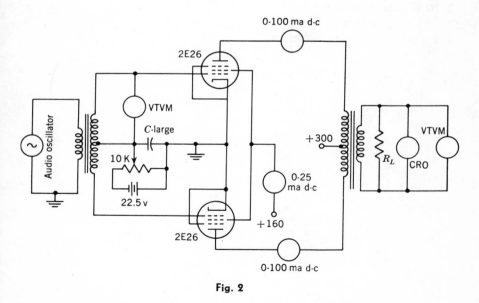

Fig. 2

References

Ryder, J. D., *Electronic Fundamentals and Applications*, 2d ed. (Englewood Cliffs, N. J.: Prentice-Hall, Inc., 1959).

Terman, F. E., and Pettit, J. M., *Electronic Measurements* (New York: McGraw-Hill Book Co., Inc., 1952).

Everitt, W. L., *Communications Engineering* (New York: McGraw-Hill Book Co., Inc., 1937).

Materials required

Components	*Equipment*
2 2A3 tubes and sockets (selected for d-c balance)	2 power supplies (one 250 to 300 volts at 150 ma and one to provide bias)
2 2E26 tubes and sockets (selected for d-c balance)	2 vacuum-tube voltmeters
1 set of 25 watt resistors to produce 3 K, 4 K, 5 K, and 10 K plate to plate resistances with output transformer	1 cathode-ray oscillograph
	1 wave analyzer
	1 audio frequency generator
	2 100 ma d-c meters
1 output transformer	1 25 ma d-c meter
1 input transformer (must provide at least 60 volts grid voltage)	1 multimeter (20,000 ohms per volt)
1 10 μf capacitor	
1 10 K potentiometer	
1 22.5 volt battery	
1 2.5 volt filament transformer	

17-A

Phase Inverters

Purpose

The object of this experiment is to aid familiarization with electronic circuits used to produce "balanced-to-ground" voltages from unbalanced sources.

Information

The widest use for phase inverters or phase splitting circuits is the driving of push-pull output stages. Other uses include balanced amplifiers for cathode-ray tubes and phase shifters. Two of the more commonly used circuits will be tested.

Preliminary

1. Derive the expressions for E_1 and E_2 of Fig. 1(a). Show that $E_1 = E_2$ if

$$R_2 = \frac{R_1[r_p + R_k(1 + \mu)]}{R_k(1 + \mu) - R_1}$$

2. Derive the expression for E_1 and E_2 in Fig. 1(b). Under what conditions does $E_1 = E_2$?
3. How will various stray shunt capacitances and coupling capacitors effect the balance of the circuits of Fig. 1?
4. Calculate the output impedances of the circuit of Fig. 1(b) at the terminals of E_1 and E_2. Let $R_L = R_k$.

Performance

5. Set up the circuit of Fig. 1(a) with the following circuit values:

T_1 and T_2 = 12AX7	R_1 = 10 K decade
R_g = 100 K	R_2 = 100 K decade (adjust for balance)
R_k = 2.7 K	$C_1 = C_2 = 0.1~\mu f$
E_{bb} = 300 volts	

With 1000 μf capacitors across E_1 and E_2 terminals (to exaggerate the affect of stray capacitance), take data for a frequency response curve. Check maximum output before noticeable distortion.

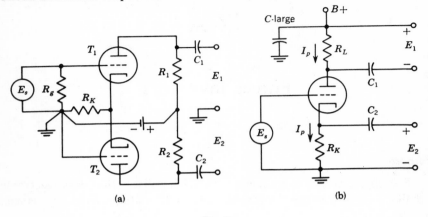

Fig. 1

6. Set up and check the circuit of Fig. 2 under the same conditions as in part 5. Adjust 4 K cathode resistor for maximum output before distortion.

Calculations and conclusions

7. Plot the curves of parts 5 and 6. How does the value of R_2 in part 6 check with the calculated value in part 1?

8. Discuss experimental inconsistencies.

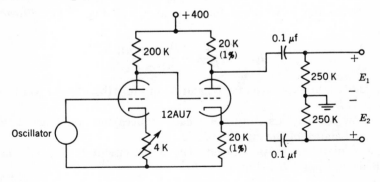

Fig. 2

References

Ryder, J. D., *Electronic Fundamentals and Applications*, 2d ed. (Englewood Cliffs, N. J.: Prentice-Hall, Inc., 1959).

Gray, T. S., *Applied Electronics* (New York: John Wiley & Sons, Inc., 1954).

Materials required

<table>
<tr><td>Components</td><td>Equipment</td></tr>
</table>

Components	Equipment
1 12AX7 and socket	1 400 volt power supply (20 ma and
1 12AU7 and socket	6.3 volts, a-c)
1 100 K, $\frac{1}{2}$ watt resistor	1 audio frequency generator
1 2.7 K, $\frac{1}{2}$ watt resistor	1 cathode-ray oscillograph
2 100 K decade resistors	1 a-c vacuum-tube voltmeter
1 200 K, 1 watt resistor	1 multimeter (20,000 ohms per volt)
1 10 K, 2 watt potentiometer	
2 20 K, $\frac{1}{2}$ watt, 1 per cent resistors	
2 0.1 μf, 400 volt capacitors	
2 250 K, $\frac{1}{2}$ watt resistors	
2 1000 $\mu\mu$f, 400 volt capacitors	

17-B

Phase Inverters

Purpose

The purpose of this experiment is to promote the understanding and to experimentally check the theory of phase inverting amplifiers.

Information

Phase inverting or "unbalanced to balanced-to-ground" amplifiers are widely used to drive push-pull amplifiers and other balanced-to-ground loads such as cathode-ray tube deflection plates. The most difficult problem in their design is the maintenance of sufficiently balanced voltages over a wide frequency range.

Two forms of phase inverters are shown in Fig. 1. These are commonly called the *paraphase inverter*, Fig. 1(a), and the *floating-paraphase inverter*, Fig. 1(b). For the paraphase inverter, it can be seen that the gain, E_1/E_{in}, is given by (1) and the conditions of balance by (2). T_1 and T_2 are assumed identical, and a frequency range where all reactances may be neglected is chosen.

$$A_1 = \frac{E_1}{E_{in}} = \frac{-\mu R_3}{r_p + R_3}, \qquad \text{where } R_3 = \frac{R_2 R_3'}{R_2 + R_3'} \tag{1}$$

$$A_2 = \frac{E_2}{E_{in}} = \frac{(K)(-\mu R_4)}{r_p + R_4} \tag{2}$$

therefore, if

$$\frac{K\mu R_4}{r_p + R_4} = 1 \quad \text{or} \quad K = \frac{r_p + R_4}{\mu R_4}$$

then

$$E_2 = -E_1$$

Usually $R_4 = R_3$, hence $K = A^{-1}$. This circuit will not be balanced at low frequency owing to C_2 and R_2, nor at any time when T_1 and T_2 are not identical.

Figure 1(b) shows one form of the floating-paraphase inverter. The input to T_2 is $R_b(I_1 + I_2)$ and R_b provides negative feedback to T_2. If this degeneration is made quite large, and the voltages are initially balanced, the circuit may be expected to retain that balance.

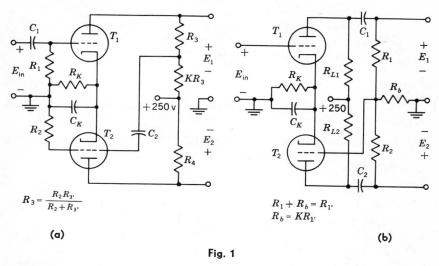

$$R_3 = \frac{R_2 R_{3'}}{R_2 + R_{3'}}$$

(a)

$$R_1 + R_b = R_{1'}$$
$$R_b = KR_{1'}$$

(b)

Fig. 1

Preliminary

1. Derive equations (1) and (2).

2. In the range where reactances may be neglected, derive an equation which, when satisfied, will assure that $E_1 = -E_2$ in Fig. 1(b).

3. How will the stray and coupling capacitances affect the balance of circuits in Fig. 1(a) and 1(b)?

Performance

4. Using the following values set up the circuits of Fig. 1 and adjust K for exact balance at 1000 cps.

Fig. 1(a)	Fig. 1(b)
$T_1, T_2 = 12AX7$	$T_1, T_2 = 12AX7$
$R_1, R_2 = 1$ megohm	$R_K = 1$ K
$R_k = 1$ K	$R_{L1}, R_{L2} = 100$ K
$R_3 = 100$ K (potentiometer)	$R_1 = 100$ K (potentiometer)
$R_4 = 100$ K	$R_2 = 100$ K
$C_K = 10$ μf (or larger)	$C_1, C_2 = 0.1$ μf
$C_1, C_2 = 0.1$ μf	$C_K = 10$ μf (or larger)

Before disconnecting either circuit, note parts 5 and 6.

5. By connecting a separate variable supply to T_2, note the unbalance that occurs in each circuit for 5, 10, and 15 per cent decrease in its filament voltage.

6. Check and take data of per cent unbalance at 10 cps, 100 cps, 1kc, 3kc, 10kc and 20kc.

Calculations and conclusions

7. Plot the results of part 6.
8. Compare the experimental and calculated values of K, as defined in equation (2).
9. Discuss any unexpected experimental observations.

References

Ryder, J. D., *Electronic Fundamentals and Applications*, 2d ed. (Englewood Cliffs, N. J.: Prentice-Hall, Inc., 1959).

Gray, T. S., *Applied Electronics* (New York: John Wiley & Sons, Inc., 1954).

Materials required

Components	*Equipment*
1 12AX7 and socket	1 250 volt power supply (10 ma and
2 1 megohm, ½ watt resistors	6.3 volts, a-c)
1 1 K, ½ watt resistor	1 variable 60 cps transformer
1 100 K, 2 watt resistor	1 cathode-ray oscillograph
1 100 K, 1 watt resistor	1 high impedance a-c vacuum-tube
1 10 μf, 10 volt capacitor (either	voltmeter
rating may be larger)	1 multimeter (20,000 ohms per volt)
2 0.1 μf, 400 volt capacitors	
1 6.3 volt transformer	

18-A

Class B and C Amplifiers

Purpose

The object of this experiment is the understanding of the properties which govern the usefulness and application of Class B and C amplifiers.

Information

The applications intended in this experiment for both amplifier types are those involving radio frequencies — although Class B push-pull amplifiers are useful for audio amplification. The Class B amplifier is useful in the amplification of amplitude modulated radio frequency waves, while the Class C amplifier is useful for unmodulated or frequency modulated signals.

The experiment will be carried out at audio frequencies with receiving type tubes in order that the more common laboratory equipment may be used. Except for radio frequency techniques involved, the results are directly applicable to higher frequency circuits.

Preliminary

1. Draw a diagram showing magnitude and phase relationship between plate current, plate voltage, grid current, and grid voltage of a Class B tuned amplifier. How do these relationships change in going to Class C operation?

2. Graphically and mathematically explain the reasons for a dip in d-c plate current as the plate tank is tuned through resonance.

3. Draw a circuit for amplitude-modulating the circuit of Fig. 1. What is the load presented to the modulator?

Performance

4. Set up the circuit of Fig. 1. Insert a 10 ma d-c meter in series with grid to indicate when the grid is driven positive. Tune the tank circuit to resonance as evidenced by: (a) maximum reading of VTVM across tank; (b) dip in reading of d-c milliammeter at X.

5. Insert a 50 ohm resistor at X. Sketch plate current pulses as viewed on a cathode-ray oscillograph. Is the class of operation B or C?

6. Vary the supply voltage from 300 volts to zero and record E_{tank} and I_b as a function of E_{bb} (modulation characteristic).

7. With $E_{bb} = 300$ volts, adjust E_c for Class B operation. Take data of E_{tank} and I_b as a function of E_g.

Calculations and conclusions

8. Plot the curves of part 6. From the slope of the E_{bb}-I_b curve, what load would the tube present to the modulator of part 3?

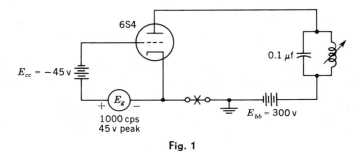

Fig. 1

9. Plot the curves of part 7. Why is a Class B radio frequency amplifier referred to as a "linear amplifier?"

10. Discuss the experiment as is appropriate.

References

Ryder, J. D., *Electronic Fundamentals and Applications*, 2d ed. (Englewood Cliffs, N. J.: Prentice-Hall, Inc., 1959).

Gray, T. S., *Applied Electronics* (New York: John Wiley & Sons, Inc., 1954).

Everitt, W. L., *Communications Engineering* (New York: McGraw-Hill Book Co., Inc., 1937).

Materials required

Components	Equipment
1 6S4 and socket	1 0–300 volt d-c supply (25 ma with 6.3 volts, a-c)
1 0.1 μf, 500 volt capacitor	
1 50 ohm resistor	1 audio frequency generator
1 45 volt bias battery	1 0–25 ma d-c meter
1 10,000 ohm potentiometer	1 0–10 ma d-c meter
1 10 μf, 100 volt capacitor	1 multimeter
1 100–500 millihenry variable inductor	1 cathode-ray oscillograph
	1 vacuum-tube voltmeter

18-B

Class B and C Amplifiers

Purpose

The object of this experiment is familiarization with these high-efficiency types of radio frequency amplifiers.

Information

Although this experiment will be carried out at audio frequencies, these types of tuned amplifiers are used almost exclusively for radio frequency power amplifiers. The distributed capacitance and inductance problems of radio frequency operation are absent at low frequencies, hence the basic amplifier principles will be easier to demonstrate.

One important feature of Class B and C tuned amplifiers is their high efficiency. Efficiency is gained by decreasing the tube losses. Tube losses are found by averaging the instantaneous product of the plate voltage and plate current as in equation (1).

$$P_p = \frac{1}{2\pi} \int_0^{2\pi} i_b e_b \, d(\omega t) \tag{1}$$

Since the plate voltage is minimum when the plate current is maximum and the supply voltage is equal to the plate plus tank voltages (instantaneously), the best way to reduce tube losses is to reduce plate voltage as much as is practical during high instantaneous plate current. See Fig. 1. The usual way of doing this is to make the load impedance high (with respect to the plate resistance) at the fundamental frequency. This is done by tuning the tank circuit to the fundamental frequency. Since E_{cc} is more than cut-off bias in Class C (equal in Class B), the plate current flows only in spurts at the minimum of plate voltage.

$$i_b = f(e_b, e_c) \tag{2}$$

$$di_b = \frac{\partial i_b}{\partial e_b} de_b + \frac{\partial i_b}{\partial e_c} de_c \tag{3}$$

$$di_b = g'_p \, de_b + g'_m \, de_c \tag{4}$$

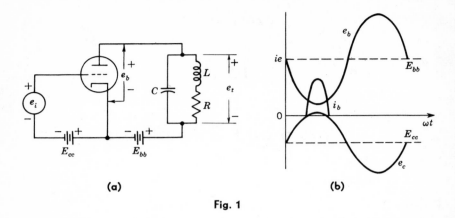

Fig. 1

In equation (4) the primes indicate variables that may be considered constant only as a first approximation. Equation (5) follows from equation (4) and the definitions of tube voltages and currents.

$$i_b = I_{bo} + di_b = I_{bo} + g'_p\, de_b + g'_m\, de_c$$
$$= I_{bo} + g'_p\, d(E_{bb} - e_t) + g'_m\, d(E_{cc} + e_i) \tag{5}$$

Since the plate circuit is tuned to the fundamental component of the plate current, de_t is given approximately by (6).

$$de_t = -I_{p1}\sqrt{2}\,R_{t1} \cos \omega t = E_t \cos \omega t \tag{6}$$

$$de_i = E_i \cos \omega t \tag{7}$$

therefore $$i_b = I_{bo} + (g'_m\, E_i - g'_p\, E_t) \cos \omega t \tag{8}$$

Equation (8) is a very rough approximation but it illustrates the following two points:

(a) Plate current, and hence power output, increases with increasing E_i, at least up to a point. That point is reached when $E_{b(min)} = e_{c(max)}$ and the grid starts taking most of the cathode current.

(b) Plate current will decrease as R_t is tuned to $\omega/2\pi$ since E_t then increases. This is the characteristic plate current dip.

Another point of interest concerns the grid current. As the plate tank is tuned to resonance, the minimum plate voltage becomes smaller with respect to the maximum grid voltage (which occurs simultaneously), hence the grid current rises. If the plate load is decreased (by coupling in another load at its resonant frequency, the grid current will dip abruptly. This is the principle of the "grid dip" oscillator which is used to determine the resonant frequency of tuned circuits.

Any of the standard texts on the subject will give additional information on the topics mentioned here and other aspects of these amplifiers.

Preliminary

1. Draw diagrams similar to Fig. 1(b) and give a short qualitative explanation for the plate current dip and grid current rise as the tank is tuned into resonance.

2. Explain the graphical procedure for finding the d-c plate current and power output using the constant current characteristics.

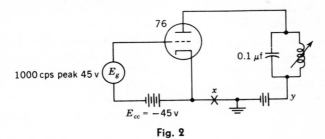

Fig. 2

3. In the circuit of Fig. 1, is the plate current dip always at the tank resonance frequency? Explain.

4. Set up the circuit shown in Fig. 2.

5. With E_b at approximately 250 volts, tune the tank into resonance as evidenced by: (a) maximum reading VTVM across tank; (b) dip in reading of d-c milliammeter at X.

6. Insert a low resistance at X and apply the drop across this resistance to CRO in order to view the waveform of the plate current. Is the operation Class B or C?

7. Take data to plot curves of a-c voltage across the tank, and I_b, as functions of E_b.

8. With E_b constant at 250 volts, adjust E_c for Class B operation. Vary E_g, measure a-c voltage drop across tank, and I_b, take data to plot these as a function of E_g.

Calculations and conclusions

9. Plot the data and draw the curves as indicated under "Performance."

10. From the plot of the data of part 7, what load would be presented to a modulator inserted at Y?

11. Why is a Class B radio frequency amplifier usually referred to as a "linear" amplifier?

12. Discuss any unexpected experimental results or phenomena.

References

Ryder, J. D., *Electronic undamentals and Applications*, 2d ed. (Englewood Cliffs, N. J.: Prentice-Hall, Inc., 1959).

Gray, T. S., *Applied Electronics* (New York: John Wiley & Sons, Inc., 1954).

Everitt, W. L., *Communications Engineering* (New York: McGraw-Hill Book Co., Inc., 1937).

Materials required

Components	Equipment
1 type 76 tube and socket	1 0–300 volt d-c supply (25 ma with 6.3 volt a-c)
1 0.1 µf, 500 volt capacitor	
1 50 ohm resistor	1 audio frequency generator
1 45 volt bias battery	1 0–25 ma d-c meter
1 10,000 ohm potentiometer	1 0–10 ma d-c meter
1 10 µf, 100 volt capacitor	1 multimeter
1 100–500 millihenry variable inductor	1 cathode-ray oscillograph
	1 a-c vacuum-tube voltmeter

19-A

Linear Oscillators

Purpose

The objectives of this experiment are to present the basic oscillator principles and verify them by experiment.

Information

The term "linear oscillator" means only that important information of the circuit's behavior may be obtained by linear circuit analysis. A truly linear oscillator cannot exist because once the oscillator had started to build up, it could not stop at any finite value.

These linear oscillators, as conceived here, will have at least a fair sinusoidal output and are mainly of interest because of their output frequencies. They comprise many assorted circuits, each having an output but no apparent (a-c) input. If any circuit carries a current without a generator present, then obviously the total series circuit impedance must be zero. This "zero impedance"* concept may be used, by inserting a series test generator, to determine the frequency and condition necessary for the start of oscillation. These two facts are found by setting the real and imaginary parts of the impedance seen by the test generator separately equal to zero.

The method to be used here is similar to the zero impedance concept but is approached differently. If the a-c circuit equations are written for the oscillator, no driving functions are found. The set of equations are homogenous, therefore a non-zero solution can be obtained only if the *system determinate is equal to zero*. Setting the system determinate equal to zero gives the frequency and condition for oscillation to start. Two examples are given in Fig. 1.

*This method was pointed out to the author by Professor W. L. Cassell of Iowa State University. It has surprising power and range of applicability.

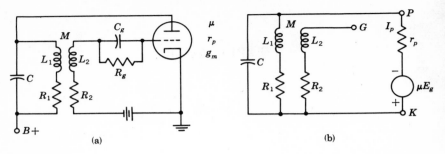

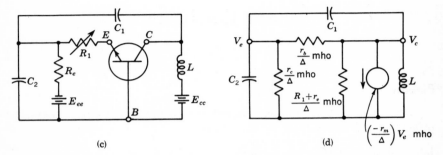

Fig. 1 **(a)** Schematic; **(b)** a-c equivalent circuit; **(c)** schematic; **(d)** a-c equivalent circuit.

For the tube

$$I_1\left[R_1 + j\left(\omega L_1 - \frac{1}{\omega C}\right)\right] + I_p(-R_1 - j\omega L_1) = 0 \tag{1}$$

$$I_1(-R_1 - j\omega L_1) + I_p(r_p + R_1 + j\omega L_1) = \mu E_g \tag{2}$$

$$E_g = -j\omega M(I_1 - I_p) \tag{3}$$

From (1), (2), and (3)

$$\omega_r^2 = \frac{1}{L_1 C}\left(\frac{r_p + R_1}{r_p}\right) \tag{4}$$

$$M = \frac{r_p R_1 C + L}{\mu} \quad \text{(minimum value)} \tag{5}$$

For the transistor

$$V_1\left[j\omega(C_1 + C_2) + \frac{r_c + r_b}{\Delta}\right] + V_2\left(-j\omega C_2 - \frac{r_b}{\Delta}\right) = 0 \tag{6}$$

$$V_1\left(-j\omega C_2 - \frac{r_b + r_m}{\Delta}\right) + V_2\left[\frac{R_1 + r_e + r_b}{\Delta} + j\left(\omega C_2 - \frac{1}{\omega L}\right)\right] = 0 \tag{7}$$

$$\Delta = (r_e + R_1 + r_b)(r_b + r_c) - r_b(r_b + r_m) \tag{8}$$

From (6), (7), and (8)

$$\omega_{r1}^2 = \frac{1}{C_1 C_2 \Delta} + \frac{1}{L[C_1 C_2/(C_1 + C_2)]} \tag{9}$$

$$\omega_{r_2}^2 = \frac{r_b + r_c}{L[C_1(r_b + r_e) + C_2(r_e + r_c - r_m)]} \tag{10}$$

Equating of (9) and (10) will indicate a minimum value of r_m for oscillations to start.

The "system determinate equals zero" criterion also applies to crystal oscillators. A reasonable electrical equivalent for a crystal is given in Fig. 2.

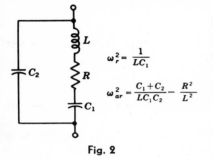

$$\omega_r^2 = \frac{1}{LC_1}$$

$$\omega_{ar}^2 = \frac{C_1 + C_2}{LC_1C_2} - \frac{R^2}{L^2}$$

Fig. 2

This tuned circuit (crystal) can be inserted in place of the normal tuned circuit of an oscillator if mutual inductance coupling is not required. Since the Q of a crystal is very high, it may be expected to provide good frequency stability.

Two additional points should be mentioned. First, amplitude of oscillation is controlled by circuit (usually tube) nonlinearities. The closer the "condition for oscillation to start" equation is to being satisfied, the smaller the nonlinearity that is necessary to stabilize the amplitude and the purer the waveform. Second, the following items have not been considered in the analysis: (1) incidental capacitances, (2) effect of parameter change due to aging or temperature, (3) amplitude stabilization to aid frequency stabilization, (4) loading effects due to output required.

Preliminary

1. In the vacuum-tube oscillator of Fig. 1, calculate the frequency of oscillation and the value of M required. $L_1 = L_2 = 150$ mh, $C = 0.1$ μf, $R_1 = R_2 = 230$ ohms, $\mu = 20$, $r_p = 7000$ ohms.

2. What per cent change would be noted in part 1 if r_p is increased by 50 per cent?

3. From the frequency expression for the transistor oscillator, what inequality must Δ satisfy in order that equation (11) be true?

$$\omega_r^2 = \frac{C_1 + C_2}{LC_1C_2} \tag{11}$$

4. Consider the following values for the transistor oscillator with $\alpha = 0.95$:

$L = 150$	$E_{ee} = 45$ volts	$r_e = 40$ ohms
$C_1 = C_2 = 0.2$ μf	$E_{cc} = 10.5$ volts	$r_b = 150$ ohms
$R_e = 50$ K	$R_1 = 10$ K potentiometer	$r_c = 10^6$ ohms

What will be the frequency of oscillation?

Performance

5. Set up the tuned plate oscillator of Fig. 1. With M set to the smallest usable value, check equations (4) and (5). (Check with your instructor as to the exact parameter values.)

6. Set up the transistor oscillator. With R_1 at its largest usable value, measure the frequency and compare with equation (9).

Calculations and conclusions

7. Tabulate the calculated versus the experimental results and the per cent error. Discuss any noticeable errors or experimental anomalies.

References

Ryder, J. D., *Electronic Fundamentals and Applications*, 2d ed. (Englewood Cliffs, N. J.: Prentice-Hall, Inc., 1959).

Corcoran, G. F., and Price, H. W., *Electronics* (New York: John Wiley & Sons, Inc., 1954.

Materials required

Components

1 calibrated triode and socket (6SN7, 6J5, 12AU7, etc.)

1 calibrated N-P-N junction transistor and socket

1 variable coupling transformer, G. R. 107-N or equivalent

1 0.1 µf capacitor

1 50 K resistor (for R_g and R_e)

1 0–10 K potentiometer

2 0.2 µf capacitors

1 0.25 µf capacitor (for C_g) batteries: 45 volt, tapped bias to 10.5 volts

Equipment

1 d-c power supply with filament output (must supply potential at which tube is calibrated)

1 oscilloscope (to observe waveforms)

1 audio oscillator (to check frequency by Lissajous figures — or an electronic counter)

1 20,000 ohm per volt multimeter

2 5 ma d-c meters

1 25 ma d-c meter

19-B

Linear Oscillators

Purpose

Both variable and crystal oscillators have important common characteristics. These will be studied by example and experiment.

Information

The following subjects will be discussed:
A. The frequency of the small amplitude oscillations
B. The conditions necessary for the start of oscillations
C. The amplitude of oscillations
D. The stability of the frequency of oscillation

Many oscillators operate Class C, others are used principally for their "switching mode," non-sinusoidal output waves, and a third class is of importance for the frequency of their sinusoidal output. This third class is the subject of this experiment.

When it is realized that a sinusoidal current is flowing in the oscillator circuit without an a-c input, subjects A and B are easily understood. If the network equations for the a-c equivalent circuit of the oscillator are written, they are homogeneous — that is, there are no driving functions. In order that any unknown voltage or current be non-zero, the "system determinate" must be equal to zero. This will be called the system determinate criterion of oscillation. With this viewpoint, it is unnecessary to classify oscillators as "two-terminal," "feedback," "negative resistance," etc. A typical example is shown in Fig. 1.

$$E_p\left(g_p + \frac{1}{R + j\omega L} + j\omega C_1\right) + E_g\left(-\frac{1}{R + j\omega L} + g_m\right) = 0 \qquad (1)$$

$$E_p\left(\frac{-1}{R + j\omega L}\right) + E_g\left(\frac{1}{R + j\omega L} + j\omega C_2\right) = 0 \qquad (2)$$

After setting *real* and *imaginary* parts of the system determinate separately equal to zero, equations (3), (4), and (5) are obtained.

Frequencies of oscillation:

$$\omega_{r1}^2 = \frac{g_p + g_m}{LC_2 g_p + RC_1 C_2}, \quad \omega_{r1}^2 = (2\pi f_{r1})^2 \tag{3}$$

$$\omega_{r2}^2 = \frac{C_1 + C_2 + C_2 g_p R}{LC_1 C_2}, \quad \omega_{r2}^2 = (2\pi f_{r2})^2 \tag{4}$$

Condition for start of oscillation:

$$\omega_{r1}^2 = \omega_{r2}^2 \quad \text{or} \quad f_{r1} = f_{r2} \tag{5}$$

Only a few general statements about the rather difficult subject of the "amplitude of oscillation" will be made. If the relation between circuit

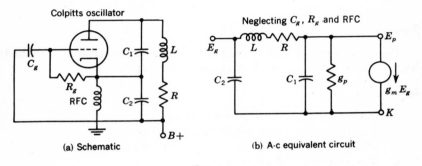

(a) Schematic   (b) A-c equivalent circuit

Fig. 1

parameters indicated by equation (5) is fulfilled, the circuit will start to oscillate and would build up indefinitely if the circuit were truly linear. On an approximate analysis, it can be said that the circuit becomes sufficiently nonlinear that g_m (or some other element) is reduced just to the point of satisfying (5). The amplitude is then stabilized at that value. Oscillators almost always use grid-leak bias to assist in starting and stabilization.

Frequency stability of oscillators depends primarily on temperature (especially for crystal oscillators), the losses in the tank circuit, changes in connected circuitry, changes in output loading, and changes in oscillation amplitude. Losses should be minimized and the other quantities stabilized to improve frequency stability.

Preliminary

1. Show that an inductor in series with the plate of Fig. 1 will make the frequency of oscillation independent of the tube parameters, if it is series resonant with C.

2. Although the classification of crystal oscillators as to series or parallel resonance is not always clear cut, discuss the mode of crystal operation in Fig. 2(a), (c), and (e). The crystal reactance diagram will prove helpful.

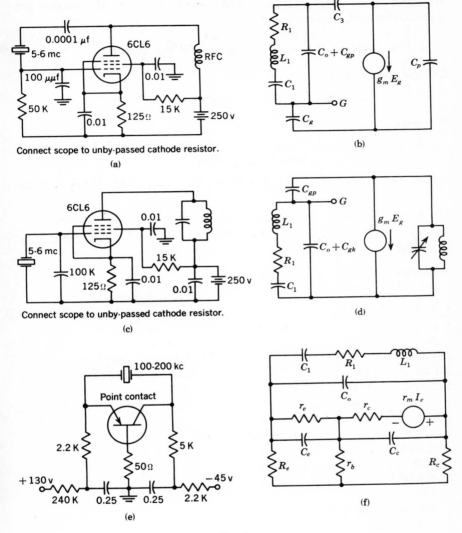

(a)

Connect scope to unby-passed cathode resistor.

(b)

(c)

Connect scope to unby-passed cathode resistor.

(d)

(e)

(f)

Fig. 2

Performance

Note: The experimental work will be for demonstration of circuits and their operation. Analytical checks of the observed results are impractical owing to component differences and circuit complexities. With accurate parameter knowledge, excellent agreement would be expected.

3. Set up circuit of Fig. 2(a). Check waveform and frequency. Without

cathode by-pass, increase R_k until oscillation almost stops. Record changes in waveform and frequency.

4. Repeat part 3 for circuit of Fig. 2(c).

5. Repeat part 3 for circuit of Fig. 2(e), except vary R_c.

Calculations and conclusions

6. Record and discuss any unforeseen experimental phenomena.

References

Ryder, J. D., *Electronic Fundamentals and Applications*, 2d ed. (Englewood Cliffs, N. J.: Prentice-Hall, Inc., 1959).

Edson, W. A., *Vacuum Tube Oscillators* (New York: John Wiley & Sons, Inc., 1953).

Lo, A. W., Endres, R. O., Zawels, J., Waldhauer, F. D. and Cheng, C. C., *Transistor Electronics* (Englewood Cliffs, N. J.: Prentice-Hall, Inc., 1955).

Materials required

Components	*Equipment*
1 6CL6 and socket	1 130–250 volt d-c supply with filament output
1 point contact transistor and socket	1 oscilloscope (5 mc response)
2 100 $\mu\mu$f capacitors	1 frequency measuring method (counter, Lissajous, beat frequency, etc.)
3 0.01 μf capacitors	1 20,000 ohm per volt multimeter
1 2.5 mh r-f choke	
1 adjustable tank circuit 5–6 mc	
2 0.25 μf capacitors	
1 0–5 K non-inductive potentiometer (R_k)	
1 0–50 K non-inductive potentiometer (R_c)	
1 5–6 mc crystal	
1 100–200 kc crystal	
1 50 K resistor	
1 100 K resistor	
2 2.2 K resistor	
1 240 K resistor	
1 50 ohm resistor	

20-A

Amplitude Modulation

Purpose

The purpose of this experiment is to present some of the concepts and associated methods of amplitude modulation.

Information

It is frequently stated that "amplitude modulation requires the mixing of the two signals in a nonlinear element." If not the only method, this is

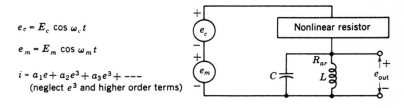

$e_c = E_c \cos \omega_c t$

$e_m = E_m \cos \omega_m t$

$i = a_1 e + a_2 e^3 + a_3 e^3 + \,\text{---}$
(neglect e^3 and higher order terms)

Fig. 1

certainly an important and easily understood method. It is illustrated in Fig. 1.

$$i = a_1 e + a_2 e^2 \tag{1}$$

$$i = a_1 E_c \cos \omega_c t + a_1 E_m \sin \omega_m t + a_2 (E_c \cos \omega_c t + E_m \sin \omega_m t)^2 \tag{2}$$

$$i = a_1 E_c \cos \omega_c t + a_2 E_c E_m [\sin (\omega_c + \omega_m)t - \sin (\omega_c - \omega_m)t] +$$
$$\frac{a_2 E_c^2}{2} (1 + \cos 2\omega_c t) + \frac{a_2 E_m^2}{2} (1 - \cos 2\omega_m t) + a_1 E_m \sin \omega_m t \tag{3}$$

If ω_m is not close to ω_c and $\omega_c^2 = 1/LC$,

$$e_{\text{out}} = a_1 R_{ar} E_c \cos \omega_c t + a_2 R_{ar} E_c E_m [\sin (\omega_c + \omega_m)t - \sin (\omega_c - \omega_m)t] \tag{4}$$

Equation (4) is of the same type as equation (5), the defining equation for amplitude modulation.

$$e = E_c(1 + m \sin \omega_m t) \cos \omega_m t =$$

$$E_c \cos \omega_m t + \frac{mE_c}{2} [\sin (\omega_c + \omega_m)t - \sin (\omega_c - \omega_m)t] \quad (5)$$

In equation (5) the coefficient $[E_c(1 + m \sin \omega_m t)]$ represents the varying amplitude. m, the modulation index, is proportional to the amplitude of the modulating voltage. $m \times 100$ per cent is termed the per cent modulation. The appearance of equation (5) as displayed on an oscillograph is illustrated in Fig. 2.

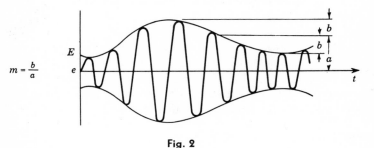

Fig. 2

Many schemes are available to produce amplitude modulation. Three common ones are listed below:

(a) Plate modulation: variation of plate supply voltage by means of the modulating voltage.

(b) Grid bias modulation: variation of bias and plate output by means of the modulating voltage.

(c) Cathode modulation: introduction of the modulating voltage into cathode circuit to produce modulation.

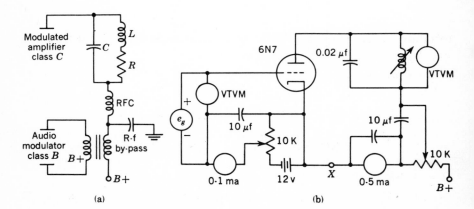

(a)   (b)

Fig. 3

At the present time, the most widely used method is plate modulation. In Fig. 3(a) is shown the usual practical circuit. R represents the reflected load, and only the plate circuits are drawn. Figure 3(b) gives the circuit to be used for experimentally testing this type of amplitude modulation.

Preliminary

1. Show that amplitude modulation can be achieved by connecting the modulating voltage and the radio frequency voltage in series in the grid circuit of a vacuum tube whose plate current is given as a function of the grid voltage by equation (1).

2. In plate modulation, what equation must relate d-c plate voltage and the fundamental component of plate current if distortionless modulation is to be accomplished?

3. List some of the characteristics of plate, grid, and cathode modulation.

Performance

4. Set up the circuit of Fig. 3(b) with $E_{bb} = 300$ volts, $E_{cc} = -12$ volts, $e_{b(min)} = 25$ volts, $e_{c(max)} = 8$ volts. Record the waveforms of tank voltage (should be sinusoidal) and plate current by inserting a 50 ohm resistor at X. Use 10,000 cps.

5. Take data to plot a curve of plate supply voltage versus a-c tank voltage.

6. By means of an isolating transformer and an adjustable autotransformer, insert a modulating voltage at X and view the modulated wave for various values of modulation index.

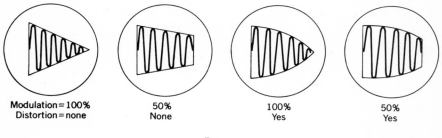

| Modulation = 100% | 50% | 100% | 50% |
| Distortion = none | None | Yes | Yes |

Fig. 4

7. By using the modulating voltage as the horizontal sweep voltage and the modulated wave for vertical deflection, view the trapezoidal modulation pattern See Fig. 4. By adjustment of grid bias, attempt to 100 per cent modulation with little distortion. It may be necessary to include about 1000 ohms and 0.1 μf as partial grid-leak bias and to make slight readjustments in the tank impedance.

Calculations and conclusions

8. Plot the data taken.

9. From the curve of part 8, what load does the Class C amplifier present to the modulator?

10. Discuss any unexpected experimental events and results.

References

Ryder, J. D., *Electronic Fundamentals and Applications*, 2d ed. (Englewood Cliffs, N. J.: Prentice-Hall, Inc., 1959).

Terman, F. E., and Pettit, J. M., *Electronic Measurements* (New York: McGraw-Hill Book Co., Inc., 1952).

Terman, F. E., *Radio Engineers' Handbook* (New York: McGraw-Hill Book Co., Inc., 1943).

Everitt, W. L., *Communications Engineering* (New York: McGraw-Hill Book Co., Inc., 1937).

Materials required

Components	*Equipment*
1 6N7 tube and socket	1 power supply (300 volts, 100 ma and 6.3 volts, a-c)
1 decade capacitor	1 audio oscillator
3 10 μf, 400 volt capacitors	1 oscillograph
1 0.1 μf, 400 volt capacitor	1 vacuum-tube voltmeter
3 10 K, 10 watt potentiometers	1 1 ma d-c meter
1 50 ohm resistor	1 5 ma d-c meter
1 12 volt (or greater) bias battery	1 25 ma d-c meter
1 5–50 mh variable inductor	1 multimeter

20-B

Amplitude Modulation

Purpose

The purposes of this experiment are two. First, experimental verification of the analytical results for the Van der Bijl system will be demonstrated. Second, the more practical plate modulation method will be tried.

Information

Amplitude modulation is the process of varying the amplitude (envelope) in direct proportion to the amplitude of an audio voltage. It is stated mathematically in equation (1).

$$e = E_c(1 + m \cos \omega_m t) \sin \omega_c t = E_c \sin \omega_c t + \frac{mE_c}{2} \sin (\omega_c + \omega_m)t +$$

$$\frac{mE_c}{2} \sin (\omega_c - \omega_m)t \tag{1}$$

where
$$m = \frac{E_m}{E_c} \quad \text{modulation index}$$

$$m \times 100 = \text{percentage modulation}$$

The amplitude of the carrier can be varied by proper introduction of the modulation voltage into the plate, grid, cathode, screen, or suppressor grid circuit. Many other methods have been used.

Preliminary

The Van der Bijl circuit for the production of an amplitude modulated waveform is shown in Fig. 1.

With the Q-point properly chosen, the a-c component of the plate current may be approximated by

$$i_p = a_1 e_g + a_2 e_g^2$$

1. Develop the equation i_p versus time in such a way as to bring out the various components.

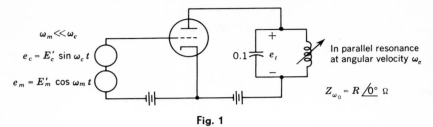

Fig. 1

2. What components of the current will produce negligible load voltage? Why? Show that the load voltage is:

$$e_t = E_c \sin \omega_c t + \frac{E_m}{2} \sin (\omega_c + \omega_m)t + \frac{E_m}{2} \sin (\omega_c - \omega_m)t$$

3. What are E_c and E_m, in terms of the grid supply voltages and other factors? Change the expression for e_t in part 2 into the following equivalent form:

$$e_t = E_c(1 + m \cos \omega_m t) \sin \omega_c t$$

where
$$m = \frac{E_m}{E_c}$$

and
$$\text{Modulation } percentage = \frac{E_m}{E_c} \times 100$$

4. Plot the amplitude modulated waveform below:

$$e = 200 \sin (\omega_c t) + 80 \sin (\omega_c + \omega_m)t + 80 \sin (\omega_c - \omega_m)t$$

where
$$f_c = 1000 \text{ cps}$$
$$f_m = 60 \text{ cps}$$

Use two sheets of graph paper pasted together. Draw the modulated wave in red and outline the envelope by dotted lines. Let 1 inch = 1/2000 second and 1 inch = 100 volts.

Performance

5. Set up the circuit of Fig. 1 using a 6J5 tube. Use operating points of $E_{bb} = 250$ volts, $E_{cc} = -11$ volts.

The carrier frequency is to be approximately 1000 cps. The modulating frequency is to be 60 cycles. The modulating source is to be variable by means of a Variac, and isolated by means of a filament transformer.

Observe the waveform of the load voltage, both without and with modulation.

Vary modulation from zero to maximum with small distortion.

6. Make a spectrum analysis of the load voltage, using a wave analyzer. Do not let modulation exceed 25 per cent in this case.

7. Set up the circuit of Fig. 2.

8. With E_{bb} at approximately 250 volts, tune the tank into resonance as shown by:

(a) Maximum reading of VTVM across tank

(b) Dip in reading of d-c milliammeter at X

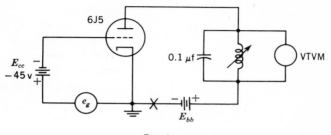

Fig. 2

9. Insert a low resistance at X and apply the drop across this resistance to a CRO to observe the waveform of the plate current.

10. Take data for and plot the curve of a-c tank voltage versus E_{bb}. From this curve estimate proper normal value of E_{bb} to give approximately the middle of linear operating range.

11. Insert a 60 cycle modulating source in series with E_{bb} at X. Observe the amplitude modulated waveform of tank voltage.

Calculations and conclusions

12. Sketch several of the patterns observed in parts 5 and 11. Give the percentage modulation and indicate some with distortion.

13. From part 10, estimate the load the amplifier would present to an audio modulator.

14. Discuss any unexpected results.

References

Ryder, J. D., *Electronic Fundamentals and Applications*, 2d ed. (Englewood Cliffs, N. J.: Prentice-Hall, Inc., 1959).

Terman, F. E., and Pettit, J. M., *Electronic Measurements* (New York: McGraw-Hill Book Co., 1952).

Terman, F. E., *Radio Engineers' Handbook* (New York: McGraw-Hill Book Co., Inc., 1943).

Everitt, W. L., *Communications Engineering* (New York: McGraw-Hill Book Co., Inc., 1937).

Materials required

Components

1 6J5 tube and socket
1 100–500 mh variable inductor
1 0.1 μf, 400 volt capacitor
1 10 μf, 100 volt capacitor
1 10 K, 10 watt potentiometer
1 45 volt battery to adjust bias

Equipment

1 power supply (250 volt, 25 ma and 6.3 volt, a-c)
1 audio oscillator
1 oscilloscope
1 wave analyzer
1 10 ma d-c meter
1 25 ma d-c meter
1 50 volt d-c meter
1 multimeter
1 a-c vacuum-tube voltmeter

21-A

Demodulation of
Amplitude-Modulated Waves

Purpose

The most common type of AM demodulator is the diode rectifier. Analytical results will be verified and automatic gain control will be applied to an associated amplifier.

Information

In Fig. 1(a), the amplitude modulated wave is shown, and in (b) the desired result from a circuit of the type of (c) is shown. Even with the distortion introduced by Fig. 1(c) at high modulation percentages, this circuit can be satisfactorily designed and is the most common detector circuit.

Many other detection circuits exist. Some of the better known ones are the grid-leak detector, plate detector, balanced detector, and infinite impedance detector. These circuits will not be examined in this experiment.

Preliminary

1. From the circuit of Fig. 1(c) and the information given below, show that $e_o = K'(E_c + E_m \cos \omega_m t)$. Given that

$$e = E_c(1 + m \cos \omega_m t) \cos \omega_c t$$

and that diode is ideal with R and C chosen so that $e_o = I_b R$, $K' = \cos \theta_o$, $\theta_0 = \frac{1}{2}$ plate current conduction angle (found from $\tan \theta_o - \theta_o = \pi r_p/R$).

2. From the circuit of Fig. 1(d), find E_o in terms of E_{a-c} and E_{d-c} at 1000 cps.

3. Show the proper connection of the filter of Fig. 1(d) to the amplifier of Fig. 2 to effect automatic gain control action.

Performance

4. Set up the circuit of Fig. 2 and adjust for maximum d-c output current.

5. With carrier of approximately 10 volts across ab, vary the modulation percentage for 0 to 50. Record the reading of the d-c milliammeter and the audio-frequency voltage across the diode load.

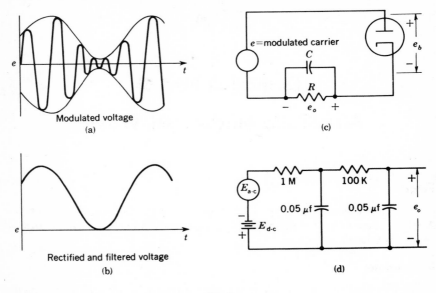

Modulated voltage
(a)

Rectified and filtered voltage
(b)

(c)

(d)

Fig. 1

6. Keep the modulation percentage constant at 50. Vary the carrier amplitude across ab from approximately 8 volts to approximately 18 volts. Record the d-c milliamperes and audio-frequency voltage across the diode load.

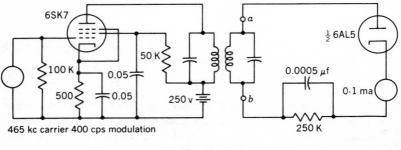

465 kc carrier 400 cps modulation

Fig. 2

7. Connect the R-C filter of part 2 to the circuit of part 4. Keep the modulation percentage constant at 50. Vary the carrier input to the 6SK7 and record this versus the audio-frequency voltage across the diode load.

Calculations and conclusions

8. Plot d-c and a-c load voltages versus per cent modulation. ·
9. (a) Plot d-c and a-c load voltages versus carrier amplitude.
   (b) Repeat (a) after the automatic gain control circuit is connected.
10. Discuss any unexpected experimental results.

References

Ryder, J. D., *Electronic Fundamentals and Applications*, 2d ed. (Englewood Cliffs, N. J.: Prentice-Hall, Inc., 1959).

Gray, T. S., *Applied Electronics* (New York: John Wiley & Sons, Inc., 1954)·

Everitt, W. L., *Communications Engineering* (New York: McGraw-Hill Book Co., Inc., 1937).

Materials required

Components	*Equipment*
1 6SK7 and socket	1 radio frequency generator with internal modulation
1 6AL5 and socket	
1 500 ohm resistor	1 power supply (250 volts, 10 ma and 6.3 volts, a-c)
2 100 K resistor	
1 50 K resistor	1 a-c vacuum-tube voltmeter
1 250 K resistor	1 1 ma d-c meter
1 1 megohm resistor	1 100 μa d-c meter
1 500 μμf capacitor	1 multimeter
4 0.05 μf capacitors	
1 456 kc i-f transformer	

21-B

Demodulation of

Amplitude-Modulated Waves

Purpose

The object of this experiment is to assist the understanding of the fundamental problem of intelligence recovery (detection or demodulation) from an amplitude modulated wave.

Information

After a little consideration, it will become apparent that even approximate filtering and rectification will effect some audio recovery or demodulation. Several possible methods are listed below in their approximate frequency of application. All except the first are very rare in present practices, and solid-state diodes are rapidly replacing vacuum diodes for demodulation

(a) Diode detector: diode rectification plus filtering

(b) Infinite impedance detector: essentially a cathode follower with filtering

(c) Plate detector: an amplifier biased Class B with filtering

(d) Grid-leak detector: essentially using grid and cathode as a diode detector and obtaining amplifier audio in the plate circuit

Since diode detection is almost universally used, this experiment will limit its discussion to that type. A complete mathematical solution for the diode detector is impractical, so that three partial analytical approaches are in common use:

(a) solution based on ideal diode and $\omega_c \gg \omega_m$

(b) solution based on rectification characteristics

(c) analysis of the effect of the load time constant

This experiment is based on the first of these.

In Fig. 1(a), if the modulation envelope changes very slowly, an analysis could be made for various carrier amplitudes on a d-c basis. Such an

144

analysis shows that the diode conduction angle $2\theta_o$ is independent of the amplitude, and equations (1) and (2) hold if diode is ideal and $\omega_c \ll \omega_m$. This experiment is based on these equations:

$$e_o = K'(E_c + E_m \cos \omega_m t) \tag{1}$$

$$K' = \cos \theta_o$$

$$\tan \theta_o - \theta_o = \frac{\pi r_p}{R} \tag{2}$$

Preliminary

1. Derive equations (1) and (2)
2. Give a one-paragraph discussion of automatic gain control and show some possible circuit arrangements.
3. At 100 cps, find e_o in terms of $E_{a\text{-}c}$ and $E_{d\text{-}c}$.

Performance

4. Set up the circuit of Fig. 1(c) and adjust for maximum rectified current, with zero modulation.
5. With carrier of approximately 10 volts across ab, vary the modulation percentage from 0 to 50. Record diode current and audio-frequency voltage across diode load.

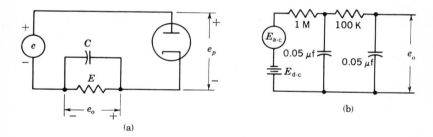

(a)

(b)

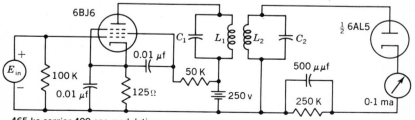

465 kc carrier 400 cps modulation

(c)

Fig. 1

6. Keep modulation percentage constant at 50. Vary carrier amplitude across *ab* from approximately 8 volts to approximately 18 volts. Record input voltage, diode current, and audio-frequency voltage across diode load.

7. Connect the *R-C* filter of part 2 to the circuit of part 4. Keep modulation percentage constant at 50. Vary the carrier input to the 6BJ6. Read input voltage and audio-frequency voltage across diode load.

Calculations and conclusions

8. Plot d-c voltage across load and audio-frequency voltage across load versus modulation percentage. Plot these on the same sheet using the same scale.

9. Plot d-c voltage across diode load and audio-frequency voltage across diode load versus carrier amplitude. Plot these on the same sheet using the same scale.

10. Plot curves of audio-frequency load voltage versus carrier input for constant modulation percentage for both cases (with and without filter).

11. Discuss results.

References

Ryder, J. D., *Electronic Fundamentals and Applications*, 2d ed. (Englewood Cliffs, N. J.: Prentice-Hall, Inc., 1959).

Gray, T. S., *Applied Electronics* (New York: John Wiley & Sons, Inc., 1954).

Everitt, W. L., *Communications Engineering* (New York: McGraw-Hill Book Co., Inc., 1937).

Materials required

Components	*Equipment*
1 6BJ6 and socket	1 power supply (250 volts 10 ma and 6.3 volts, a-c)
1 6AL5 and socket	1 radio frequency generator with internal modulation
1 125 ohm resistor	1 a-c vacuum-tube voltmeter
1 50 K resistor	1 1 ma d-c meter
1 100 K resistor	1 100 μa d-c meter
1 250 K resistor	1 multimeter
1 megohm resistor	
2 0.01 μf capacitors	
2 0.05 μf capacitors	
1 465 kc i-f transformers	

22-A

Demodulation of
Frequency-Modulated Waves

Purpose

The purpose of this experiment is the experimental verification of the theoretical analysis of the Foster-Seeley discriminator type of frequency-modulation detector. One limiter circuit and the ratio detector will also be tested.

Information

The detection of frequency modulated waves, from at least one point of view, depends upon changing them to amplitude-modulated waves and then detecting the latter. The proper operation of these devices depends upon the elimination of incidental amplitude modulation caused by static or interference before detection.

The Foster-Seeley amplitude discriminator of Fig. 1(a) utilizes one or more limiters to eliminate AM, then generates its own in the tuned circuitry, while the gated beam limiter-disciminator (or locked oscillator) receives pulses of plate current proportional to frequency deviation. The varying amplitude pulses are thus an amplitude modulated wave even though unidirectional and detectable by simple filtering.

Several other very good FM detection methods exist, but only the much-used discriminator and the gated beam circuit will be studied, the latter because of the novel principles involved. All tests will be made around 455 kc, to reduce stray capacitance and wiring problems.

Preliminary

1. Show by means of a vector diagram that E_o of Fig. 1(a) is zero at the frequency to which the primary and secondary are tuned. Also show that E_o became of opposite polarity for deviations around the carrier frequency.

2. How does the coefficient of coupling in a discriminator compare to that in a normal i-f transformer? Why?

3. It is sometimes stated that the Foster-Seeley circuit is insensitive to amplitude modulation. Is this ever true? Describe the difference between amplitude limiter stages and normal amplifiers.

4. Draw a modification of Fig. 1(a) to illustrate the ratio detector. Explain its operation briefly.

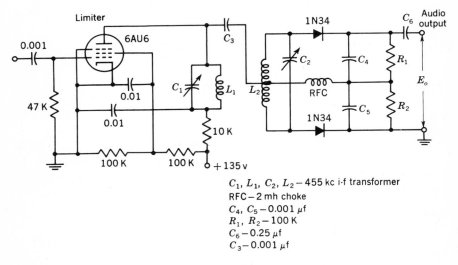

$C_1, L_1, C_2, L_2 - 455$ kc i-f transformer
RFC $-$ 2 mh choke
$C_4, C_5 - 0.001 \mu f$
$R_1, R_2 - 100$ K
$C_6 - 0.25 \mu f$
$C_3 - 0.001 \mu f$

Fig. 1(a)

5. Explain briefly the operation of the gated beam FM detector and limiter. What advantages does it have over the limiter-discriminator arrangement, if any?

Performance

6. Set up and adjust the circuit of Fig. 1(a). For the initial tests the driving stage will be modified to reduce limiting. Increase the grid resistor to 300 K. Increase E_{bb} to 200 volts. Short circuit the 10 K resistor. Put in a 1 K by-passed cathode resistor. Use a procedure similar to the following:

(a) Adjust the transformer for maximum unloaded r-f output with a 1 volt, 455 kc input (no modulation).

(b) With load, adjust C_1 (or primary slug) to maximum d-c output voltage and then C_2 (or secondary slug) to zero output.

(c) Adjust C_1 to equal magnitude of output voltage at ± 5 kc input (from 455 kc).

(d) Recheck for zero output at 455 kc and then recheck (c).

7. Take data for an output voltage (d-c) versus frequency deviation curve.

8. With 30 per cent modulation applied, take data of a-c output voltage versus deviation.

9. Modify the amplifier to the limiter circuit and repeat part 8.

10. Connect the circuit of Fig. 1(b) and take data for an output versus deviation curve. Note limiting action.

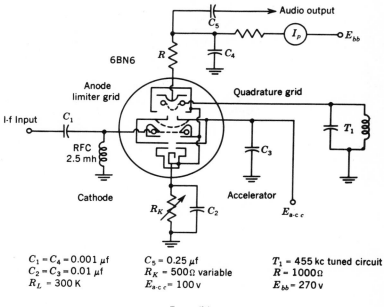

$C_1 = C_4 = 0.001\ \mu f$	$C_5 = 0.25\ \mu f$	$T_1 = 455$ kc tuned circuit
$C_2 = C_3 = 0.01\ \mu f$	$R_K = 500\Omega$ variable	$R = 1000\Omega$
$R_L = 300$ K	$E_{a\text{-}c\ c} = 100$ v	$E_{bb} = 270$ v

Fig. 1(b)

Calculations and conclusions

11. Plot the curves for which data were taken and discuss briefly.

12. List and explain, if possible, any experimental difficulties.

References

Ryder, J. D., *Electronic Fundamentals and Applications*, 2d ed. (Englewood Cliffs, N. J.: Prentice-Hall, Inc., 1959).

Terman, F. E., *Radio Engineers' Handbook* (New York: McGraw-Hill Book Co., Inc., 1943).

Materials required

Components

1 6AU6 tube and socket
1 6BN6 tube and socket
2 1N34 diodes with mounts
1 500 ohm variable resistor
1 10 K, 10 watt potentiometer (to adjust supply potentials)
1 1 K resistor
1 10 K resistor
1 47 K resistor
4 100 K resistors
1 330 K resistor
1 455 kc i-f transformer (center-tapped)
1 2.5 mh choke
1 455 kc resonant circuit (high-Q)
3 0.001 μf capacitors
3 0.01 μf capacitors
2 0.25 μf capacitors

Equipment

1 power supply (200–300 volts at 10 ma and 6.3 volts, a-c)
1 radio frequency generator
1 a-c vacuum-tube voltmeter
1 10 ma d-c meter
1 multimeter

22-B

Demodulation of

Frequency-Modulated Waves

Purpose

The purpose is to promote familiarity, both theoretical and practical, with the Foster-Seeley frequency discriminator for detection of frequency modulated waves.

Information

While several circuits are used to accomplish the detection of frequency modulated waves, the most commonly used type is the conventional discriminator. In this experiment the performance of this circuit and the ratio detector variation will be tested along with the associated amplitude limiter.

Preliminary

1. How can a parallel tuned circuit be used for FM detection? What are its limitations?

2. Given the circuit of Fig. 1, derive expressions for $|E_1|$ and $|E_2|$, as-

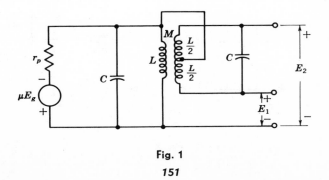

Fig. 1

suming $r_p \gg x_c$ and that the Q of the primary and secondary (which are identical) is large.

3. Show the general shape of the curve defined by

$$E = |E_1| - |E_2|$$

Use expressions derived for $|E_1|$ and $|E_2|$ in part 2.

4. What is the purpose of amplitude limiters as used with FM receivers?

Performance

5. Set up the circuit of Fig. 2(a). Balance the detector by the following methods:

(a) Adjust C_1 (or L_1 by slug) to maximum E_{out} with a 465 kc, 1 volt input.

(b) Adjust C_2 (or L_2 by slug) to zero output voltage at 465 kc.

(c) Adjust C_1 so that the output voltages at ± 5 kc (from 465 kc) are equal in magnitude.

(d) Recheck (b), then (c).

6. Take data of E_{out} against deviation from 465 kc. Use at least 20 kc on either side.

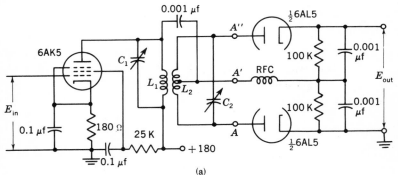

(a)

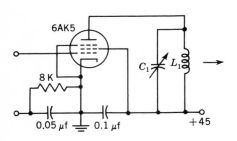 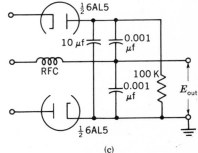

(b)   (c)

Fig. 2

7. Take data of E_{out} against E_{in} at 470 kc.

8. Apply 20 per cent, 1000 cps amplitude modulation to the 470 kc input. Observe and record the output on an oscillograph. Changing the input frequency, find the frequency of minimum audio output.

9. Replace the circuit to the right of AA'' by the circuit of Fig. 2(b). *Note:* Leave the i-f transformer adjusted as in part 5.

10. Take data of E_{out} against deviation for the new circuit as in part 6.

11. Replace the amplifier circuit by the limiter circuit of Fig. 2(c). This limiter operates for input voltages above about one volt. Repeat parts 7 and 8.

Calculations and conclusions

12. Plot the curves for which data was taken under "Performance."

13. Explain how the ratio detector reduces amplitude modulation.

14. Discuss any unusual experimental observations.

References

Ryder, J. D., *Electronic Fundamentals and Applications*, 2d ed. (Englewood Cliffs, N. J.: Prentice-Hall, Inc., 1959).

Martin, T. L., *Electronic Circuits* (Englewood Cliffs, N. J.: Prentice-Hall, Inc., 1955).

Receiving Tube Manual, Radio Corporation of America.

Materials required

Components	*Equipment*
1 6AK5 tube and socket	1 power supply (45 and 180 volts
1 6AL5 tube and socket	at 10 ma and 6.3 volts, a-c)
1 465 kc i-f transformer with secondary center tap (or special 465 kc discriminator transformer	1 radio frequency generator with internal amplitude modulation (must be readable to 1 kc difference)
2 0.1 µf, 100 volt capacitors	
3 0.001 µf capacitors	
1 0.05 µf capacitor	1 a-c vacuum-tube voltmeter
1 10 µf, 50 volt capacitor	1 d-c vacuum-tube voltmeter (zero center-scale preferable)
2 100 K resistors	1 multimeter
1 2.5 mh radio frequency choke	

23-A

Noise in Vacuum-Tube Amplifiers

Purpose

The purpose of this experiment is to study the noise characteristics of vacuum-tube amplifiers.

Information

No system is free of noise, and when extremely small signals are to be detected or precise measurements made, this imposes a limit on all efforts. The purposes of studying the noise characteristics of amplifiers or other devices is to recognize the limitations and find methods for partially alleviating them.

The two noise figures normally used are termed "single-frequency" and "integrated." Either may be obtained by the "noise-generator" or "signal-generator" method. In this experiment the single-frequency, signal-generator method will be used for the sake of brevity and equipment availability.

Note: It must be recognized that the measurement of noise voltages and powers is rather exacting. In some laboratories shielded benches or even shielded rooms may be necessary because of excessive ambient noise. Battery operation and other isolation methods are also helpful.

Preliminary

1. Define the noise figure of an amplifier.

2. If two amplifiers are cascaded with noise figure of F_1 and F_2, respectively, what is the overall noise figure F? If the noise figure of each is 10, what must be the gain of the first if the increase of noise power output due to the second stage is just one per cent?

3. Assume a perfect filter passing the frequencies of $f_1 \leq f \leq f_2$ without attenuation as shown in Fig. 1. Show that the noise figure can be written as

$$F = \frac{V_n^2}{4kTR_g(f_2 - f_1)A_v^2}$$

where

V_n = rms noise voltage output

R_g = source resistance

A_v = voltage gain of the device tested in the frequency range $f_1 \leq f \leq f_2$

It should be noted that A_v is defined as $A_v = V_o/E_g$ when E_g is increased sufficiently large to render all noise voltages ineffective. This definition of voltage gain is not the usual one.

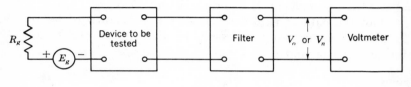

Fig. 1

4. Explain the relationship between noise figure and signal to noise ratio.

Performance

5. Set up the circuit of Fig. 2 with as short leads as possible. Record voltages. Take data for a frequency response curve with $R_g = 500$ ohms. Use a wave analyzer as the voltmeter. Note: The vacuum-tube voltmeter may give less difficulty on the generator side of the transformer and may have to be removed while taking readings.

6. With the signal generator of, measure the noise spectrum over the audio range. Check and reduce the 60 cps pick-up to the lowest value possible.

7. Replace the wave analyzer with a 1000 cps null detector (thermocouple meter or balometer) and check the noise output at 1000 cps. The

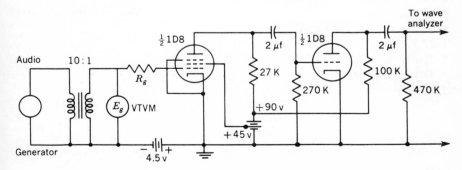

Fig. 2

signal generator may be used to calibrate the null detector whose response must be known or checked with the wave analyzer and oscillator.

8. (a) With the setup as in part 7, vary R_g from zero to 1 megohm and record results. (b) Check all 1D8 tubes available to compare their noise figures.

Calculations and conclusions

9. Plot the frequency response curve and the noise spectrum.

10. Calculate a single-frequency noise figure from the data of parts 5 and 6 and also from parts 5 and 7. Do these differ? Why?

11. Plot the data of part 8(a). Does this substantiate the theory?

12. Discuss the experimental results briefly, with particular emphasis on difficulties encountered.

References

Ryder, J. D., *Electronic Fundamentals and Applications*, 2d ed. (Englewood Cliffs, N. J.: Prentice-Hall, Inc., 1959).

Terman, F. E., and Pettit, J. M., *Electronic Measurements* (New York: McGraw-Hill Book Co., Inc., 1952).

Goldman, S., *Frequency Analysis, Modulation and Noise* (New York: McGraw-Hill Book Co., Inc., 1948).

Van Der Ziel, A., *Noise* (Englewood Cliffs, N. J.: Prentice-Hall, Inc., 1954).

Materials required

Components	*Equipment*
1 1D8 tube and socket (with as many spare tubes as possible)	1 wave analyzer
1 approximately 10:1 audio transformer	1 audio frequency generator
1 7.5 volt bias battery	1 1000 cps null detector with square-law meter
2 45 volt batteries	1 sensitive vacuum-tube voltmeter
1 1 megohm decade resistor	1 multimeter (20,000 ohms per volt)
1 27 K resistor	
1 270 K resistor	
1 470 K resistor	
2 2µf capacitors	

23-B

Noise in Vacuum-Tube Amplifiers

Purpose

The purpose of this experiment is to increase familiarity with amplifier noise. This will be achieved through testing an amplifier by means of a noise generator.

Information

Every amplifier generates some noise. The *noise figure* of an amplifier is defined as the ratio of the *available* signal-to-noise ratio at the input to the *available* signal-to-noise ratio at the output.

$$F' = \frac{\left(\dfrac{\text{available signal power input}}{\text{noise power input}}\right)}{\left(\dfrac{\text{available signal power output}}{\text{noise power output}}\right)} = \frac{\dfrac{S_{\text{in}}}{KTB}}{\dfrac{S_{\text{out}}}{N_{\text{out}}}} \tag{1}$$

In definition (1), the word "available" indicates the power that could be transferred under matched conditions. This definition gives a unique noise figure, but one that is somewhat difficult to apply to amplifiers with indeterminate input impedances. In this experiment, the noise figure will be defined as in equation (2), or actually the decibel ratio of the right-hand term of (2).

$$F = \frac{\text{actual noise power output}}{\text{noise output if amplifier were noise free}} \tag{2}$$

In most cases, any attempt to amplify a signal whose output is comparable to the actual noise power output is fruitless.

In this experiment several different tubes, in a common amplifier circuit, will be tested for noise figure by the noise generator method. The bandwidth of the amplifier will be artificially restricted so that no chance of its exceeding the bandwidth of the noise generator or detector will exist.

Note: Noise measurements are very difficult to make in most laboratories, owing to high electrical noise levels. Signals induced at power frequencies are particularly troublesome when wide-band, low-frequency measurements are being made. Some or all of the following precautions may be necessary to obtain good noise measurements:

(a) Use a grounded metal-top bench.

(b) Use shielding wherever possible.

(c) Use complete battery sources.

(d) Use battery-operated test equipment.

(e) Use a shielded room (or box).

Preliminary

1. (a) Describe and draw block diagrams for the determination of integrated noise figures by the noise-generator and wide-band detector method. (b) Repeat for a signal generator and narrow-band detector.

2. (a) Describe and draw block diagrams for the determination of the single-frequency noise figure by the noise generator and narrow-band detector method. (b) Repeat for a signal generator and narrow-band detector.

3. How will the following factors affect noise measurements?

(a) the type of meter indicator (square law, average, etc.)

(b) the time constant of the measuring device

(c) dynamic range of measuring device

4. In Fig. 1, what must the power gain of the first stage be if the noise of the second stage is not to increase the noise figure by more than 0.1 decibel?

Performance

5. Set up the circuit of Fig. 1 with T_1 and T_2 a 12AU7. With noise generator input and a wide-band, sensitive, average reading voltmeter on

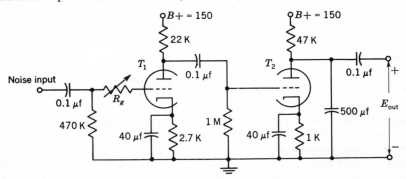

Fig. 1

the output, determine the noise figure for R_g equal to 1 K, 50 K, and 2.5 megohms.

6. Repeat part 5, with a wide-band square-law detector.

7. With $R_g = 100$ K, check and record the noise figure using all available 12AU7, 12AT7, 12AX7, and 12AY7 tubes.

Calculations and conclusions

8. Plot the results of parts 5 and 6. What effect does R_g have on noise figure?

9. Tabulate the results in decibels versus tube type. What tube gave the lowest average noise figure?

10. Discuss briefly any experimental difficulties encountered.

References

Ryder, J. D., *Electronic Fundamentals and Applications*, 2d ed. (Englewood Cliffs, N. J.: Prentice-Hall, Inc., 1959).

Terman, F. E., and Pettit, J. M., *Electronic Measurements* (New York: McGraw-Hill Book Co., Inc., 1952).

Valley, G. E., and Wallman, H., *Vacuum Tube Amplifiers*, vol. 18, Rad. Lab. Series (New York: McGraw-Hill Book Co., Inc., 1948).

Goldman, S., *Frequency Analysis, Modulation and Noise* (New York: McGraw-Hill Book Co., Inc., 1948).

Materials required

Components	*Equipment*
several 12AU7, 12AT7, 12AX7, and 12AY7 tubes with socket	1 power supply (300 volts at 20 ma, very low ripple, and 6.3 volts a-c)
1 1 megohm decade resistor	1 a-c vacuum-tube voltmeter (at least 10^{-3} volts full scale and 100 kc bandwidth)
1 10 K, 10 watt potentiometer	
1 1 K resistor	
1 2.7 K resistor	1 wide-band, sensitive detector with square-law indicator
1 22 K, 1 watt resistor	
1 47 K, 2 watt resistor	1 multimeter
1 50 K resistor	1 noise generator with calibrated output
1 1 megohm resistor	
1 1.5 megohm resistor	
1 500 μf capacitor	
2 0.1 μf capacitors	
1 8μf, 300 volt capacitor	
2 40 μf, 25 volt capacitors	

24-A

Frequency Conversion

Purpose

The purpose of this experiment is to study the principle of frequency translation and to operate practical converter and mixer circuits.

Information

Although the frequencies concerned are usually different, the problem of frequency conversion or translation is primarily one of modulation. Since efficiency and power are unimportant in the usual superheterodyne receiver application, simple nonlinear mixing arrangements are used.

Preliminary

1. Describe the construction of the 6BE6 heptode.
2. Explain the operation of the 6BE6 as a converter as shown in Fig. 1.
3. Define conversion transconductance.
4. Consider that the transconductance of the tube can be expressed as

$$g_m = a_0 + a_1 e_{g1} + a_2 e_{g1} + \cdots$$

where $g_m = \partial i_p / \partial e_{g3}$; $a_0, a_1, a_2, \cdots$ are constants; e_g is the a-c voltage on grid No. 1, and e_{g3} is the a-c voltage on grid No. 3.

Using the relationships $i_p = g_m e_{g3}$, $e_{g1} = E_o \sin \omega_o t$ (oscillator), and $e_{g3} = E_s \sin \omega_s t$ (signal), find the conversion transconductance g_c.

5. A superheterodyne receiver has an intermediate frequency of 465 kc. The signal-frequency circuits cover the range 550–1600 kc. What two oscillator tuning ranges are possible? Why is it customary for the oscillator to operate at higher frequency than the signal frequency?

6. With the oscillator frequency higher than the signal frequency of 800 kc, find the frequency of the undesired "image" for an intermediate frequency of 465 kc. Repeat for an intermediate frequency of 175 kc. Why is the higher value of i-f preferable? What is the only remedy for "image interference?"

Performance

7. Set up the circuit of Fig. 1. Set the signal generator to 465 kc and tune the i-f transformer. Next, set the signal generator to 800 kc and adjust

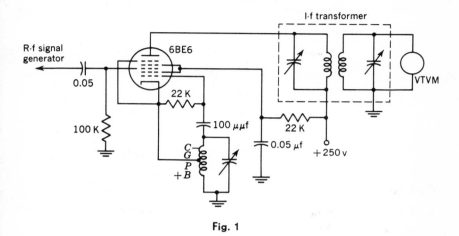

Fig. 1

oscillator above 800 kc to produce a 465 kc signal. Verify the existence of the image. Read input and output voltages in each case.

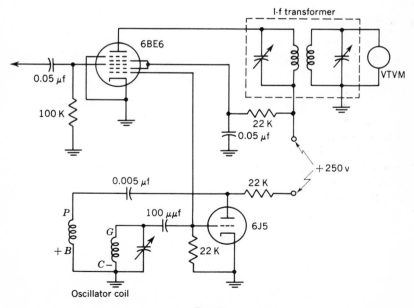

Fig. 2

8. Set up the circuit of Fig. 2 and repeat.

9. Replace the input circuit with the circuit of Fig. 3 tuned to 800 kc. Repeat part 7.

Calculations and conclusions

10. Discuss any unusual experimental phenomena.

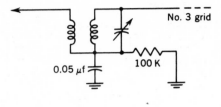

Fig. 3

References

Ryder, J. D., *Electronic Fundamentals and Applications*, 2d ed. (Englewood Cliffs, N. J.: Prentice-Hall, Inc., 1959).

Martin, T. L., *Electronic Circuits* (Englewood Cliffs, N. J.: Prentice-Hall, Inc., 1955).

Receiving Tube Manual, Radio Corporation of America.

Materials required

Components	*Equipment*
1 6BE6 tube and socket	1 power supply (250 volts at 20 ma and 6.3 volts, a-c)
1 6J5 tube and socket	1 radio frequency generator
1 oscillator coil	1 a-c vacuum-tube voltmeter
1 r-f input transformer	1 multimeter
1 i-f transformer	
2 0.05 μf capacitors	
1 0.005 μf capacitor	
2 250–450 μμf variable capacitors	
3 22 K resistors	
1 100 K resistor	

24-B

Frequency Conversion

Purpose

The purpose of this experiment is to study the principle of frequency conversion, as applied to the superheterodyne radio receiver.

Information

If two signals are caused to pass through any linear element (resistor, capacitor, inductance, oscillator, etc.,) no mixing or heterodyning occurs. Sum and difference frequencies are not generated. On the other hand, if these same two signals are passed through nonlinear elements these frequencies are generated as shown below. This is a modulation process.

$$e = a_1 i + a_2 i^2 + \text{neglected terms} \tag{1}$$

$$i = I_1 \sin \omega_1 t + I_2 \sin \omega_2 t \tag{2}$$

therefore

$$e = a_1 I_1 \sin \omega_1 t + a_1 I_2 \sin \omega_2 t + a_2 \left(\frac{I_1^2}{2} + \frac{I_2^2}{2} \right) - \left(\frac{a_2 I_1^2}{2} \right) \cos 2\omega_1 t -$$

$$\left(\frac{a_2 I_2^2}{2} \right) \cos 2\omega_2 t + a_2 I_1 I_2 \left[\cos (\omega_1 - \omega_2)t - \cos (\omega_1 + \omega_2)t \right] \tag{3}$$

If I_1 or I_2 are not constants but varying, as in amplitude modulation, then either of the sum or difference frequencies (last two terms of 3) may be used to translate the incoming signal to the intermediate frequency in a superheterodyne receiver.

Several minor variations of circuitry are used in frequency conversion. Each involves mixing of signals in a nonlinear element (tube, transistor, or diode). Each has some advantages and disadvantages which will not be emphasized here.

Preliminary

1. Given the circuit of Fig. 1, with the Q-point properly chosen, the a-c component of plate current may be expressed as

$$ip = a_1 e_g + a_2 e_g^2$$

Prove that the a-c load voltage is

$$e_L = K \cos \omega_i t$$

2. Take ω_s as fixed. Show that two values of ω_o will produce the same load voltage e_L.

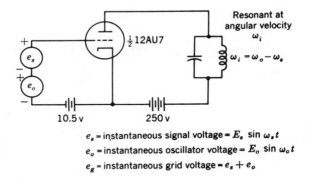

e_s = instantaneous signal voltage = $E_s \sin \omega_s t$

e_o = instantaneous oscillator voltage = $E_o \sin \omega_o t$

e_g = instantaneous grid voltage = $e_s + e_o$

Fig. 1

3. A superheterodyne receiver has an intermediate frequency of 465 kc. The signal-frequency circuits cover the range from 550–1600 kc. What two oscillator tuning ranges are possible? Why is it customary for the oscillator to operate at higher frequency than the signal frequency?

4. With the oscillator frequency higher than the signal frequency of 800 kc, find the frequency of the undesired "image" for an intermediate frequency of 465 kc. Repeat, for an intermediate frequency of 175 kc. Why is the higher value of i-f preferable? What is the only remedy for "image interference?"

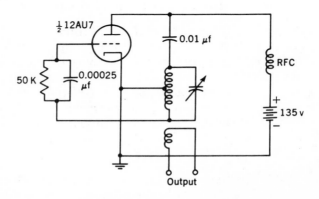

Fig. 2

5. Describe the construction of a type 6A8 pentagrid converter tube. Explain the operation of the converter circuit of part 9.

6. What is meant by the term "conversion transconductance?"

Performance

7. Set up the circuit of Fig. 1 using one half of a 12AU7 tube. The load consists of an i-f transformer tuned to 465 kc, with a VTVM across the secondary. Supply signal voltage from a standard signal generator. Use the oscillator circuit of Fig. 2.

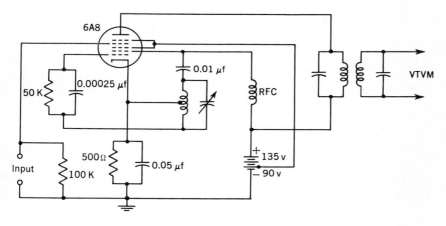

Fig. 3

8. With the signal voltage at 800 kc, tune the oscillator to produce 465 kc output. Adjust the signal frequency to verify the existence of the image.

9. Set up the circuit of Fig. 3.

Repeat part 8, measuring the 465 kc output voltage at both the desired signal frequency of 800 kc and at the image signal frequency. Repeat, replacing the untuned resistive input circuit by a tuned radio-frequency transformer.

Calculations and conclusions

10. How many decibels improvement were noted when the tuned circuit was added?

11. Discuss any unusual experimental phenomena.

References

Ryder, J. D., *Electronic Fundamentals and Applications*, 2d ed. (Englewood Cliffs, N. J.: Prentice-Hall, Inc., 1959).

Martin, T. L., *Electronic Circuits* (Englewood Cliffs, N. J.: Prentice-Hall, Inc., 1955).

Receiving Tube Manual, Radio Corporation of America.

Materials required

Components	*Equipment*
1 12AU7 tube and socket	1 power supply (250 volts at 10 ma and 6.3 volts, a-c)
1 6A8 tube and socket	
1 oscillator transformer (this can be a commercial model but needs a few turns loosely coupled for output, see Fig. 2)	1 radio frequency signal generator
	1 a-c vacuum-tube voltmeter
	1 multimeter
1 antenna input transformer	
1 intermediate transformer, 465 kc	
1 2.5 mh radio frequency choke	
2 25–450 $\mu\mu$f variable capacitors	
1 250 $\mu\mu$f capacitor	
1 0.01 μf capacitor	
1 0.05 μf capacitor	
1 500 ohm resistor	
1 50 K resistor	
1 100 K resistor	

25-A

Vacuum-tube Voltmeters

Purpose

The purpose of this experiment is to study the response of various commercial vacuum-tube voltmeters to voltages of different waveforms. The frequency response will also be studied.

Preliminary

1. The voltage whose waveform is shown in Fig. 1 is applied to the

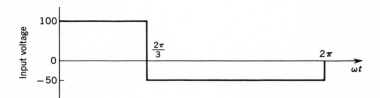

Fig. 1 Waveform of a periodic voltage.

vacuum-tube voltmeters whose response and calibration are described below. What will be the scale indication in each case?
   (a) peak-reading meter (two answers)
   (b) half-wave average-reading meter
   (c) full-wave average-reading meter
   (d) rms-reading meter

2. Suppose the meters in part 1 were each calibrated with a sine wave and the meter scale marked in rms volts, based on a sine wave. What would be the scale indications under these conditions?

3. Describe the meaning of waveform and turnover error in terms of the calculations in parts 1 and 2.

4. What factors limit the low- and high-frequency responses of vacuum-tube voltmeters?

5. What method is used in most vacuum-tube voltmeter circuits to eliminate any d-c component of the input voltage so that the a-c component alone of the voltage wave may be measured?

Performance

6. The following vacuum-tube voltmeters are to be used in this experiment: Hewlett Packard Model 400A, Ballantine Model 300, and General Radio Type 726A. From instruction manuals obtain and record the following data for each instrument.

    (a) voltage ranges

    (b) frequency ranges

    (c) accuracy

    (d) voltmeter indication (type of waveform response)

    (e) voltmeter calibration (method of scale calibration)

    (f) input shunt capacitance

    (g) input shunt resistance

7. Connect the three voltmeters and a cathode-ray oscillograph in parallel. Use care that ground terminals are properly connected. Set the meters to the following scales: H. P., 10 volt scale, G. R., 15 volt scale. Al-

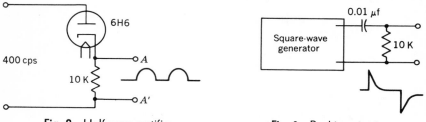

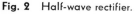   

Fig. 2 Half-wave rectifier.   **Fig. 3** Peaking circuit.

low several minutes warmup time, then short circuit the terminals and adjust the zero adjustment of the meters for which such an adjustment is provided.

8. Apply a source of sinusoidal voltage of approximately 5 volts at 400 cps to the circuit. Adjust the oscillograph trace so that the peaks fall on the plus and minus 1 inch horizontal lines. Secure the gain adjustment in this position with a strip of scotch tape. Record the indication of each meter and the position of the plus and minus peaks on the oscillograph.

9. Connect the circuit of Fig. 2 to obtain a source of half-wave rectified voltage. Connect this circuit to the voltmeters and oscillograph with terminal A' connected to the ground bus. Adjust the voltage to 5 volts as read on the Hewlett-Packard meter. Record the meter indications and oscillograph peaks. Repeat, with terminals A and A' reversed.

10. Apply a 5-volt 400-cps square wave to the circuit and record the same data as before.

11. Apply a peaked wave obtained by the use of the circuit of Fig. 3 to the voltmeters and oscillograph. Record the same data as before. Note: The Hewlett-Packard and Ballantine meters may be changed to a lower scale if necessary. The General Radio meter should be left on the 15-volt scale.

12. Connect the meters to an oscillator. Record the meter readings as the frequency is varied up to 5 mc. (Above 20 kc a signal generator may be used as a source.) Adjust the voltage to a value of approximately 1 volt as read on the General Radio meter, for each setting. If, as the frequency is raised, a meter reading drops off, that meter may be removed from the circuit.

Calculations and conclusions

13. Arrange the data in parts 8, 9, 10, 11 in a tabular form for easy comparison. Discuss the specific reason for the different responses of the meters to each waveform of voltage.

14. Compare the reading of the General Radio meter to the positive peak of the oscillograph trace for the various waveforms. Do they tend to follow each other? Explain.

15. Plot data of part 12 on 5-cycle semi-log paper. Adjust all readings to 1 volt as indicated by the General Radio meter. Discuss the curves. What major difference in the meter circuits caused the General Radio instrument to have a much wider frequency response?

16. Discuss the overall significance of the various tests performed in this experiment.

References

Ryder, J. D., *Electronic Fundamentals and Applications*, 2d ed. (Englewood Cliffs, N. J.: Prentice-Hall, Inc., 1959).

Terman, F. E., and Pettit, J. M., *Electronic Measurements* (New York: McGraw-Hill Book Co., Inc., 1952).

Terman, F. E., *Radio Engineers' Handbook* (New York: McGraw-Hill Book Co., Inc., 1943).

Materials required

Components	Equipment
1 6H6 tube and socket	1 audio oscillator
1 10 K resistor	1 square-wave generator
1 0.01 µf capacitor	1 cathode-ray oscillograph
	1 Hewlett-Packard Model 400A vacuum-tube voltmeter
	1 Ballantine Model 300 vacuum-tube voltmeter
	1 General Radio Type 726A vacuum-tube voltmeter

EXPERIMENT

25-B

Vacuum-tube Voltmeters

Purpose

The purpose of this experiment is to familiarize the student with some aspects of vacuum-tube voltmeter theory, practice, advantages, and errors.

Information

A few points will be mentioned here that will be emphasized in the experimental section. Direct-current vacuum-tube voltmeters are only as stable as the associated amplifiers. In the more refined d-c meters, many stabilizing procedures such as push-pull, difference amplifiers, and chopper amplifiers are used.

Alternating-current vacuum-tube voltmeters are inherently more stable than d-c meters since negative feedback can stabilize a-c gain to any degree desired. Feedback amplifiers, however, are difficult to design for more than 10 megacycles bandwidth, so very wide-band voltmeters usually employ rectification followed by a d-c voltmeter circuit.

Preliminary

1. Define the following terms and explain their significance as applied to vacuum-tube voltmeters:

(a)	input impedance	(f)	zero drift
(b)	turnover	(g)	series resonance error
(c)	grounding error	(h)	peak reading
(d)	waveform error	(i)	rms reading
(e)	transit-time error	(j)	average reading

2. Suppose that the zero signal plate current ($i_b = i_{bo}$) for the circuit of Fig. 1(a) is 0.50 ma. What must be the value of R_1 in the zeroing circuit of Fig. 1(b) to just balance out the zero-signal current in Fig. 1(a)?

3. Discuss significant causes of error peculiar to a slide-back voltmeter when used to measure a-c voltages.

Performance

The triode vacuum-tube voltmeter will be used for illustration.

D-c triode voltmeter

4. Connect the circuit as shown in Fig. 1 with $R = 0$. Set V_2 to 90 volts. Read I_1 for values of V_1 from 0 to 3.5 volts in 0.5-volt steps. Measure I_1 with a 0–5 ma d-c milliammeter.

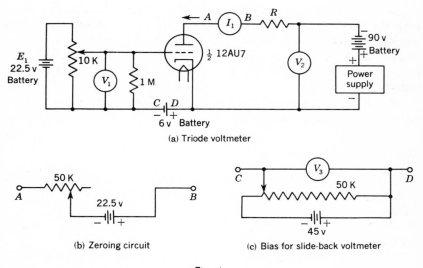

(a) Triode voltmeter

(b) Zeroing circuit   (c) Bias for slide-back voltmeter

Fig. 1

5. Repeat part 4 with $R = 10,000$ ohms. Read values of V_1 up to 6 volts or I_b up to 5 ma, which ever occurs first.

6. Repeat part 5 with $R = 20,000$ ohms.

7. With $R = 20,000$ ohms, set V_1 equal to 3 volts. Vary V_2 from 70 to 120 volts and read I_1.

A-c triode voltmeter

8. Replace battery E_1 with an oscillator, V_1 with a vacuum-tube voltmeter, and I_b with a 0–1 ma d-c milliammeter. Set the frequency at 500 cps. Repeat parts 4, 5, and 6 except that the source of grid voltage is now the oscillator.

Zeroing circuit

9. Connect terminal A of the zeroing circuit of Fig. 1(b) to terminal A in Fig. 1(a). Make certain that all of the resistance of the 50 K potentiometer R_1 is in the circuit. Set V_2 to cause approximately full-scale current I_1 to flow. Connect terminal B of Fig. 1(b) to terminal B of Fig. 1(a) and

adjust R_1 until I_1 is zero. Then raise V_2 a few volts and readjust R_1 until I_1 is again zero. Continue this process until V_2 is 150 volts. Repeat part 8 for $R = 0$ and 20,000 ohms only.

Note: It is important that the procedure as outlined above be followed. Otherwise the meter may be damaged. Reverse the procedure before removing the zeroing circuit or turning off the power supply.

Slide-back voltmeter

10. Return the circuit to that of Fig. 1(a) with the bias battery replaced with the bias circuit in Fig. 1(c). Leave the oscillator and vacuum-tube voltmeter connected to the circuit. Set V_1 equal to zero, V_2 to 90 volts, and adjust V_3 so that $I_1 = 0.02$ ma. Record value of V_3. Adjust V_3 to a large negative value (30 to 35 volts), and set V_1 to 5 volts (rms). Adjust V_3 until 0.02 ma plate current flows. Read V_3.

Repeat for $V_1 = 10, 15, 20,$ and 25 volts. Use care to always return V_3 to its most negative value before increasing V_1.

Calculations and conclusions

11. Plot V_1 vs I_1 for parts 4, 5, and 6 on a single curve sheet. Discuss the characteristics of the circuit of Fig. 1(a) and a d-c vacuum-tube voltmeter.

12. Plot V_2 vs I_1 for part 7. Discuss significance of results in terms of plate voltage supply regulation.

13. Plot V_1 vs I_1 for parts 8 and 9. Discuss the characteristics of the circuits involved as a-c vacuum-tube voltmeters. Discuss the operation and desirability of the zeroing circuit.

14. Compute the peak values of V_1 in part 10. Compare to the value determined from V_3. Show also the per cent error based on the known peak values. Discuss the reasons for any discrepancies.

References

Ryder, J. D., *Electronic Fundamentals and Applications*, 2d ed. (Englewood Cliffs, N. J.: Prentice-Hall, Inc., 1959).

Terman, F. E., and Pettit, J. M., *Electronic Measurements* (New York: McGraw-Hill Book Co., Inc., 1952).

Henney, K., and Richardson, G. A., *Principles of Radio*, 6th ed. (New York: John Wiley & Sons, Inc., 1952).

Terman, F. E., *Radio Engineers' Handbook* (New York: McGraw-Hill Book Co., Inc., 1937).

Materials required

Components

1 12AU7 tube and socket
2 45 volt batteries with 22.5 volt taps
1 7.5 volt bias battery
1 10 K, 10 watt potentiometer
1 50 K, 2 watt potentiometer
1 10 K, 2 watt resistor
1 20 K, 2 watt resistor
1 1 megohm resistor

Equipment

1 power supply (either 0–150 volts or to be reduced as in Fig. 1(a), with 6.3 volts a-c)
1 audio oscillator
1 250 volt d-c voltmeter
1 100 volt d-c voltmeter
1 25 volt d-c voltmeter
1 1 ma d-c meter
1 10 ma d-c meter
1 multimeter

26-A

R-C Transients

Purpose

The object of this experiment is to familiarize students with some of the many phenomena associated with R-C circuits, which are of such wide application in electronic circuits.

Information

This experiment is facilitated by a knowledge of Laplace transform or some other operational method; however, elementary differential equations can be used.

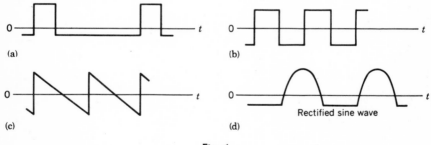

Rectified sine wave

Fig. 1

Preliminary

1. The driving voltages shown in Fig. 1 are applied across a series R-C circuit. Sketch the steady-state waveform across R if the time constant of the R-C circuit is short in comparison with the period of the applied wave. Sketch also the waveform of steady-state voltage across C if the time constant is long in comparison with the period of the applied wave.

2. The average control characteristics of a type 2D21 shield-grid thyratron ($E_{c2} = 0$ volts, $R_g = 100$ K), are given below. If the plate

supply voltage in Fig. 2 is 200 volts, and C is initially uncharged, how long
will it be after switch S is thrown before the tube conducts?

Control grid volts	Anode volts
−1.00	50
−1.75	100
−2.00	150
−2.25	200
−2.45	250
−2.70	300

Performance

3. Connect a 100 K resistor and decade capacitor in series across the
output terminals of a square-wave generator with the capacitor on the
grounded side. Connect a cathode-ray oscillograph across C, and another
oscillograph across the R-C combination. Set the frequency (repetition
rate) to 500 cps.

Set $C = 0$ (actually about 30 $\mu\mu f$, the distributed capacitance of the
decade capacitor). Observe and sketch the waveform of the voltage
across C.

Repeat for $C = 0.001, 0.005, 0.01, 0.05,$ and 0.1 μf. Note any change in
amplitude of voltage across C. Use the oscillograph across the R-C combination to monitor the input voltage waveform. Inform your instructor if
the input voltage waveform shows any change.

4. Interchange positions of R and C in part 3. With $R = 100$ ohms,
observe and sketch the waveform across R for $C = 0.002$ μf. Repeat for
$C = 0.01, 0.05, 0.1, 0.5,$ and 1.0 μf. Note any change in the amplitude of the
voltage across R.

5. Replace the square-wave generator with the half-wave rectifier of
Fig. 3(a).

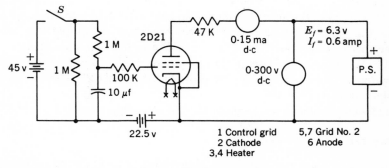

Fig. 2

With $R = 100$ K, and in the same position as in part 3, observe and
sketch the waveform across C for values of $C = 0.001, 0.01, 0.05,$ and 0.5 μf.

Interchange positions of R and C. With $R = 100$ K, observe and sketch the voltage waveform across R for $C = 0.002$, 0.05, and 0.5 μf.

6. Connect the circuit of Fig. 3(b). With the capacitor short circuited, record the input voltage V and the current I. Remove the short circuit on the capacitor and measure the time required for the current to drop to 0.368 times its initial value. Take five independent readings.

7. Connect the circuit of Fig. 2. Set the plate supply voltage to 200 volts. Measure the time required for the tube to fire after the switch is

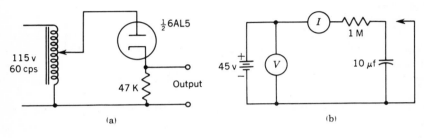

Fig. 3

closed. At least three readings should be taken. After each reading the switch S and power supply must both be turned off and the capacitor allowed to discharge. The capacitor may be short circuited with a lead to insure that it is discharged.

Calculations and conclusions

8. Show the waveforms obtained in parts 3, 4, and 5 in a neat arrangement. Compare these waveforms with those predicted for similar circuit arrangements in part 1. Explain any differences.

9. Compute the actual value of R in part 6 from the experimental data. Using this value of R and the average time constant, compute the value of C Show the measured and rated values of R and C in tabular form.

10. What was the average time required for the tube to fire in part 7? How does this compare to the time predicted in part 2? Discuss possible reasons for discrepancies.

11. Discuss the general significance of this experiment.

References

Ryder, J. D., *Electronic Fundamentals and Applications*, 2d ed. (Englewood Cliffs, N. J.: Prentice-Hall, Inc., 1959).

Von Tersch, L. W., and Swago, A. W., *Recurrent Electrical Transients* (Englewood Cliffs, N. J.: Prentice-Hall, Inc., 1953).

Materials required

Components

1 2D21 tube and socket
1 6AL5 tube and socket
1 45 volt battery
1 22.5 volt battery
2 1 megohm resistors
1 100 K resistor
1 47 K resistor
1 10 μf paper capacitor
1 variable transformer (Variac)
1 1 μf decade capacitor
1 10 K decade capacitor

Equipment

1 power supply (200 volts at 20 ma and 6.3 volts, a-c)
1 square-wave generator
1 100 μa d-c meter
1 15 ma d-c meter
1 50 volt d-c meter
1 300 volt d-c meter
1 multimeter

26-B

R-C Transients

Purpose

The object of this experiment is familiarization with waveforms obtainable in R-C circuits, with mathematical derivations and experimental verification.

Information

The extremely wide use of R-C circuits justifies a great deal of practice with these circuits.

Preliminary

1. A periodic signal is to be supplied to the circuit of Fig. 1(a). For linear circuit elements, show the relationship among the following quantities: (a) average value of the input voltage, (b) average value of the voltage across the capacitor, (c) average value of the output voltage.

2. Let the voltage of Fig. 1(b) be applied to the circuit of Fig. 1(a). Sketch the steady-state output voltage, labeling all critical points in terms of Δe, E_o, Δt_1, and Δt_2.

3. Using the results of part 2 sketch and label the steady-state output voltage for (a) $RC \rightarrow 0$ (b) $RC \rightarrow \infty$. The time intervals Δt_1 and Δt_2 remain finite in length. (c) What are the circuits of (a) and (b) called?

4. Alter the circuit of Fig. 1(a) by placing a resistor R_c in parallel with C. (a) Using the input waveform of Fig. 1(b) sketch and label the steady-state output voltage. (b) Sketch and label the potential drop across the capacitor using the R-R_c junction as a reference.

5. Let the voltage of Fig. 1(c) be applied to the circuit of Fig. 1(a). Sketch the steady-state output voltage, labeling all critical points in terms of Δe, E_o, RC, Δt_1, and Δt_2.

6. Let the voltage of Fig. 1(d) be applied to the circuit if Fig. 1(a). Sketch and label the steady-state output voltage.

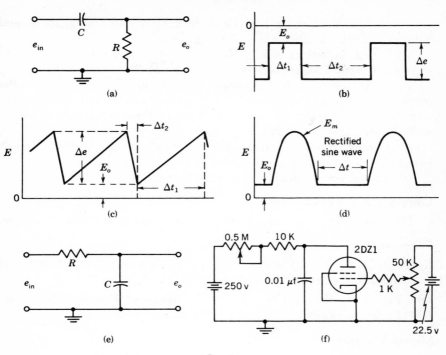

Fig. 1

7. (a) Develop an approximate equation for the output of an R-C differentiating circuit with an arbitrary input voltage. (b) Repeat for an R-C integrating circuit.

8. Plot three cycles of a sawtooth voltage having a linear rise time of 2500 μsec and linear return time of 400 μsec. The peak-to-peak amplitude is 100 volts. Plot the derivative and integral of this voltage showing the correct time relationships among the three curves.

9. The sawtooth voltage of part 8 is applied to the circuit of Fig. 1(a) where R is 25 K and C is 0.001 μf. Plot and label the steady-state output voltage. Compare with the true derivative as obtained in part 8. What are the chief differences?

10. The sawtooth voltage of part 8 is applied to the circuit of Fig. 1(e) where R is 250 K and C is 0.1 μf. Compare the steady-state output voltage to the true integral as obtained in part 8. What are the chief differences?

Performance

11. Apply a square wave of 500 cps to the circuit of Fig. 1(a). Sketch the output voltage for several values of $\Delta t/RC$ ranging from 0.02 to 100. For two values of $\Delta t/RC$ measure the output voltage and compare to calculated values.

12. Set up the circuit of part 4 and show the output voltage for several values of $\Delta t/RC$. Explain any differences.

13. Using the circuit of Fig. 1(e) and a square-wave input signal, observe the output voltage for several values of $\Delta t/RC$.

14. Construct a sawtooth generator as shown in Fig. 1(f) and sketch the output waveshape. Using the sawtooth source as an input signal to the circuit of Fig. 1(a), sketch the output for several values of RC. Compare with the results obtained in part 9.

15. Connect the sawtooth generator to the circuit of Fig. 1(e). Repeat part 14 and compare the results to those of part 10.

16. Obtain results similar to those of part 6.

Calculations and conclusions

17. Discuss any unexpected phenomena observed under performance.

References

Ryder, J. D., *Electronic Fundamentals and Applications*, 2d ed. (Englewood Cliffs, N. J.: Prentice-Hall, Inc., 1959).

Von Tersch, L. W., and Swago, A. W., *Recurrent Electrical Transients* (Englewood Cliffs, N. J.: Prentice-Hall, Inc., 1953).

Materials required

Components	*Equipment*
1 2D21 tube and socket	1 power supply (250 volts at 10 ma and 6.3 volts, a-c)
1 1N34 diode (mounted)	
1 1 K resistor	1 square-wave generator
1 3.3 K resistor	1 audio oscillator
2 10 K resistors	1 d-c oscillograph
1 33 K resistor	1 multimeter
1 100 K resistor	
1 330 K resistor	
1 1 megohm resistor	
1 50 K potentiometer	
1 500 K potentiometer	
1 100 $\mu\mu$f capacitor	
1 330 $\mu\mu$f capacitor	
1 1000 $\mu\mu$f capacitor	
1 3300 $\mu\mu$f capacitor	
1 0.01 μf capacitor	
1 0.033 μf capacitor	
1 0.1 μf capacitor	
1 0.33 μf capacitor	
1 22.5 volt battery	

EXPERIMENT

27-A

Ringing Circuits

Purpose

The purpose of this experiment is to study RLC transients and their use in ringing circuits.

Information

Rather than approaching the general problem of RLC transients, this experiment will deal primarily with ringing circuits. Ringing circuits have many applications in pulse generation and time measurement. In addition, the method used applies to many other devices exhibiting resonant properties.

Preliminary

1. Explain the operation of the circuit of Fig. 1 if the input is a symmetrical square wave of 40 volts amplitude. Sketch the plate and grid voltages showing their relationships with respect to time. Assume that $2\pi\sqrt{LC}$ is very much less than the period of the input square wave.

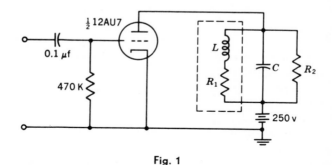

Fig. 1

2. A system similar to that of Fig. 1 may be used to measure the Q of a coil or the Q of a tuned circuit. A CRO is needed to measure voltage and

time. If R_2 is very large, describe a system, including any necessary equations, to experimentally determine the Q of a coil using a CRO and this circuit. What type of tuned circuit might be very susceptible to this type of measurement?

3. Assume the Q of the coil to be very large (R_1 very small). At some value of R_2 the circuit is said to be critically damped. Explain this condition, showing what value of R_2 would critically damp the circuit. Sketch the output of Fig. 1 if the circuit is critically damped, again showing the square-wave input as a reference. Discuss the use of the critically damped circuit as a pulse generator.

4. Figure 1 may be modified into the circuit of Fig. 2. Sketch the cathode voltage showing the input square wave as a reference. Describe

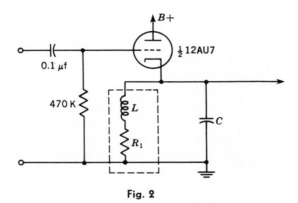

Fig. 2

any differences between the voltage waveforms in this circuit and the circuit of Fig. 1.

5. The circuits of Figs. 1 and 2 are quite often used as standards for measuring time intervals, since the oscillations always start at the same time with respect to the input waveform. Why may this be important?

Performance

6. Set up the circuit of Fig. 1 omitting R_2. Using a square-wave input frequency of 300–600 cps, measure the frequency of oscillation. Sketch the plate voltage waveform. Measure the circuit components on the bridge and compute the resonant frequency.

7. Measure the Q of the coil using the method of part 2. Compare with the Q obtained from the bridge values.

8. Add R_2 to the circuit and adjust until the system is critically damped as indicated by the CRO. Sketch the plate voltage waveform. Compare the experimental value of R_2 with the computed critical value.

9. Set up the circuit of part 4. Sketch the cathode voltage.

Calculations and conclusions

10. Is there any difference in the amplitude of the square-wave input needed to keep the tube cut off for parts 6 and 9?

11. Do the parameters of the tube have any effect on the frequency of oscillation in part 6? Explain.

12. Do the parameters of the tube have any effect on the frequency of oscillation in part 9? Explain.

13. Discuss briefly any unusual experimental observations.

References

Von Tersch, L. W., and Swago, A. W., *Recurrent Electrical Transients* (Englewood Cliffs, N. J.: Prentice-Hall, Inc., 1953).

Chance, B., *et al.*, *Waveforms* (New York: McGraw-Hill Book Co., Inc., 1949).

Ryder, J. D., *Electronic Fundamentals and Applications*, 2d ed. (Englewood Cliffs, N. J.: Prentice-Hall, Inc., 1959).

Materials required

Components	*Equipment*
1 12AU7 tube and socket	1 power supply (250 volts at 20 ma
1 approximately 25 mh inductance	and 6.3 volts, a-c)
1 5 K potentiometer	1 cathode-ray oscillograph
1 470 K resistor	1 square-wave generator
1 100 K decade resistor	1 25 ma d-c meter
1 100 $\mu\mu$f capacitor	1 multimeter
1 1000 $\mu\mu$f capacitor	1 audio-frequency impedance bridge
1 0.01 μf capacitor	setup (to be available)
2 0.1 μf capacitors	
1 50 μf, 50 volt capacitor	
1 2 K potentiometer	
1 470 K resistor	
1 100 K decade resistor	
1 100 $\mu\mu$f capacitor	
1 1000 $\mu\mu$f capacitor	
1 0.01 μf capacitor	
2 0.1 μf capacitors	
1 50 μf, 50 volt capacitor	

27-B

Ringing Circuits

Purpose

The object of this experiment is a limited study of RLC circuits and their particular application to ringing circuits.

Preliminary

1. The switch in the circuit of Fig. 1(a) has been closed for a long time and is opened at $t = 0$. Sketch and label the voltage from point A to ground for all different forms of operation that may occur. Indicate the relationships existing among the circuit parameters to produce the various forms of operation. If the switch has been opened for a long time and is closed at $t = 0$, repeat the above.

2. The time constant in the grid circuit of Fig. 1(b) is long compared to the period of the input square wave. The peak-to-peak amplitude of the square wave is 75 volts. Compare the operation of this circuit with that of Fig. 1(a).

3. Is there any use for the circuit of Fig. 1(b) operating under conditions of critical damping?

4. A system similar to that of Fig. 1(a) or (b) may be used to measure the Q of a coil or tuned circuit. Describe a system and pertinent equations to make such a determination. Could this method be used on cavities not containing lumped constants? How?

5. The circuit of Fig. 1(b) may be modified into that of Fig. 1(c). Sketch the cathode voltage showing the input square wave as a reference. Describe any differences between the voltage waveforms in this circuit and the circuit of Fig. 1(b). If the coil, capacitor, and tube are used in both the circuits will the frequencies of oscillation be the same?

6. How can the circuits of Fig. 1 be used to measure time?

7. How can a diode be used, in Fig. 1, to limit the ringing to one-half cycle? What limits the pulse amplitude?

Performance

8. Set up the circuit of Fig. 1(b) omitting R_2. Using a square-wave input frequency of 300–600 cps, measure the frequency of oscillation. Sketch

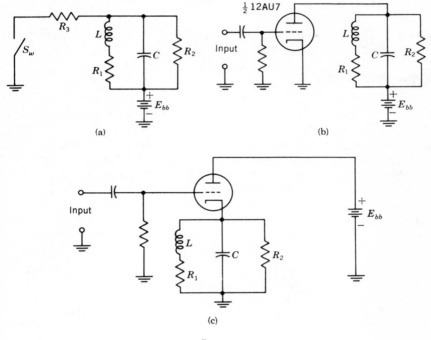

(a)   (b)

(c)

Fig. 1

the plate voltage waveform. Be sure to record the value of the components used. Use the larger of the two inductances.

9. Measure the Q of the larger coil using the method of part 4.

10. Add R_2 to the circuit and adjust until the system is critically damped. Sketch the plate voltage waveform. Compare the value of R_2 obtained here with a value computed from the measurements of part 8 and part 9.

11. Set up the circuit of part 5. Sketch the cathode voltage.

12. Using the smaller coil and diode as in Fig. 1(b), measure the pulse height and duration. Use no additional capacitance or resistance.

Calculations and conclusions

13. Is the amplitude of square wave necessary for Fig. 1(b) and (c) different? Why?

14. Discuss any unexpected experimental phenomena and observations.

References

Von Tersch, L. W., and Swago, A. W., *Recurrent Electrical Transients* (Englewood Cliffs, N. J.: Prentice-Hall, Inc., 1953).

Chance, B., *et al.*, *Waveforms* (New York: McGraw-Hill Book Co., Inc., 1949).

Ryder, J. D., *Electronic Fundamentals and Applications*, 2d ed. (Englewood Cliffs, N. J.: Prentice-Hall, Inc., 1959).

Materials required

Components

1 12AU7 tube and socket
1 1N34 diode or equivalent
1 approximately 25 mh inductance
1 small, high-Q, single-layer inductance having a resonant frequency of around 500 to 1000 kc when connected in the 12AU7 plate circuit

Equipment

1 power supply (250 volts at 50 ma and 6.3 volt, a-c)
1 cathode-ray oscillograph
1 square-wave generator
1 25 ma d-c meter
1 multimeter

EXPERIMENT

28-A

Clipping Circuits

Purpose

The purpose of this experiment is familiarization with some of the aspects of clipping circuits.

Information

The name "clipping" is applied to functions which result in removal of a wave above some level, below some level, above and below two levels, respectively, or between two levels. It is allied closely to "amplitude discrimination" and often used with "clamping" circuits. The variety of the circuits and combinations is so great that complete survey is impossible. Only limited examples will be covered here.

Preliminary

1. Suppose in Fig. 1(a) that one diode plate is disconnected. For $E_{in} = 50$ volts peak, $E_1 = 10$ volts, $R = 5000$ ohms, plot to scale the waveforms of V_1 and V_2, each on its own axis, if (a) $r_p = 0$, (b) $r_p = 1000$ ohms. Show 0 and π radian points.
2. Repeat part 1 if both diodes are connected and $E_1 = E_2 = 10$ volts.
3. Explain how the triode clipper of Fig. 1(b) works. Illustrate by the use of typical triode dynamic transfer characteristics and show typical waveforms. Waveforms for two cases should be shown, i.e. for positive and for negative peak clipping.

Performance

4. Set up the diode peak clipper of Fig. 1(a) leaving one diode plate disconnected.

   (a) Set E_{in} to 50 volts and E_1 to 0 volts. Sketch waveforms of V_1 and V_2 for $R = 10,000, 47,000, 100,000$, and $1,000,000$ ohms.

   (b) Set E_1 to 6 volts and R to 47 K. Vary E_{in} from 0 to greater than 50 volts and sketch typical waveforms of V_1 and V_2.

5. Connect both diode plates in the circuit of Fig. 1(a).

(a) Repeat part 4(a) except with $E_1 = E_2 = 6$ volts.

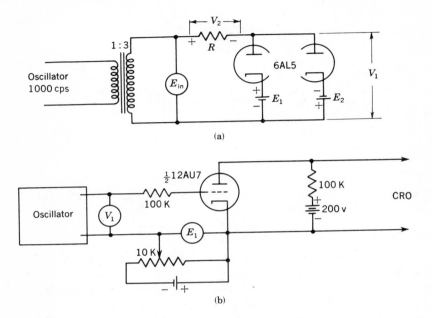

(a)

(b)

Fig. 1 **(a)** Diode clipper; **(b)** triode clipper.

(b) Set $E_1 = E_2 = 6$ volts and $R = 1$ megohm. Vary E_{in} and sketch typical waveforms of V_1 and V_2.

(c) Repeat part (b) with $E_1 = 3$ volts and $E_2 = 6$ volts.

6. Set up the circuit of Fig. 1(b).

(a) Adjust E_1 and V_1 to obtain positive peak clipping. Record values of E_1 and V_1 and sketch output waveform.

(b) Repeat for negative peak clipping.

(c) Repeat for equal clipping of both peaks.

Calculations and conclusions

7. (a) Reproduce typical waveforms observed in part 4(a). Discuss the waveforms and explain how the value of R affects the waveform. (b) Reproduce typical waveforms observed in part 4(b). Discuss the effect on the waveform which occurs as a result of varying E_{in}.

8. Repeat part 7 for the data of part 5.

9. Reproduce typical waveforms observed in part 6. Discuss.

10. Compare the results obtained by use of the diode and triode clippers. Discuss good and bad features of each.

References

Ryder, J. D., *Electronic Fundamentals and Applications*, 2d ed. (Englewood Cliffs, N. J.: Prentice-Hall, Inc., 1959).

Von Tersch, L. W., and Swago, A. W., *Recurrent Electrical Transients* (Englewood Cliffs, N. J.: Prentice-Hall, Inc., 1953).

Chance, B., *et al.*, *Waveforms* (New York: McGraw-Hill Book Co., Inc., 1949).

Materials required

Components	*Equipment*
1 12AU7 tube and socket	1 power supply (200 volts at 10 ma
1 6AL5 tube and socket	and 6.3 volts, a-c)
1 input transformer (to increase oscillator output voltage)	1 audio oscillator
2 7½ volt bias batteries with taps	1 cathode-ray oscillograph
1 10 K, 2 watt, potentiometer	1 100 volt a-c meter
1 10 K resistor	1 10 volt d-c meter
1 47 K resistor	1 multimeter
3 100 K resistor	
1 1 megohm resistor	

EXPERIMENT

28-B

Clipping Circuits

Purpose

The purpose of this experiment is to study methods of clipping and squaring voltage waveforms.

Information

"Clipping" is usually understood to mean a process whereby a portion or portions of a voltage wave is removed. The parts removed are usually selected by an amplitude selection — as contrasted to time selection, etc. These circuits differ primarily from "clamping circuits" in that they intentionally change the waveshape.

The experiment will be performed entirely with vacuum tubes, only because the equipment is available. Solid-state diodes and amplifiers are available for almost any purpose, but their characteristics have not been standardized among various manufacturers.

Preliminary

1. Describe a generalized input voltage-output voltage characteristic which is common to all clipping circuits.

2. Sketch and label the clipping characteristic for the circuits of Figs. 1(a) and (b) if (a) the diode resistance $\bar{r}_p$ is very much less than R, (b) if $\bar{r}_p$ is appreciable in magnitude with respect to R. Assume $\bar{r}_p$ to be linear. (c) Compare the use of crystal and thermionic diodes in the circuits of Fig. 1.

3. (a) Assuming the diodes in the circuit of Fig. 1(c) have a constant static conducting resistance of 100 ohms, plot the output voltage for a 15-volt rms sine-wave input signal. (b) Repeat for the circuit of Fig. 1(d) if a 10-volt rms input signal is used. (c) Redesign the circuit of Fig. 1(d) using the vacuum diodes and but one source of bias voltage.

4. Explain the operation of the circuit shown in Fig. 2(a). The 15-volt rms sine-wave input signal has a frequency 10 times that of the square wave. The square wave varies from 0–25 volts with the polarity shown. Sketch the output voltage.

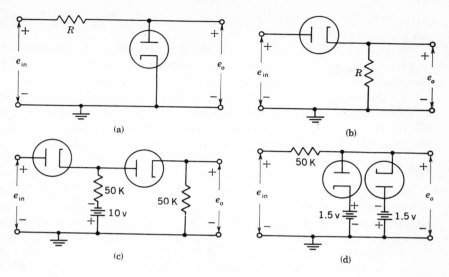

Fig. 1

5. The amplifier of Fig. 2(b) may be used to obtain approximate square waves from a sine-wave input signal. Discuss this circuit, including in the discussion such items as (a) use of series grid resistor, (b) magnitude

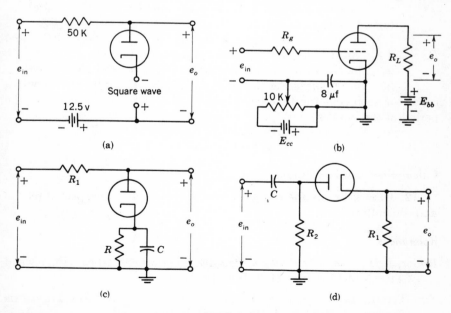

Fig. 2

of bias, (c) effect of change in input signal amplitude, plate supply voltage, and plate load resistance.

6. In a great number of diode circuits difficulty arises owing to the fact that the volt-ampere characteristic does not have a sharp break. Show and discuss one circuit which tends to overcome this disadvantage.

7. The circuit of Fig. 2(c) will operate as a self-biased clipper if $R_2C \gg \Delta t$, where Δt is the period of the input signal. (a) Discuss the operation of this circuit for the case of a square-wave input signal, including any appropriate equations. (b) Repeat part 7(a) for the circuit of Fig. 2(d).

Performance

8. Set up the circuit of Fig. 1(a). Let R be successively 25 K, 50 K, and 250 K. For a constant sine-wave input, compare the results obtained with each resistor. With $R = 250$ K, use three widely different values of sine-wave input signal. Sketch the input and output voltages for each case.

9. Repeat part 8 for the circuit of Fig. 1(b).

10. Reverse the plate and cathode of the circuit of Fig. 1(d) and insert a bias voltage of 10 volts, negative terminal at ground, in the shunt branch. Repeat part 8.

·11. Set up and operate the following circuits. Record all pertinent waveforms.

(a) The circuit of Fig. 1(c)

(b) The circuit of Fig. 1(d) using the modification of part 3(c)

(c) The circuit of Fig. 2(a)

(d) The circuit of Fig. 2(b). Let $R_g = 250$ K, $E_{bb} = 250$ volts, $R_L = 50$ K. Adjust the bias to give a symmetrical output.

(e) The circuit of Fig. 2(b) with the 250 K resistor shorted out

(f) The circuit of Fig. 2(b) with the 250 K resistor by-passed with a capacitor such that the time constant of the combination is equal to the period of the input signal

(g) The circuit of Fig. 2(c)

(h) The circuit of Fig. 2(d)

Calculations and conclusions

12. Discuss briefly the results observed, particularly unexpected results and difficulties.

References

Ryder, J. D., *Electronic Fundamentals and Applications*, 2d ed. (Englewood Cliffs, N. J.: Prentice-Hall, Inc., 1959).

Von Tersch, L. W., and Swago, A. W., *Recurrent Electrical Transients* (Englewood Cliffs, N. J.: Prentice-Hall, Inc., 1953).

Chance, B., *et al.*, *Waveforms* (New York: McGraw-Hill Book Co., Inc., 1949).

Materials required

Components	*Equipment*
1 6AL5 tube and socket	1 power supply (250 volts at 20 ma and 6.3 volts, a-c)
1 12AU7 tube and socket	1 d-c cathode-ray oscillograph
1 10 K potentiometer	1 audio frequency oscillator
1 8 μf paper capacitor	1 multimeter
1 1 μf decade capacitor	
1 10 K resistor	
1 27 K resistor	
1 47 K resistor	
1 100 K resistor	
1 270 K resistor	
1 470 K resistor	
1 22.5 volt battery	
2 7.5 volt bias batteries with 1.5 volt taps	

Clamping Circuits

Purpose

The purpose of this experiment is the study of various types of clamping circuits and some possible uses.

Information

In terms of components and circuit arrangements "clamping" and "clipping" circuits are similar. Clipping circuits, however, alter waveshape while clamping circuits merely change the average value or fix one voltage extremity at some desired d-c potential. These circuits are also called d-c restorers or d-c reinsertion circuits.

Preliminary

1. If a symmetrical square wave is applied to the circuit of Fig. 1(a), sketch the output wave with (a) the tube in the circuit; (b) the tube out of the circuit.

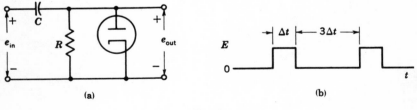

(a)   (b)

Fig. 1

2. Using the input voltage of Fig. 1(b), repeat part 1.
3. Repeat part 2 for each of the circuits of Fig. 2.
4. Describe the need and use of clamping circuits in television receivers
5. Name and describe two other uses for clamping circuits.
6. What is meant by synchronized clamping?

7. Draw a circuit for grid clamping, and explain the conditions under which clamping may occur in R-C coupled amplifiers. Is clamping possible in tetrode and pentode circuits?

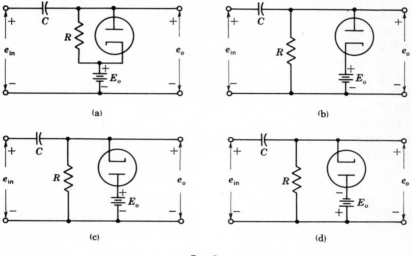

Fig. 2

Performance

8. Set up the circuit and check the results of part 1. Calibrate the oscillograph and sketch results with voltage check points. Use a time constant long compared to the square wave.

9. Repeat part 8 with a sine-wave input.

10. Repeat part 8 for the circuits of Fig. 2.

Calculations and conclusions

11. Discuss briefly comparisons of calculations and experimental results. Also discuss any unexpected experimental occurrences.

References

Ryder, J. D., *Electronic Fundamentals and Applications*, 2d ed. (Englewood Cliffs, N. J.: Prentice-Hall, Inc., 1959).

Chance, B., *et al.*, *Waveforms* (New York: McGraw-Hill Book Co., Inc., 1949).

Von Tersch, L. W., and Swago, A. W., *Recurrent Electrical Transients* (Englewood Cliffs, N. J.: Prentice-Hall, Inc., 1953).

Materials required

Components

1 6AL5 tube and socket
1 45 volt battery
1 10 K potentiometer
1 1 K resistor
1 10 K resistor
1 100 K resistor
1 1 megohm resistor
1 0.001 µf capacitor
1 0.01 µf capacitor
1 0.1 µf capacitor
1 1.0 µf capacitor
1 8 µf paper capacitor
1 6.3 volt transformer

Equipment

1 d-c cathode-ray oscillograph
1 square-wave generator
1 audio frequency generator
1 multimeter

EXPERIMENT

29-B

Clamping Circuits

Purpose

The object of this experiment is to make familiar some of the many aspects of circuits used to fix points of waveforms at predetermined d-c potentials.

Preliminary

1. Consider the circuit of Fig. 1(a). The resistor R is a nonlinear resistor having the volt-ampere characteristic of Fig. 1(b). For an arbitrary periodic input calculate the ratio of the area above the zero axis in the output voltage to that below the zero axis. Write an expression for the average value of the output voltage.

2. Let the voltage of Fig. 1(c) be applied to the circuit of Fig. 1(a). Sketch and label the output voltage for the general values of $C_1, R_1, R_2, \Delta t_1,$ $\Delta t_2,$ and Δe.

3. If $R_2 = 3R_1,$ $\Delta t_1 = 2\Delta t_2,$ $\Delta e = 100$ volts, and $R_1 C \gg \Delta t_1,$ sketch and label the output voltage (system similar to part 2).

4. If $R_1 \gg R_2$ and CR_1 is large with respect to any time interval in the input signal, what form of operation will result? What is such a circuit called? What is the easiest practical way to construct such a circuit? Is this a linear circuit?

5. What types of diodes are available for use in clamping circuits? What are the advantages and disadvantages of each? Can triodes be used in clamping circuits? Can pentodes be used in clamping circuits?

6. In the waveform of Fig. 1(c), $\Delta t_1 = 4\Delta t_2$. Apply this voltage to each of the circuits of Fig. 1(d), (e), (f), (g), (h), (i). If operation should depend upon the relationship between Δe and E_o, indicate all possible relationships. Sketch also the output voltage for each of the circuits if the diode is removed from the circuit. In all cases $RC \gg \Delta t_1$.

7. Describe the need and use of clamping circuits in television receivers.

8. Describe two other uses for clamping circuits.

9. Draw and explain a synchronized clamping circuit. What could it be used for advantageously?

10. Explain the similarity between the circuits of Fig. 1(d) and Fig. 2.

Performance

11. Set up a circuit which will operate in a manner similar to that of Fig. 1(a). Use a time constant that is large with respect to a period of the square-wave driving voltage. Apply the output voltage directly to the de-

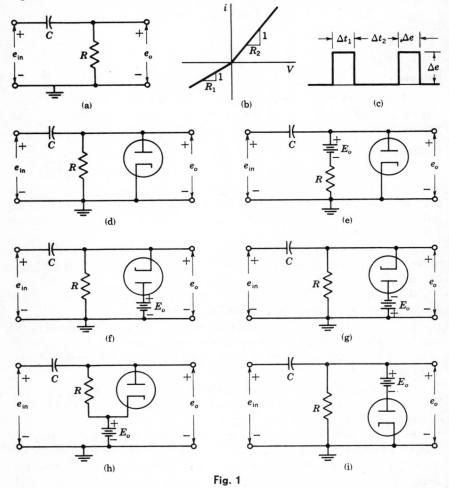

Fig. 1

flection plates of a CRO or to the normal input of d-c CRO. Determine the output voltage waveform for several ratios of R_2 to R_1.

12. Set up the circuits of Fig. 1(d), (e), (f), (g), (h), (i), using a time constant that is large with respect to the square-wave input period. Sketch and label the CRO presentation with the tube both in and out of the circuit.

Use a potentiometer and battery for the source E_o. Explain any discrepancies.

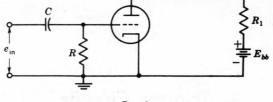

Fig. 2

13. Apply a sine-wave input signal to the circuit of Fig. 2. Sketch and label the output voltage, with the tube in and out of the circuit.

Calculations and conclusions

14. What effects were noted in this experiment that could be attributed to diode capacitance?

15. Discuss any unexpected experimental observations.

References

Von Tersch, L. W., and Swago, A. W., *Recurrent Electrical Transients* (Englewood Cliffs, N. J.: Prentice-Hall, Inc., 1953).

Chance, B., *et al.*, *Waveforms* (New York: McGraw-Hill Book Co., Inc., 1949).

Ryder, J. D., *Electronic Fundamentals and Applications*, 2d ed. (Englewood Cliffs, N. J.: Prentice-Hall, Inc., 1959).

Materials required

Components	*Equipment*
1 6AL5 tube and socket	1 power supply (0–300 volts at 20
1 12AU7 tube and socket	ma and 6.3 volts, a-c)
1 45 volt battery	1 d-c cathode-ray oscillograph
1 10 K, 2 watt potentiometer	1 square-wave analyzer
1 10 μf paper capacitor	1 audio frequency oscillator
1 330 ohm resistor	1 multimeter
1 1 K resistor	
1 3.3 K resistor	
1 10 K resistor	
1 33 K resistor	
1 100 K resistor	
1 330 K resistor	
1 1 megohm resistor	
1 0.001 μf capacitor	
1 0.01 μf capacitor	
1 0.1 μf capacitor	
1 1.0 μf capacitor	

EXPERIMENT

30-A

Trigger Circuits

Purpose

The object of this experiment is a study of bistable thyratron circuits as an example of the larger class of trigger circuits.

Information

The term "trigger circuit" as used here covers all circuits that have more than one stable state. These stable states are naturally separated by unstable states.

The list of circuits satisfying the above definition is large and growing continuously. The first was the Eccles-Jordan trigger circuit, flip-flop, or bistable multivibrator. Now there are also thyratron trigger circuits, Schmidt trigger circuits, phantastron trigger circuits, beam switching tube circuits, transistor trigger circuits, magnetic amplifier trigger circuits, and many others. Trigger circuits are classified as bistable, monostable, and astable. Bistable circuits have two stable states and switch from one to the other when a sufficient or greater signal is received. Monostable circuits switch only for the duration of the trigger or for a fixed period. Astable circuits are oscillators.

Preliminary

1. Draw the waveform of the voltage across one tube of Fig. 1(a) to scale for at least two complete cycles of operation. Assume a trigger signal with a repetition rate of approximately 100 times per second. The transient portions of the waveform may be sketched, but the terminal voltages should be shown to scale.

2. How could the circuit be modified so that the deionization time T_D would fix the upper limit of the switching rate?

3. (a) What maximum current flows in a plate load resistor during the time its associated tube is conducting?

   (b) What should be the power rating of the 10 K resistors assuming the maximum current flows for one half of each cycle?

4. (a) Show two possible connections to indicate the condition of a particular tube of a trigger pair using the circuit of Fig. 1(c).

(b) What will be the approximate current in the indicator circuit for each of the two connections of part 4(a)?

(c) Compute the ratio of the indicator circuit currents of part 4(b) to the maximum plate load resistor current of part 3(a). This ratio gives an indication of the "loading" imposed by the indicator circuit.

5. A signal for triggering a second trigger pair is to be obtained from the circuit of Fig. 1(a). Where should the connection be made? How? Show necessary connections and any electrical components needed.

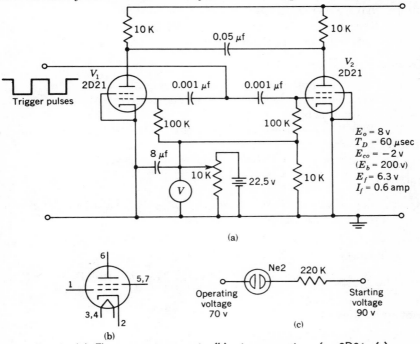

Fig. 1 **(a)** Thyratron trigger pair; **(b)** pin connections for 2D21; **(c)** interpolation light circuit.

Performance

6. (a) Set up the circuit of Fig. 1(a), with provisions for measuring the d-c supply voltage, direct current to entire circuit, bias voltage, and waveforms of various voltages. Set bias voltage to -5 volts for the 2D21 tubes.

(b) Connect neon indicator lamps to each tube so they will light when the tube with which each is associated is conducting.

(c) Check general features of operation of the circuit with a square-wave generator as a trigger source.

7. Starting with the lowest trigger repetition rate available, vary the repetition rate in several steps until triggering action ceases. Record or sketch:

    (a) Trigger repetition rate

    (b) D-c supply voltage

    (c) Total direct current

    (d) Bias voltage

    (e) Peak triggering voltage required

    (f) Waveform of tube voltage

8. Sketch the waveform of voltage across the 0.05 μf capacitor at a low, intermediate, and high trigger signal repetition rate.

9. Repeat part 9 for waveform of cathode-grid voltage of one of the tubes. Note *very* sharp spike in the waveform.

Calculations and conclusions

10. Include complete diagrams if not previously drawn.

11. What maximum switching rate was obtained experimentally? What are the limiting factors?

12. Discuss waveforms obtained with particular emphasis on the changes with frequency.

13. Discuss any unexpected experimental observations.

References

Ryder, J. D., *Electronic Fundamentals and Applications*, 2d ed. (Englewood Cliffs, N. J.: Prentice-Hall, Inc., 1959).

Von Tersch, L. W., and Swago, A. W., *Recurrent Electrical Transients* (Englewood Cliffs, N. J.: Prentice-Hall, Inc., 1953).

Chance, B., *et al.*, *Waveforms* (New York: McGraw-Hill Book Co., Inc., 1949).

Materials required

Components	Equipment
2 2D21 tubes and sockets	1 power supply (200 volts at 50 ma,
1 22.5 volt battery	and 6.3 volts, a-c)
2 0.001 μf capacitors	1 d-c cathode-ray oscilloscope
1 0.05 μf capacitor	1 square-wave generator
1 8 μf, 50 volt capacitor	1 25 volt d-c meter
2 10 K, 5 watt resistors	1 multimeter
1 10 K resistor	
2 100 K resistors	
1 220 K resistor	
1 10 K potentiometer	
1 ne-2 neon tube with mounting	

EXPERIMENT

30-B

Trigger Circuits

Purpose

The purpose of this experiment is to investigate the characteristics and uses of some of the more common trigger circuits.

Preliminary

1. To investigate the suitability of a device as a trigger circuit, the volt-ampere characteristic can be examined. (a) What form of volt-ampere characteristic is necessary to produce a trigger circuit? (b) The sketches of Fig. 1(a) and (b) show an Eccles-Jordan trigger circuit and Schmitt trigger circuit, respectively. Where does the required volt-ampere characteristic appear in these two circuits? (c) Sketch a volt-ampere characteristic for the circuit of Fig. 1(a). (d) Show mathematically the possibility of a trigger action in the two circuits. (e) What is the relationship between the volt-ampere characteristic previously sketched and these calculations? (f) Name and explain briefly three other circuits which will give a trigger action.

2. (a) Does the circuit of Fig. 1(a) have an unstable point of operation if $R_{c1} = R_{c2} = 100$ K, $R_{g1} = R_{g2} = 50$ K, $R_{b1} = R_{b2} = 50$ K, $E_{cc} = 40$ volts, and $E_{bb} = 300$ volts? The tube type is 12AU7. (b) Calculate the input resistance to $P_1 - P_2$ at the point where the tubes are operating linearly and carrying equal plate current. (c) Find the electrode voltages and currents if the circuit is operating at a stable point.

3. (a) What general conditions must be satisfied in order to transfer conduction from one tube to the other in the circuit of Fig. 1(a)? (b) Calculate the approximate value of the voltage pulse necessary to transfer conduction if the pulse is applied to the grid of the "on" tube; the "off" tube. (c) What effect do the interelectrode capacitances have upon the dependability and speed of response of the trigger circuit? (d) What methods

can be used to partially overcome the effect of these capacitances? (e) Is it feasible to use cathode bias instead of the bias battery E_{cc} as shown in

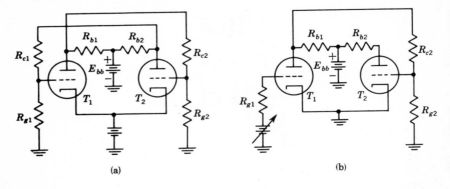

(a)   (b)

Fig. 1

Fig. 1(a)? (f) What would be the value of the bias resistor? (g) Quite often it is desirable to know which tube in an Eccles-Jordan trigger pair is conducting. Show two ways in which neon lamps can be used to supply this information.

4. Eccles-Jordan trigger pairs may be cascaded to form scaling or counting circuits. (a) Show two ways in which one trigger pair may be coupled to the next. (b) Show that the total pulse division or count-down ratio is 2^n, where n is the total number of trigger pairs. (c) Four trigger pairs are properly connected for pulse division with the last pair operating into a mechanical counter. Since the mechanical counter will register only once for every 16 input pulses, show how the neon lamps of part 3 may be used to interpolate between mechanical counts. (d) If one counting operation has been finished and a new one is to begin, some method of fixing the starting point must be used. How can this be done? (e) Sufficient energy to move the armature of a mechanical counter cannot usually be obtained directly from the trigger circuit. Draw and explain a circuit that will receive an input from the trigger circuit, and then operate the mechanical counter. A typical counter might require 50 ma for operation and have resistance of 50 ohms and an inductance of 50 mh.

5. (a) Explain two ways in which trigger circuits can be arranged to count down by an integral value. (b) Explain briefly three different applications of the Eccles-Jordan circuit.

6. (a) Assume that the parameters of the circuit of Fig. 1(b) are such that an instability can exist. If the magnitude of E_{cc} is slowly increased from zero what will happen? (b) If E_{cc} is increased still more does any further significant action take place? (c) If E_{cc} is then decreased back

toward zero what will happen? (d) What is meant by the hysteresis of the circuit? (e) Devise an experimental setup which will allow the hysteresis effect to be observed. (f) Discuss briefly one application of the Schmitt circuit.

Performance

7. (a) Set up the circuit of Fig. 1(a) using the parameters of part 2(a). The cathode bias should be obtained by the use of a 10 K variable resistor shunted by a capacitor. Use two milliammeters to indicate proper operating conditions, these meters being placed in the cathode circuit. The plate supply voltage and cathode resistance should be varied until proper operation is obtained. The trigger pair should be sufficiently sensitive to operate when touched by a finger. When the system is working properly replace the meters with a neon lamp indicator. (b) Observe the plate-plate volt ampere characteristic on the CRO by driving the trigger pair from a sine-wave source in series with a 20 K variable resistor. Compare the slope of the negative resistance portion of the characteristic with the calculations of part 2(b). Note the effect of changes in the cathode resistance and plate supply voltage.

8. Place a 15 K resistor in the plate supply lead. Drive the trigger circuit with a square wave, coupled to the junction of the 15 K resistor and the plate load resistors with a 50 μf capacitor. Adjust the system until the pair is properly counting down.

9. Set up the circuit of Fig. 1(b) using $R_{b_1} = 10$ K, $R_{b_2} = 5$ K, $R_{c_2} = 100$ K, $R_{g_2} = 50$ K, and $R_k = 10$ K variable. Observe the hysteresis effect discussed in part 6(d). Note the effect of changes in plate supply voltage and cathode resistance.

Calculations and conclusions

10. Discuss briefly the experimental results with emphasis on the unexpected ones.

References

Ryder, J. D., *Electronic Fundamentals and Applications*, 2d ed. (Englewood Cliffs, N. J.: Prentice-Hall, Inc., 1959).

Chance, B., *et al.*, *Waveforms* (New York: McGraw-Hill Book Co., Inc., 1949).

Von Tersch, L. W., and Swago, A. W., *Recurrent Electrical Transients* (Englewood Cliffs, N. J.: Prentice-Hall, Inc., 1953).

Materials required

<table>
<tr><td colspan="2">Components</td><td colspan="2">Equipment</td></tr>
<tr><td>1</td><td>12AU7 tube and socket</td><td>1</td><td>power supply (300 volts at 25 ma and 6.3 volts, a-c)</td></tr>
<tr><td>1</td><td>10 K potentiometer</td><td></td><td></td></tr>
<tr><td>1</td><td>20 K potentiometer</td><td>1</td><td>d-c cathode-ray oscilloscope</td></tr>
<tr><td>1</td><td>4.7 K, 1 watt resistor</td><td>1</td><td>square-wave generator</td></tr>
<tr><td>1</td><td>10 K, 1 watt resistor</td><td>1</td><td>audio-frequency generator</td></tr>
<tr><td>1</td><td>15 K, 1 watt resistor</td><td>2</td><td>10 ma d-c meters</td></tr>
<tr><td>4</td><td>47 K resistors</td><td>2</td><td>25 ma d-c meters</td></tr>
<tr><td>2</td><td>100 K resistors</td><td>1</td><td>multimeter</td></tr>
<tr><td>2</td><td>20 $\mu\mu$f capacitors</td><td></td><td></td></tr>
<tr><td>1</td><td>50 μf capacitor</td><td></td><td></td></tr>
<tr><td>2</td><td>0.1 μf capacitors</td><td></td><td></td></tr>
<tr><td>1</td><td>8 μf capacitor</td><td></td><td></td></tr>
<tr><td>1</td><td>45 volt battery</td><td></td><td></td></tr>
</table>

31-A

Multivibrators

Purpose

The purpose here is to study the operation of univibrators and multivibrators; to measure time delay in a univibrator; to measure repetition rate of a multivibrator; and to observe effects of nonsymmetry in a multivibrator.

Preliminary

1. (a) Draw the waveforms of grid and plate voltage to scale for the circuit of Fig. 1.

(b) Estimate the time delay afforded by this circuit.

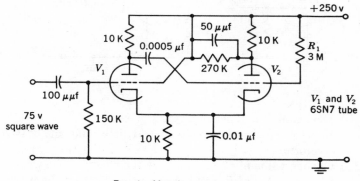

Fig. 1 Univibrator circuit.

2. (a) Draw the waveforms of grid and plate voltage to scale for the circuit of Fig. 2.

(b) Estimate the repetition rate.

Performance

3. Set up the circuit of Fig. 1.

(a) Make a preliminary observation of grid and plate voltage waveforms using a trigger frequency of about 250 cps.

(b) Connect a 50 volt square wave to the CRO and adjust the gain so that 1 inch = 50 volts. Do not readjust the gain until after waveforms have been observed.

(c) Observe waveforms of both grid and plate voltages. Determine voltage values from the calibrated scope.

(d) Set the trigger rate to 1000 cps. Adjust horizontal gain of the CRO to give 1 inch per complete period. Determine the delay time by observing plate voltage waveform of V_1.

(e) Vary d-c supply voltage from 160 to 300 volts and observe qualitatively the effect on the operation of the univibrator.

(f) Change value of C_1 and observe qualitatively the effect on delay time and waveform.

(g) Change value of R_1 and observe qualitatively the effect on delay time and waveform.

4. Set up the circuit of Fig. 2. Make a preliminary observation of the waveforms.

(a) With a calibrated CRO observe waveforms of plate and grid voltages and determine the amplitude of various parts of the waveforms.

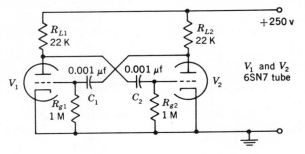

Fig. 2 Multivibrator circuit.

(b) Determine the repetition rate.

(c) Vary the d-c supply voltage and determine qualitatively the effect on waveform.

(d) Change value of C_2 and observe the effect on the waveform.

(e) Change value of R_{g2} and observe the effect on the waveform.

Calculations and conclusions

5. Univibrator

(a) Compare predicted and observed waveforms. Explain differences.

(b) Compare estimated and observed delay times.

(c) Discuss effect of varying plate supply voltage.

(d) Discuss the effect of varying C_1 and R_1.

6. Multivibrator

(a) Compare predicted and observed waveforms. Explain differences.

(b) Compare estimated and observed repetition rates.

(c) Discuss effect of varying the plate supply voltage.

(d) Discuss the effect of varying C_2 and R_{g2}.

References

Ryder, J. D., *Electronic Fundamentals and Applications*, 2d ed. (Englewood Cliffs, N. J.: Prentice-Hall, Inc., 1959).

Von Tersch, L. W., and Swago, A. W., *Recurrent Electrical Transients* (Englewood Cliffs, N. J.: Prentice-Hall, Inc., 1953).

Chance, B., *et al.*, *Waveforms* (New York: McGraw-Hill Book Co., Inc., 1949).

Materials required

Components	*Equipment*
1 6SN7 tube and socket	1 power supply .(160 to 300 volts at
1 50 $\mu\mu$f capacitor	50 ma and 6.3 volts, a-c)
2 100 $\mu\mu$f capacitors	1 square-wave generator
1 500 $\mu\mu$f capacitor	1 d-c cathode-ray oscillograph
2 1000 $\mu\mu$f capacitors	1 300 volt d-c meter
1 5000 $\mu\mu$f capacitor	1 multimeter
1 0.01 μf capacitor	
3 10 K, 2 watt resistors	
2 220 K, 2 watt resistors	
2 47 K, 1 watt resistors	
1 150 K resistor	
1 270 K resistor	
1 470 K resistor	
2 1 megohm resistors	
1 2.2 megohm resistor	

31-B

Multivibrators

Purpose

The purpose of this experiment is to make a study of the simple free-running and single-cycle multivibrators, along with some allied circuits.

Preliminary

1. Discuss briefly the similarities and differences in the following three circuits: (a) Eccles-Jordan trigger circuit; (b) plate-coupled multivibrator; (c) plate-coupled single-cycle multivibrator.

2. Repeat part 1 for (a) the Schmitt trigger circuit, (b) the cathode-coupled multivibrator.

3. (a) What is the purpose of using a positive grid return in a multivibrator? (b) What is the purpose of using a series grid resistance in multivibrator circuits?

4. Consider the plate-coupled single-cycle multivibrator circuit shown in Fig. 1(a). (a) If the tube is a type 12AU7, what is the minimum value of E_{cc} necessary to keep T_1 cut off in the interval between trigger pulses? (b) Take the actual value of E_{cc} as 1.8 times the value calculated, and sketch the plate and grid voltage waveforms for both tubes when a large narrow positive pulse is applied at A. Label all important time and voltage points.

5. (a) To what potential should point B be returned [Fig. 1(a)] in order that the "off" time of T_2 be reduced to 80 per cent of the value it had in part 4(b)? (b) Repeat part 4(b) if a 250 K resistor is inserted in series with the grid at point C (no plus voltage at point B).

6. (a) Give a qualitative description of the cathode-coupled multivibrator shown in Fig. 1(b). (b) Can this circuit be free-running? (c) What advantage does this circuit have over the circuit of Fig. 1(a)? (d) Sketch a set of waveforms for a typical plate-coupled free-running multivibrator.

7. (a) Describe qualitatively the operation of the circuit shown in Fig. 1(c). (b) Repeat for the circuit of Fig. 1(d).

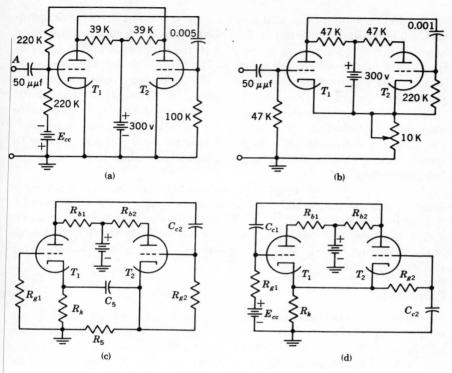

Fig. 1

8. Show how to alter the circuit of Fig. 1(a) to use pentodes so that an electron-coupled output may be obtained.

9. In the Miller type sweep circuit of Fig. 2(a), $r_p = 180$ K and $g_m = 3000$ micromhos. If the type operates in a linear region, calculate V_1, V_2, V_3, V_4, V_5, and V_6 of Fig. 2(b).

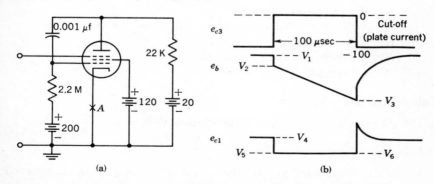

Fig. 2

10. In the circuit of Fig. 2(a) insert a resistor at point A. (a) For operation similar to that shown in Fig. 2(b) sketch the screen voltage. (b) Show how this screen voltage may be coupled to the suppressor grid in order to furnish the suppressor voltage shown in Fig. 2(b). The driving signal need now be only a narrow positive pulse on the suppressor, the complete suppressor voltage being supplied by the screen. (c) What is the circuit of (b) called? (d) In the original circuit, operation stopped when the input square wave dropped below the plate current cut-off value. What will stop operation in the modified circuit? (e) Show how to use a cathode follower to speed the charging of the 0.001 μf capacitor immediately following the 100 μsec period.

11. It is possible to replace the positive gate on the suppressor by a negative gate on the cathode, generated most easily by the insertion of a resistor in the cathode circuit. (a) What is this circuit called? (b) Sketch a circuit of this type showing a method of continuously varying the length of the operating period. What is the form of the driving pulse needed for this circuit?

Performance

12. Set up and operate the following circuits. Record the actual circuit used and all pertinent voltage waveforms. Calibrate the voltage and time axis of the CRO in order to approximately label the curves.

(a) The circuit of Fig. 1(a). Show the effect of altering the time constant in the grid circuit of T_2.

(b) A circuit to illustrate part 5(a)

(c) A circuit to illustrate part 5(b)

(d) The circuit of Fig. 1(b). Show the effect of altering the time constant in the grid circuit of T_2.

(e) A circuit to illustrate part 6(d)

(f) The circuit of Fig. 1(c)

(g) The circuit of Fig. 1(d)

(h) A circuit to illustrate part 8

(i) A circuit to illustrate part 9

(j) A circuit to illustrate part 10

(k) A circuit to illustrate part 11

Calculations and conclusions

13. Discuss any unexpected experimental difficulties.

References

Ryder, J. D., *Electronic Fundamentals and Applications*, 2d ed. (Englewood Cliffs, N. J.: Prentice-Hall, Inc., 1959).

Receiving Tube Manual, Radio Corporation of America.

Von Tersch, L. W., and Swago, A. W., *Recurrent Electrical Transients* (Englewood Cliffs, N. J.: Prentice-Hall, Inc., 1953).

Materials required

Components

1 12AU7 tube and socket
1 6AS6 tube and socket
1 45 volt battery
1 7.5 volt battery
1 50 $\mu\mu$f capacitor
1 500 $\mu\mu$f capacitor
1 1000 $\mu\mu$f capacitor
1 0.005 μf capacitor
1 0.01 μf capacitor
1 0.05 μf capacitor
1 0.1 μf capacitor
1 10 K, 2 watt potentiometer
1 22 K, 2 watt resistor
2 39 K, 2 watt resistors
2 47 K, 2 watt resistors
1 100 K resistor
2 220 K resistors
1 470 K resistor
1 1 megohm resistor
1 2.2 megohm resistor

Equipment

1 power supply (160–300 volts at 50 ma and 6.3 volts, a-c)
1 square-wave generator
1 d-c cathode-ray oscillograph
1 10 ma d-c meter
1 25 ma d-c meter
1 multimeter

EXPERIMENT

32-A

Blocking Oscillators

Purpose

The object of this experiment is an increased understanding of blocking oscillators by experimental verifications of their theory.

Information

Operation of blocking oscillators is simply explained on an approximate level, but is almost impossible to explain on an exact basis. Some of the reasons for this will be mentioned after an introductory explanation.

Basically any of the several oscillator types can be caused to "block." If the gain of the oscillator is much higher than is required for oscillation, and an R-C bias arrangement exists in the grid circuit, the circuit will start into oscillation so violently that the grid will charge the bias capacitor and go beyond cutoff when its induced driving signal is lost owing to falling plate current. The circuits (see Fig. 1) may not appear conventional, but distributed transformer capacitances have not been drawn. Transformers for blocking oscillators are purposefully designed for low-Q, tight coupling, and saturation.

From the brief discussion above, it can be seen that exact analysis is difficult owing to the very nonlinear operation of the tube and transformer. To make it worse, these nonlinearities are functions of frequency.

Preliminary

1. (a) To what type (Hartley, TPTG, etc.) of oscillator does Fig. 1(a) correspond? (b) Describe briefly the circuit operation. Sketch waveforms. (c) How does the blocking oscillator transformer design differ from audio transformer design? (d) What tube ratings are most important for blocking oscillator application?

2. What determines the blocking oscillator pulse length?

3. Show how it may be modified for synchronized and driven operation both by series and parallel triggering.

4. How does the operation of the circuits of Fig. 1(a) and (b) differ?

5. Sketch circuits for transformer windings in the plate and cathode circuits and also in the grid and cathode circuits.

6. Show several output methods.

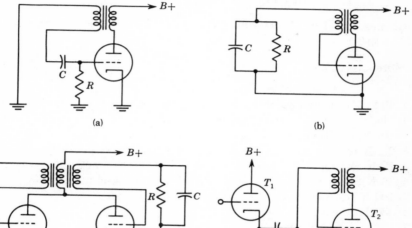

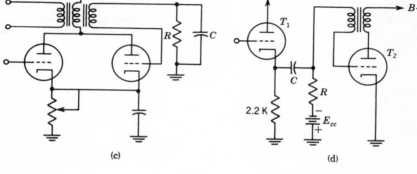

Fig. 1

Performance

7. Set up and operate the circuit of Fig. 1(a) with $C = 1000$ $\mu\mu$f and R from 2 megohms down. Record voltages, time intervals, and waveforms.

8. Return the grid bias resistor to a variable positive bias and take data and waveforms as the positive bias is varied.

9. Check the circuit of Fig. 1(b).

10. Check the series and parallel triggering arrangements of Fig. 1(c) and (d).

Calculations and conclusions

11. Plot the period versus the grid time constant and bias, respectively, in parts 7 and 8.

12. Discuss briefly the operational difficulties and experimental results, particularly the unexpected ones.

References

Ryder, J. D., *Electronic Fundamentals and Applications*, 2d ed. (Englewood Cliffs, N. J.: Prentice-Hall, Inc., 1959).

Von Tersch, L. W., and Swago, A. W., *Recurrent Electrical Transients* (Englewood Cliffs, N. J.: Prentice-Hall, Inc., 1953).

Chance, B., *et al.*, *Waveforms* (New York: McGraw-Hill Book Co., Inc., 1949).

Materials required

Components	*Equipment*
1 12AU7 tube and socket	1 power supply (170–300 volts at
1 blocking oscillator transformer	50 ma and 6.3 volts, a-c)
1 10 K potentiometer	1 d-c cathode-ray oscillograph
1 2.2 K resistor	1 square-wave generator
1 10 K resistor	1 50 volt d-c meter
1 33 K resistor	1 250 volt d-c meter
1 100 K resistor	1 multimeter
1 330 K resistor	
1 1 megohm resistor	
1 2.2 megohm resistor	
1 100 μμf capacitor	
1 1000 μμf capacitor	
1 0.01 μf capacitor	
1 0.1 μf capacitor	
1 8 μf paper capacitor	
1 7.5 volt bias battery	
1 22.5 volt battery	

EXPERIMENT

32-B

Blocking Oscillators

Purpose

The purpose of this experiment is to make an elementary study of the blocking oscillator and some of its simple applications.

Preliminary

1. (a) Explain the operation of the circuit shown in Fig. 1(a), noting the sense of the transformer windings. (b) Sketch the approximate waveforms for the plate voltage and grid voltage, indicating the correct time relationships.

2. (a) What factors determine the width of the current pulse in the blocking oscillator? (b) What are the chief differences between a transformer designed for audio service and a transformer designed for use in a fast blocking oscillator circuit?

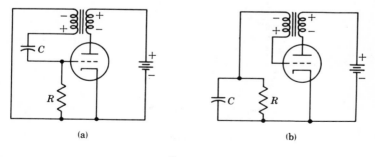

(a)   (b)

Fig. 1

3. In many types of vacuum-tube oscillators the output power is limited by the allowable plate dissipation. What other factors may be important in pulsed circuits such as the blocking oscillator circuit?

4. (a) Compare the circuits of Fig. 1(a) and (b). (b) Explain the system of Fig. 2. What particular use might this circuit have? (c) Sketch and explain a blocking oscillator circuit which has the transformer windings in the grid and cathode circuits; in the plate and cathode circuits.

5. The blocking oscillator may be free-running, may be synchronized by an external signal, or may be completely driven by an external signal. In the second case, removal of the driving signal will not stop operation, but in the third case removal of the driving signal will stop the oscillations. Show how the circuit of Fig. 1(a) may be modified to permit operation similar to the second and third cases.

6. (a) Show three ways in which an output signal may be taken from a blocking oscillator. (b) Show how a blocking oscillator may be used as a frequency divider. Consider the input signal to be a series of narrow positive pulses.

Performance

7. Determine the relative polarity of the windings of the transformer which has been supplied.

8. Set up the circuit of Fig. 1(a) using a type 12AU7 tube with E_{bb} = 175 volts. Let R = 100 K and C = 0.001 μf. Sketch the plate voltage, plate current, and grid voltage, indicating the correct time relationship. Note very carefully the height and width of the plate current pulse.

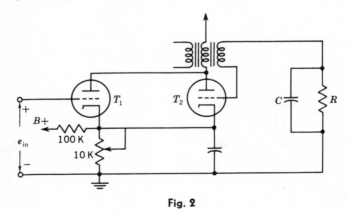

Fig. 2

9. Using values of R from 2 megohms down, record the period $(1/f)$ as a function of the time constant.

10. Return the grid resistor R to a positive potential E_{cc} instead of ground. Record and plot period as a function of E_{co}. Use any time constant for which the circuit operates satisfactorily.

11. Alter the circuit of Fig. 1(a) into that of Fig. 1(b), and note any changes in operation.

12. Parallel triggering of the blocking oscillator may be accomplished by the circuit of Fig. 2. Set up this circuit and make it operate correctly.

13. The circuit of figure 3(a) is an example of series triggering. Repeat part 12.

14. The step-counting circuit of Fig. 3(b) also uses a blocking oscillator as a switch element. Put this circuit into operation, sketching the resulting waveforms. Include a brief description of the form of operation.

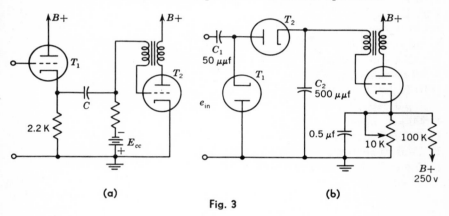

(a)

(b)

Fig. 3

Calculations and conclusions

15. What form should the data in parts 9 and 10 approach when plotted?

16. What differences were noted in the operation of circuits of Fig. 1(a) and (b)?

17. Discuss any unusual experimental behavior noted.

References

Ryder, J. D., *Electronic Fundamentals and Applications*, 2d ed. (Englewood Cliffs, N. J.: Prentice-Hall, Inc., 1959).

Von Tersch, L. W., and Swago, A. W., *Recurrent Electrical Transients* (Englewood Cliffs, N. J.: Prentice-Hall, Inc., 1953).

Chance, B., *et al.*, *Waveforms* (New York: McGraw-Hill Book Co., Inc., 1949).

M.I.T. Radar School Staff, *Principles of Radar* (New York: McGraw-Hill Book Co., Inc., 1953).

Materials required

Components

1 12AU7 tube and socket
1 6AL5 tube and socket
1 blocking oscillator transformer (approximately 1:1)
1 1 K resistor
1 2.2 K resistor
1 10 K resistor
1 33 K resistor
1 100 K resistor
1 330 K resistor
1 1 megohm resistor
1 2.2 megohm resistor
1 10 K potentiometer
1 50 $\mu\mu$f capacitor
1 500 $\mu\mu$f capacitor
1 1000 $\mu\mu$f capacitor
1 0.5 μf capacitor
1 45 volt battery with 22.5 volt tap
1 7.5 volt bias battery

Equipment

1 power supply (170–300 volts at 50 ma and 6.3 volts, a-c)
1 d-c cathode-ray oscilloscope
1 square-wave generator
1 10 ma d-c meter
1 50 ma d-c meter
1 multimeter

33-A

Electrostatic Sweep Circuits

Purpose

The object of this experiment is the study of *R-C* controlled oscillators in general and thyratron-controlled sweep circuits in particular.

Information

The gas diode makes a satisfactory "saw tooth" or sweep generator if connected similar to the plate circuit of Fig. 2. Its greatest difficulty is the instability of the firing and extinction potentials that vary considerably with temperature and tube life.

For many purposes, including oscilloscope sweep circuits, the gas triode is preferred since the oscillator may then be synchronized externally. In any case, the cycle consists of sections of two exponential curves between the firing and extinction potentials of the tube.

Preliminary

1. Assume a firing potential of 180 volts and an extinction potential of 50 volts with a resistance of 100 K and a capacitance of 0.01 μf. The supply voltage is 200 volts. Draw the waveshape and calculate the frequency and period.

2. What effect will supply voltage have on the above oscillator?

3. (a) Explain a method of synchronization for thyratron oscillators.

(b) What is the usual method of frequency control?

Performance

4. Connect the thyratron as shown in Fig. 1.

5. Adjust R_1 to about 1500 ohms. Set V_1 at -1 volt with V_2 at zero. Increase V_2 until the tube fires. Record V_1 and V_2. Repeat at 1-volt intervals for V_1 out to -7 volts. Return V_2 to zero each time before setting V_1. Note change in V_1 as V_2 is increased.

6. Set V_1 to -2 volts with V_2 at zero. Increase V_2 until the tube fires. Record V_2 and I for values ranging from 5 to 70 ma. Repeat for V_1 set at -4 volts. Note: R_1 should never be reduced to zero.

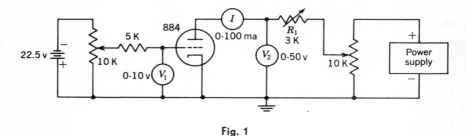

Fig. 1

7. Connect the relaxation oscillator circuit as in Fig. 2.

8. Set V_1 at -4 volts with V_2 at zero. Set V_2 to 250 volts. Connect AA' to the vertical input of a cathode-ray oscillograph. Sketch the trace. Note linearity and retrace characteristics.

9. Connect AA' to horizontal input and an audio oscillator to vertical input of the oscillograph. Determine the frequency (repetition rate) of the relaxation oscillator for values of C_1 from 0.1 to 1.0 μf in 0.1 μf steps.

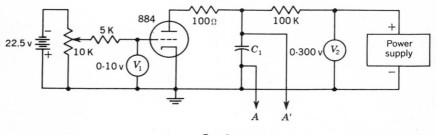

Fig. 2

10. With C_1 set at 0.5 μf observe qualitatively the effect of varying V_1.

11. With C_1 set at 0.5 μf observe qualitatively the effect of varying V_2.

Calculations and conclusions

12. Plot the firing curve, volt-ampere characteristic, and frequency calibration curve.

13. Discuss any unexpected experimental occurrences.

References

Ryder, J. D., *Electronic Fundamentals and Applications,* 2d ed. (Englewood Cliffs, N. J.: Prentice-Hall, Inc., 1959).

Von Tersch, L. W., and Swago, A. W., *Recurrent Electrical Transients* (Englewood Cliffs, N. J.: Prentice-Hall, Inc., 1953).

Chance, B., *et al.*, *Waveforms* (New York: McGraw-Hill Book Co., Inc., 1949).

Materials required

Components	Equipment
1 884 tube and socket	1 power supply (170–300 volts at
2 10 K, 20 watt resistors	100 ma and 6.3 volts, a-c)
1 5 K, 50 ma variable resistor	1 cathode-ray oscillograph
1 100 ohm resistor	1 10 volt d-c meter
1 100 K resistor	1 50 volt d-c meter
1 1 μf decade capacitor	1 300 volt d-c meter
1 22.5 volt battery	1 100 ma d-c meter
1 5 K resistor	1 multimeter

33-B

Electrostatic Sweep Circuits

Purpose

The purpose of this experiment is to study circuits which use either gas or high vacuum tubes as discharge elements in sweep generators.

Information

Although several types of sweep circuits are used in this experiment, the use of blocking oscillators and multivibrators as sweep circuits will be delayed until the principles of these circuits have been discussed in later experiments.

Preliminary

1. (a) Why is it desirable that a time base voltage be a linear function of time? (b) If a constant current source supplies 3.5 ma to a capacitor, what size must the capacitor be in order to have a voltage change of 25 volts per millisecond across its terminals? (c) If this capacitor is charged from a 300 volts source through a series resistor, what must be the value of the resistor to obtain an initial rate of change of voltage equal to 25 volts per millisecond? (d) How much time will have elapsed when the rate of change has decreased to 12 volts per millisecond?

2. A capacitor may be charged from a voltage source through a particular form of nonlinear resistor in order to achieve a constant charging current. (a) Sketch the volt-ampere characteristic of a resistor suitable for this use. (b) Show how a pentode might be connected to charge a capacitor linearly. (c) With 150 volts on the screen of a type 6CB6 tube, what grid-cathode voltage will allow a plate current of 4.0 ma? (d) If this pentode is used to charge a capacitor from a 300 volt supply, at approximately what capacitor voltage will the rate of change of voltage cease to be a constant? (e) What effect will an unby-passed cathode resistor have on the circuit? (f) In the circuit of Fig. 1(a) the tube is a 12AU7, E_{cc} is 130 volts, E_{bb} is 300 volts. Sketch and label the volt-ampere characteristic looking to the

left from point A to ground. (g) If the switch has been shut for a long time and is opened at zero time, sketch and label the voltage from point A to ground.

3. In general, there are two types of electrostatic sweep circuits. The first is a free-running sweep which may or may not be influenced by some external signal. The second is a completely synchronized sweep which pro-

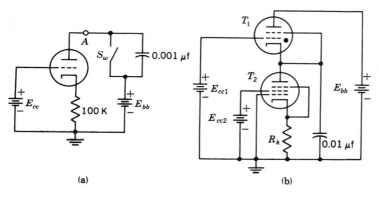

(a)   (b)

Fig. 1

duces a sawtooth only when triggered by an external signal. (a) What particular use does each type of sweep circuit have? (b) Can gas tubes be used for either type? (c) Can vacuum tubes be used for either type? (d) What are some of the limitations on the use of gas tubes in sweep circuits?

4. (a) What advantage does the thyratron sweep circuit have over the gas diode sweep circuit? (b) In the circuit of Fig. 1(b) T_1 is a type 2D21 tube and T_2 is a type 6CB6, $E_{bb1} = 300$ volts, $E_{cc2} = 150$ volts. If R_K is 2 K, plot frequency as a function of E_{cc1} for $50 < E_{cc1} < 300$ volts. (c) For $E_{cc1} = 150$ volts, plot frequency of oscillation as a function of R_K for $500 < R_K < 5$ K.

5. (a) The circuit of Fig. 2(a) is driven by a symmetrical square wave of 100 volts peak-peak amplitude. The period of the input square wave is 1500 μsec. If the tube is type 12AU7, sketch and label the plate voltage showing the relationship between the grid and plate voltages. (b) Show how to modify the circuit of Fig. 2(a) into the bootstrap sweep circuit. (c) The input to the circuit of Fig. 2(b) is similar to that of Fig. 2(a). Sketch and label the voltage from A to ground. The tube T_1 is a type 12AU7 and T_2 is a type 6CB6.

Performance

6. Using the type 2D21 tube and a 50-ohm current-limiting resistor directly in series with the plate, set up a sweep generator with a resistive

charging circuit. Note the linearity and ratio of charge to discharge time. Measure and plot the frequency as a function of thyratron bias for a fixed charging time constant. For a constant bias and fixed supply voltage, measure and plot frequency as a function of charging resistance.

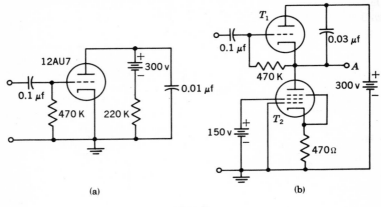

(a)   (b)

Fig. 2

7. For a convenient value of charging resistance and grid bias, replace the current-limiting resistor in the plate circuit with an inductance. Note the effect on the output voltage and frequency.

8. Set up the circuit of Fig. 1(b). Take data similar to that of parts 4(b) and 4(c). Record one set of waveforms.

9. Set up the circuit of Fig. 2(a). Note the effect of varying the time constant.

10. Modify the circuit of Fig. 2(a) into a bootstrap sweep circuit. Set up the circuit such that the sweep is slightly nonlinear without feedback. Then connect the feedback capacitor to show the effect of feedback. Record all waveforms.

11. Alter the circuit of Fig. 2(a) by making the grid circuit time constant very small, and by adding a source of bias sufficiently large to keep the tube cut off except on the positive peaks of the input voltage. Record all waveforms, noting any differences from part 9.

12. Set up and operate the circuit of Fig. 2(b).

Calculations and conclusions

13. In part 6, what happens when an attempt is made to increase the frequency to a large value by using a small charging resistor? What happens when an attempt is made to decrease the frequency to a small value by using a large resistance?

14. Explain the effects noted in parts 7, 9, and 11.

15. Discuss any unusual results.

References

Ryder, J. D., *Electronic Fundamentals and Applications*, 2d ed. (Englewood Cliffs, N. J.: Prentice-Hall, Inc., 1959).

Von Tersch, L. W., and Swago, A. W., *Recurrent Electrical Transients* (Englewood Cliffs, N. J.: Prentice-Hall, Inc., 1953).

Chance, B., *et al.*, *Waveforms* (New York: McGraw-Hill Book Co., Inc., 1949).

Materials required

Components

1 2D21 tube and socket
1 12AU7 tube and socket
1 6CB6 tube and socket
2 10 K, 10 watt potentiometers
1 470 ohm resistor
1 1 K resistor
1 3.3 K resistor
1 10 K resistor
1 33 K resistor
1 100 K resistor
1 330 K resistor
1 1 megohm resistor
1 3.3 megohm resistor
1 1 µf decade capacitor
2 8 µf paper capacitors
2 0.1 µf capacitors
2 45 volt batteries

Equipment

2 power supplies (150–300 volts 50 ma and 6.3 volts, a-c
1 cathode-ray oscillograph
1 square-wave generator
1 multimeter

34-A

Sweep Circuits for Magnetic Deflection

Purpose

The purpose of this experiment is to make a study of some common sawtooth current generators.

Preliminary

1. (a) Under what conditions is the spot deflection in a magnetic cathode-ray tube proportional to the deflection current? (b) Explain a system of magnetic focusing. In what two ways can a magnetic field be obtained for focusing purposes? What are some advantages and disadvantages of each method? (c) The screens of magnetic-type cathode-ray tubes are quite often subject to damage near the center. What is the source of this damage? Why are tubes using electric deflection not affected? What can be done about it?

2. (a) To produce a sawtooth current similar to that of Fig. 1(a), in a coil of 1000 ohms resistance and 40 mh inductance, what must be the voltage applied to the coil? Sketch and label this voltage showing the relationship to the resulting current. Consider both the rise and the fall of the current waveform to be linear. (b) If the coil current is to be $i = 200 \sinh (2000t)$ ma defined over the period $0 < t_0 < 1000$ μsec, what should be the applied voltage?

3. (a) What must be the input voltage to the circuit of Fig. 1(b) if the current is to be of the form $i_L = kt$? (b) to the circuit of Fig. 1(c)? (c) Why is a damping resistor R_d shown in Fig. 1(b) but not in Fig. 1(c)?

4. A circuit which can provide the input voltage for part 3 is shown in Fig. 1(d). (a) Explain the operation of this circuit. (b) Show how a triode may be used as the resistor $\bar{r}_p$ and the switch S_w. (c) If $\bar{r}_p$ is assumed to be linear and equal to 10 K, $R_1 = 75$ K, $R_2 = 4$ K, $C_1 = 0.025$ μf, $E_{bb} = 300$ volts, and the effective switch is open for 100 μsec and closed for 20 μsec, find the steady-state output voltage.

5. (a) Show how a diode might be used in place of the damping resistance in the circuit of Fig. 1(b). (b) If the trace on the CRT is blanked

out during the retrace time, are oscillations during this time necessarily bad? (c) Show how a pair of 6BC6 tubes and an associated trapezoidal generator could be used in a "push-pull" deflection circuit if the coils are

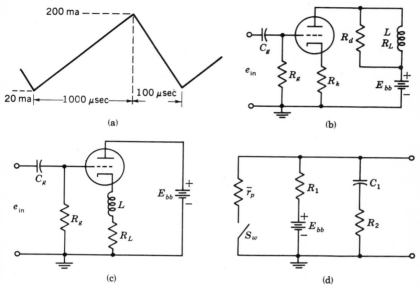

Fig. 1

connected so that their fields subtract in the neck of the tube. (d) How could it be arranged so that the sweep would start on one side of the tube? (e) For this condition sketch each coil current and the total force on the beam. (f) What is the effect on magnetic coupling between the coils?

6. (a) What effect may the distributed capacitance of the deflection coils have upon the linear current sweep? (b) Show two ways of charging this distributed capacitance at the start of the sweep. (c) Redraw and explain a complete horizontal sweep system used in any commercial television receiver.

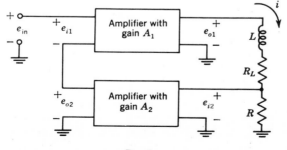

Fig. 2

7. It is possible to arrange a general system in which the current in a deflection coil can be made proportional to an applied voltage. Consider the system of Fig. 2. The amplifiers have gains as indicated and very high input impedances. Show that the coil current becomes proportional to the input voltage as the gain A_1 becomes large.

8. Design a circuit using type 12AU7 and 6V6 tubes which is the practical equivalent of the circuit of Fig. 2. The deflection coil has an inductance of 0.25 henry and a resistance of 840 ohms.

Performance

9. Set up the circuit of Fig. 1(d) using a type 12AU7 tube. Let $R_1 =$ 100 K, $R_2 = 10$ K variable, and $C_1 = 0.01$ μf. The input signal should be a square wave of approximately 10 kc. After an acceptable trapezoidal output waveform is obtained, attach the 6V6 sweep amplifier. Use a 10 K variable resistance in the cathode circuit of the 6V6. Do not use a cathode by-pass capacitor. Use a 15 K damping resistor and 100 ohm resistance in series with the coil in order that the coil current may be observed. Adjust the system for the best current waveform. Record all waveforms. Show the effect of an incorrect jump-slope ratio.

10. Alter the circuit of part 9 by constructing a blocking oscillator to operate the trapezoidal generator. Record the actual circuit used and all pertinent waveforms.

11. Put a 2 μf capacitor across the cathode resistance of the 6V6. Resketch and explain any waveforms which differ from those of part 10.

12. To determine the effect of the damping resistor, the plate waveform of the sweep amplifier may be observed. The 100 ohm resistance must be removed. Sketch the plate waveform of the 6V6 with and without the 15 K damping resistor.

13. Use the other half of the 12AU7, two 100 K resistors, and a 50 μf capacitor to form one of the circuits of part 6(c). The sweeps may be so slow that over-compensation will be obtained. Sketch all waveforms.

14. Set up the circuit of part 8. Drive the circuit with a simple sawtooth voltage generator. Record the actual circuit used and all pertinent voltage and current waveforms.

Calculations and conclusions

15. Discuss briefly the circuits tested with emphasis on unexpected behavior and difficulties encountered.

References

Ryder, J. D., *Electronic Fundamentals and Applications*, 2d ed. (Englewood Cliffs, N. J.: Prentice-Hall, Inc., 1959).

Von Tersch, L. W., and Swago, A. W., *Recurrent Electrical Transients* (Englewood Cliffs, N. J.: Prentice-Hall, Inc., 1953).

Chance, B., *et al.*, *Waveforms* (New York: McGraw-Hill Book Co., Inc., 1949).

Materials required

Components	*Equipment*
2 12AU7 tubes and sockets	1 power supply (170–300 volts 50
1 6V6 tube and socket	ma and 6.3 volts, a-c)
1 2D21 tube and socket	1 d-c cathode-ray oscillograph
2 10 K potentiometers	1 square-wave generator
1 100 ohm resistor	1 multimeter
4 10 K resistors	
1 15 K resistor	
4 100 K resistors	
2 470 K resistors	
3 1 megohm resistors	
1 50 $\mu\mu$f capacitor	
1 1000 $\mu\mu$f capacitor	
1 0.01 μf capacitor	
2 0.1 μf capacitors	
2 2 μf paper capacitors	
1 blocking oscillator transformer	

34-B

Sweep Circuits for Magnetic Deflection

Purpose

The object of this experiment is familiarization with some of the methods and circuits for magnetic deflection.

Information

Although the general theory of magnetic deflection should consider an arbitrary current waveshape, the sawtooth generator only is analyzed since it is one of the most important. Only a few of the sawtooth current generators will be considered, since the more refined circuits of the feedback type are not suitable for introductory work.

Preliminary

1. An example of the type of current waveform generally desired for magnetic deflection is given in Fig. 1(a). The shape of the short portion (retrace) is not important. (a) Find the voltage across a 50 mh choke that would cause this current to flow. (b) Repeat (a) if the coil has 100 ohms resistance. (c) What change in waveshape is necessary if distributed capacitance is present?

2. If the tube in Fig. 1(b) operates class A, sketch the grid voltage necessary to give a linear coil current.

3. Sketch the output of the circuit of Fig. 1(c) if a large square wave is applied to its input.

4. Explain the action of the circuit of Fig. 1(d), and pick suitable components, if L is 50 mh with 100 ohms resistance.

Performance

5. Set up and adjust for trapezoidal output the circuit of Fig. 1(c), with one half of a 12AU7 tube and 10,000 cps square-wave input. Record all waveforms as displayed by the cathode-ray oscillograph.

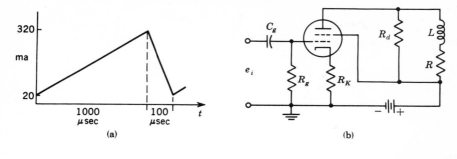

(a)   (b)

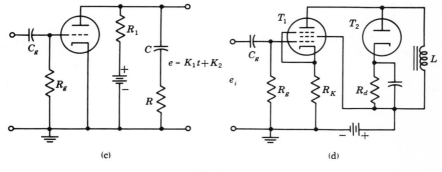

(c)   (d)

Fig. 1

6. Attach a 6AQ5 amplifier of the type of Fig. 1(b). $L = 50$ mh, $E_{bb} = 250$ volts, $R_K = 10$ K variable, $R_d = 100$ K variable. View the coil current with a 50 ohm series resistor. Record all waveforms.

7. Set up the circuit of Fig. 1(d) and drive it by means of the trapezoidal generator. Use a 6AQ5 and 6AL5 tube. Observe coil current and circuit waveforms.

Calculations and conclusions

8. Discuss briefly the results, particularly difficulties, of each part of the experiment.

References

Ryder, J. D., *Electronic Fundamentals and Applications*, 2d ed. (Englewood Cliffs, N. J.: Prentice-Hall, Inc., 1959).

Chance, B., *et al.*, *Waveforms* (New York: McGraw-Hill Book Co., Inc., 1949).

Von Tersch, L. W., and Swago, A. W., *Recurrent Electrical Transients* (Englewood Cliffs, N. J.: Prentice-Hall, Inc., 1953).

Materials required

Components	Equipment

Components

1 12AU7 tube and socket
1 6AQ5 tube and socket
1 6AL5 tube and socket
1 approximately 50 mh air-core choke
1 1 K potentiometer
2 10 K potentiometers
1 50 ohm resistor
1 10 K resistor
1 15 K resistor
3 100 K resistors
2 470 K resistors
1 1 megohm resistor
1 0.001 µf capacitor
2 0.01 µf capacitors
2 0.1 µf capacitors
2 2 µf capacitors

Equipment

1 power supply (170–300 volts 50 ma and 6.3 volts, a-c)
1 d-c cathode-ray oscillograph
1 square-wave generator
1 multimeter

EXPERIMENT

35-A

Thyratron Rectifiers

Purpose

The purpose of this experiment is to study the methods for controlling a gaseous triode (thyratron) rectifier.

Information

Although this experiment deals mainly with rectifying circuits, many facets of other thyratron applications are incidentally covered. The uses of these tubes in amplitude discriminators, oscillators. trigger circuits, and pulse generators are important and advantageous in many respects. From this standpoint, it would be well to consider this experiment as a possible method of illustrating important thyratron characteristics.

Preliminary

1. Explain the meaning of the following rating for thyratron tubes. What damage or difficulty will result in each case if the ratings are not observed?
   - (a) Average anode current
   - (b) Peak anode current
   - (c) Surge current
   - (d) Averaging time
   - (e) Tube drop
   - (f) Peak inverse voltage
   - (g) Temperature limits
     - (1) Upper
     - (2) Lower
   - (h) Cathode heating time

2. Explain and illustrate with circuit diagrams and other graphs the following methods of control of thyratron rectifiers: (a) d-c (bias) control; (b) phase shift control. Show a circuit which can be used to obtain the phase shift.

3. The average control characteristic of an FG-27-A thyratron at a condensed mercury temperature of 40° C is given below.

Grid volts	Anode volts
−0.0	45
−0.5	50
−1.0	60
−1.5	80
−2.0	110
−2.5	145
−3.0	180
−3.5	250
−4.0	310
−5.0	485
−6.0	660
−7.0	845

Plot the control curve.

4. An FG-27-A thyratron is used with bias control and an anode voltage of 120 volts rms.

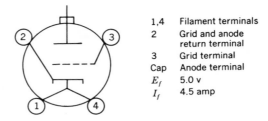

1,4	Filament terminals
2	Grid and anode return terminal
3	Grid terminal
Cap	Anode terminal
E_f	5.0 v
I_f	4.5 amp

Fig. 1 Socket connections of FG-27-A.

(a) At what angle does conduction begin if the grid voltage is set at zero volts?

(b) What value of grid voltage is required to cause the tube to begin to conduct at the maximum point of the anode voltage cycle?

Performance

5. Connect the circuit as shown in Fig. 2 using d-c control in the grid circuit. *Important:* Connect the filament transformer first and allow tube to warm up several minutes before applying anode voltage.

6. With V_1 set to 120 volts and V_2 to zero, adjust load resistance R_L to give a current I of 600 ma. Leave R_L at this setting for remainder of experiment.

(a) Lower V_1 to a voltage slightly larger than that required to cause the tube to fire. Record V_1, K, and $V_2 = 0$. Sketch waveform of tube voltage and load current.

(b) Repeat part (a) for $V_1 = 80$ and 120 volts.

7. Set V_1 to 120 volts. Vary V_2 in 0.5 volt steps to the value necessary to stop conduction. For each step record V_1, V_2, and I and sketch the waveform of a load current. Observe if there is any instability when V_2 was set for the last reading.

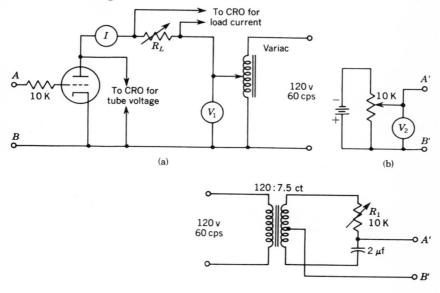

Fig. 2 Thyratron rectifier and control circuits: **(a)** thyratron rectifier; **(b)** d-c control.

8. Replace the d-c control circuit with the phase-shift control circuit. Set V_1 to 120 volts. Test polarity of voltage to phase-shift control circuit by varying R_1 and observing if I varies smoothly from maximum to zero. If I drops to zero suddenly at some setting of R_1, the plug to the transformer of the control circuit should be reversed.

(a) With R_1 set for maximum current, record V_1 and I and sketch the waveform of the load current.

(b) Repeat part (a) for values of R_1 which give 75, 50, 25, and 5 per cent maximum current.

Calculations and conclusions

9. Discuss the waveforms observed in part 6 in detail. Sketch the waveforms as a part of the discussion.

10. What are the limits of control for the circuit of part 7? Express both in total angle of conduction per cycle and direct current values. Discuss.

Was any instability noticed for the last reading of part 7? If so, discuss the reasons.

11. What are the limits of control for the circuit of part 8?

12. Compare d-c and phase-shift control on the following points: ease of control, control range, instability, and circuit complexity.

References

Ryder, J. D., *Electronic Fundamentals and Applications*, 2d ed. (Englewood Cliffs, N. J.: Prentice-Hall, Inc., 1959).

Gray, T. S., *Applied Electronics* (New York: John Wiley & Sons, Inc., 1954).

Terman, F. E., *Radio Engineers' Handbook* (New York: McGraw-Hill Book Co., Inc., 1937).

Materials required

Components	*Equipment*
1 FG-27-A tube and socket	1 d-c cathode-ray oscillograph
1 5 volt, 4.5 ampere filament transformer	1 750 ma d-c meter
1 5 ampere, 0–135 volt variable transformer (Variac)	1 10 volt d-c meter
1 7.5 volt filament transformer with CT	1 150 volt a-c meter
1 10 K, 2 watt potentiometer	1 multimeter
1 10 K resistor	
1 22.5 volt battery	
1 2 μf paper capacitor	
1 100–500 ohm, 1 ampere variable resistor	

35-B

Thyratron Rectifiers

Purpose

This experiment is intended to aid in the familiarization with thyratrons in general and their application in rectifier circuits in particular.

Preliminary

1. What ratings are important in limiting the application of a particular gaseous triode or tetrode (thyratrons)?

2. Define the following terms for thyratrons:
    (a) Critical grid voltage
    (b) Negative grid tube
    (c) Positive grid tube
    (d) Ionization time
    (e) Relaxation time

3. Using the FG-27-A tube, calculate the following with an applied voltage of 110 volts, a-c:

    (a) Average plate current for a grid voltage of -3 volts d-c, tube drop of 10 volts and load of 500 ohms.

    (b) Average plate loss in watts.

    (c) Plot to scale the plate current waveform obtained, the applied voltage, and the tube drop all on the same axis.

    (d) Check the result of (a) only, by graphical integration.

Performance

Note: Allow heater to warm up for 5 minutes before applying anode potential.

4. Take data [Fig. 1(c)] to check the firing characteristics of Fig. 1(b) from $E_b = 50$ to 400 volts.

5. (a) Replace the d-c plate voltage and circuitry with 110 volts a-c and appropriate meters. With zero grid volts and a load of 500 ohms, record I_{d-c}, V_{d-c}, and V_{a-c}. Observe output on oscillograph. (b) Repeat for firing angles of 30, 60, and 90 degrees.

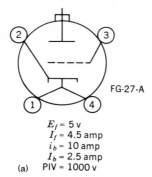

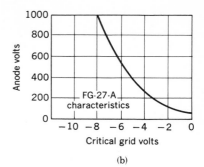

$E_f = 5$ v
$I_f = 4.5$ amp
$i_b = 10$ amp
$I_b = 2.5$ amp
(a)   PIV = 1000 v

(b)

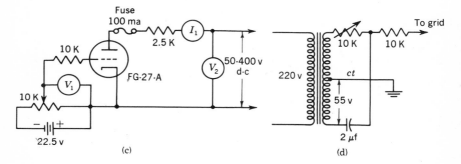

(c)   (d)

Fig. 1

6. Under conditions of part 5, plot $I_{d\text{-}c}$ versus grid voltage.

7. Substitute the grid control circuit of Fig. 1(d) with other conditions as in part 5. Note that phase of grid voltage must be checked. Take data of $I_{d\text{-}c}$ versus angle of grid voltage. (Record the phase-shift resistance and convert to phase angles.) Observe load voltage for all settings.

Calculations and conclusions

8. Compare analytical and experimental results.

9. Plot applicable data.

10. Were any difficulties encountered in part 5(b)? Explain.

11. Discuss briefly the experimental results, in particular anything unexpected.

References

Ryder, J. D., *Electronic Fundamentals and Applications*, 2d ed. (Englewood Cliffs, N. J.: Prentice-Hall, Inc., 1959).

Gray, T. S., *Applied Electronics* (New York: John Wiley & Sons, Inc., 1954).

Terman, F. E., *Radio Engineers' Handbook* (New York: McGraw-Hill Book Co., Inc., 1943).

Materials required

Components

1 FG-27-A tube and socket
1 5 volt, 4.5 ampere filament transformer
1 220–110 CT transformer
1 2.5 K, 10 watt resistor
1 10 K resistor
1 500 ohm, 50 watt resistor
1 10 K decade resistor
1 300 ohm, 1 ampere load resistor
1 10 K, 2 watt potentiometer
1 2 μf paper capacitor
1 100 ma fuse with mount
1 22.5 volt battery

Equipment

1 d-c cathode-ray oscillograph
1 d-c power supply
1 1.5 ampere d-c meter
1 100 ma d-c meter
1 500 volt d-c meter
1 50 volt d-c meter
1 250 volt a-c meter
1 multimeter

36-A

Photoelectric Cells

Purpose

The object of this experiment is familiarization with photoelectric cells and their applications.

Information

The subject of photoelectric devices is generally relegated to a rather minor roll in most study programs, as perhaps it should be. Modern developments, however, such as improved photoelectric cells, secondary emission

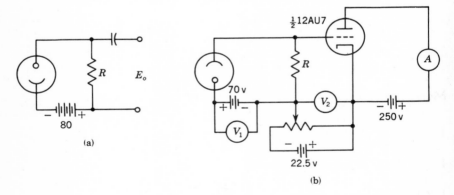

Fig. 1

photocell amplifiers, and solar batteries indicate that the subject should not be entirely neglected.

Preliminary

1. Name and describe briefly the action of the three basic photoelectric cells.

2. Why are gas photoemission cells limited in voltage which may be applied? Discuss differences in characteristics of vacuum and gas cells.

3. List some advantages for each of the cell types.

4. From the characteristics, obtain the rms output voltage for a 930 photocell used in the circuit of Fig. 1(a), for a sinusoidal light variation from 52 to 156 foot-candles (peak to peak) and $R = 4$ megohms.

5. (a) Describe the action in a photomultiplier cell. (b) Describe the phototransistor types.

Performance

6. Connect the circuit of Fig. 1(b) using a gas phototube. Use 2 megohms for R and adjust V_2 for 1.0 ma plate current at no light. Take data from meters versus light intensity with circuit fixed.

7. Repeat part 6 with a vacuum phototube.

8. With a vacuum photocell plot A vs R from zero to 2 megohms.

9. With a vacuum photocell plot A vs V_1 from zero to 135 volts.

Calculations and conclusions

10. Discuss briefly the experimental results and plot the data.

References

Ryder, J. D., *Electronic Fundamentals and Applications*, 2d ed. (Englewood Cliffs, N. J.: Prentice-Hall, Inc., 1959).

Millman, J., and Seeley, S., *Electronics* (New York: McGraw-Hill Book Co., Inc., 1941).

Terman, F. E., *Radio Engineers' Handbook* (New York: McGraw-Hill Book Co., Inc., 1943).

Materials required

Components	*Equipment*
1 type 929 phototube and socket (R.C.A.)	2 power supplies (one 0–135 volts, one 250 volts at 20 ma and 6.3 volts, a-c)
1 type 930 photocell and socket (R.C.A.)	1 illumination meter
1 2 megohm potentiometer	1 1 ma d-c meter
2 10 K potentiometers	1 20 ma d-c meter
1 22.5 volt battery	1 20 volt d-c meter
	1 150 volt d-c meter
	1 multimeter

EXPERIMENT

36-B

Photoelectric Cells

Purpose

A better understanding of some photoelectric devices is the object of this experiment.

Information

The following list of photo devices and terms should be reviewed:

(a) Photoemissive cell, vacuum type: a vacuum diode that generates current owing to electron emission when light falls on its cathode.

(b) Photoemissive cell, gas tube: similar to vacuum type with low pressure gas added to increase sensitivity by ionization.

(c) Photovoltaic or barrier-layer cell: a non-vacuum cell that generates electricity by a process similar to the phototransistor junction diode.

(d) Photoconductive cell: a resistor that changes resistance when illuminated. Semiconductors all have this property.

(e) Point-contact phototransistor: a point-contact diode with light focused on base material to generate hole-electron pairs.

(f) P-N junction phototransistor: similar to the point-contact unit except that this is a "junction" device.

(g) N-P-N junction phototransistor: a transistor in which light can be focused on the base (or emitter) section.

(h) Spectral sensitivity: response versus frequency of incident light. Devices are available with good sensitivity for each spectral region from infrared to ultraviolet. None, however, covers the entire spectrum well.

(i) Sensitivity: usually given as microamperes per microwatt (or microamperes per lumen) at a specified wavelength.

(j) Dark current: phototube current when shielded from radiation.

(k) Frequency response: the response of the device versus frequency of variation of the light intensity.

(l) Photomultiplier: an emission cell integral with a secondary-emission multiplier used for amplification.

Ideally all of the above should be covered in this experiment; however, since laboratory periods are usually limited in time only a few are included here.

Preliminary

1. From the characteristics of the 921 and 922 photocells, find the change in output voltage as light is varied from 25 to 50 foot-candles with 0.1, 1, and 10 megohms load at 80 volts.

2. (a) Give a brief discussion of photoemissive, barrier-layer, and photoconductive cells. (b) List some of the advantages of each type.

3. Why are gas photoemissive cells limited in plate voltage?

4. From the characteristics, calculate the light intensity necessary to cause the relay to close (20 ma closing current): $V_2 = 200$ volts, $V_1 = 70$ volts, $E_{cc} = -15$ volts.

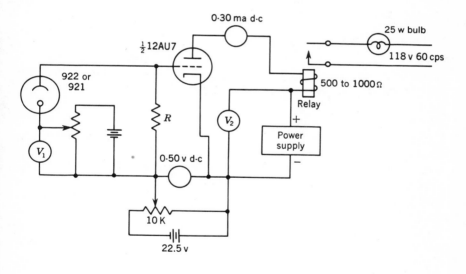

Fig. 1

Performance

5. Set up a circuit and check the two phototube volt-ampere characteristics for at least three light levels including the dark current.

6. Set up a circuit and take data on each cell of light intensity versus output for 80 volts applied.

7. Set up the circuit of part 4 and check the calculated values.

Calculations and conclusions

    8. Could the circuit of Fig. 1 be caused to oscillate? How?

    9. Plot the data taken in parts 5 and 6.

   10. Discuss briefly any unusual experimental results.

References

Ryder, J. D., *Electronic Fundamentals and Applications*, 2d ed. (Englewood Cliffs, N. J.: Prentice-Hall, Inc., 1959).

Lo, A. W., Endres, R. O., Zawels, J., Waldhauer, F. D., and Cheng, C. C., *Transistor Electronics* (Englewood Cliffs, N. J.: Prentice-Hall, Inc., 1955).

Fink, D. G., *Television Engineering* (New York: McGraw-Hill Book Co., Inc., 1952).

Anner, G. E., *Elements of Television Systems* (Englewood Cliffs, N. J.: Prentice-Hall, Inc., 1951).

Materials required

Components	*Equipment*
1 921 tube and socket	2 power supplies (200 volts at 50 ma and 6.3 volts, a-c)
1 922 tube and socket	1 50 volt d-c meter
1 12AU7 tube and socket	1 100 volt d-c meter
1 relay (20 ma pull in current and 1000 ohm coil, add resistance if lower)	1 250 volt d-c meter
1 25 watt light bulb	1 50 μa d-c meter
1 10 K, 10 watt potentiometer	1 250 μa d-c meter
1 10 K potentiometer	1 1 ma d-c meter
1 0.1 megohm resistor	1 30 ma d-c meter
1 1 megohm resistor	1 light intensity meter
1 2.5 megohm resistor	1 variable light intensity source (constant spectral distribution if possible)
1 10 megohm resistor	
1 22.5 volt battery	

EXPERIMENT

37-A

Solid-State Rectifiers

Purpose

The purpose of this experiment is the study of the several types of solid-state diodes now in common use.

Information

Unilateral elements are almost as common in electronic circuits as resistors. For any particular purpose a variety of rectifiers or diodes is available. It is important that the capabilities and limitations be understood.

In this experiment various unilateral elements will be considered as to their power rectification capabilities. Copper-oxide, selenium, germanium point-contact, silicon point-contact, germanium junction, and silicon junction rectifiers will be considered. For availability low current units will be tested and compared with a low current vacuum diode.

Preliminary

1. In Fig. 1 the volt-ampere characteristics of several diodes are illustrated. These are approximate only for rectifiers of similar current ratings with the reverse current shown to an expanded scale.

List each of the rectifiers as to their rectification efficiency and inverse peak voltage.

2. What current capabilities would ordinarily be available in each type of rectifier?

3. (a) For a particular rectification problem of 500 volts at 2 amperes, d-c, rate the diodes as to weight.

(b) Repeat (a) except rate on a volume basis.

4. Give typical temperature ranges for each type.

Performance

5. Set up the circuit of Fig. 2(a) and sketch the volt-ampere characteristic of each rectifier supplied. Calibrate the CRO so that quantitative

247

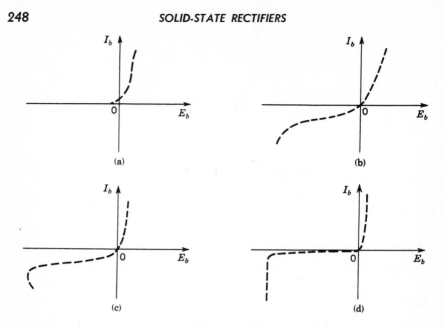

Fig. 1 **(a)** Vacuum diode; **(b)** copper oxide or selenium diode; **(c)** point-contact diodes (silicon and germanium); **(d)** junction diodes (silicon and germanium).

sketches can be made. Use milliampere representation for forward current and microamperes for reverse current.

6. Set up the circuit of Fig. 2(b) and test the rectification efficiency of each rectifier at the highest allowable power rating. The input voltage and R_2 may be adjusted so that the current rating and inverse peak rating are approached simultaneously. Note that the power input is the 60 cps voltage, 60 cps current component product.

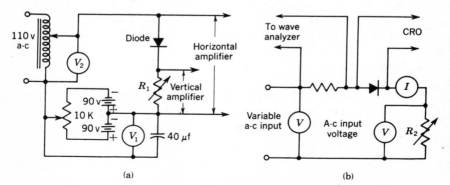

Fig. 2

Calculations and conclusions

7. Adjust the listings of part 1, if the experimental results so indicate.

8. Discuss briefly any unusual experimental difficulties or observations.

References

Young, M. G., and Bueche, H. S., *Fundamentals of Electronics and Control* (New York: Harper and Brothers, Publishers, 1952).

Chance, B., *et al.*, *Waveforms* (New York: McGraw-Hill Book Co., Inc., 1949).

Gray, T. S., *Applied Electronics* (New York: John Wiley & Sons, Inc., 1954).

Ryder, J. D., *Electronic Fundamentals and Applications*, 2d ed. (Englewood Cliffs, N. J.: Prentice-Hall, Inc., 1959).

Materials required

Components	*Equipment*
1 6AL5 tube and socket	1 d-c cathode-ray oscillograph (both
1 1N34 diode	amplifiers capable of calibration)
1 low current selenium rectifier	1 wave analyzer (to determine 60
1 low current copper-oxide rectifier	cps component of input current)
1 germanium junction diode	1 100 volt d-c meter
1 silicon junction diode	1 10 ma d-c meter
1 variable transformer	1 100 ma d-c meter
1 500 ohm, 10 watt potentiometer	1 20 volt a-c meter
2 10 K, 10 watt potentiometers	1 d-c vacuum-tube voltmeter
1 40 μf paper capacitor	
4 45 volt batteries	
1 6.3 volt transformer	

37-B

Solid-State Rectifiers

Purpose

The purpose of this experiment is familiarity with the characteristics of solid-state diodes.

Information

Diodes have many uses in addition to their use in a-c to d-c conversion. Triggering, clamping, clipping, and amplitude discrimination are a few of the more common uses.

Perhaps for the above purposes the most important characteristics are: reverse to forward resistance ratio, sharpness of break, temperature stability, capacitance, contact potential (for vacuum diodes). Each of these will be briefly investigated for the germanium point-contact, germanium junction, silicon point-contact, silicon junction, and compared with the vacuum-diode. Copper-oxide and selenium diodes will not be tested since they are not usually made for these purposes.

Preliminary

1. Sketch typical volt-ampere characteristics of the following diode types: (a) vacuum, (b) point-contact germanium, (c) point-contact silicon, (d) junction germanium, (e) junction silicon.

2. If the voltage of Fig. 1(a) is applied to the circuit of Fig. 1(b), find the output. Assume the diode to be perfect.

3. Repeat part 2, if the forward resistance is 100 ohms and the reverse resistance is 1 megohm. $\Delta t = 5$ μsec, $C = 0.01$ μf. Repeat for a reverse resistance of 10,000 ohms.

4. (a) How could the circuit of Fig. 1(b) be modified to make a simple amplitude discriminator? (b) How would the expanded break defects of Fig. 1(c) affect the discriminator operation? (c) How would diode capacitance affect its operation?

5. How will temperature affect diode characteristics?

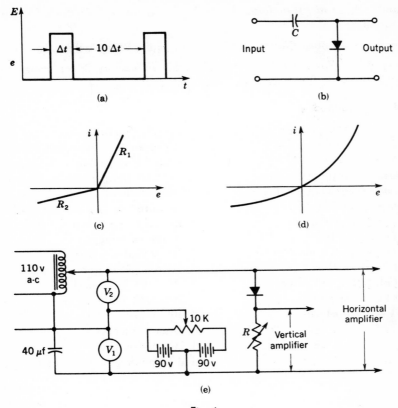

Fig. 1

Performance

6. Test all of the rectifiers for forward current at 1 and 2 volts (or less if maximum rated current is exceeded) and for reverse current at 1 and 10 volts.

7. Using a circuit similar to that in Fig. 1(d), examine and sketch quantitatively the volt-ampere characteristics of the diodes provided from the lowest temperature available to 100° C. The behavior at low voltages and currents near the break point is of most interest.

Calculations and conclusions

8. Tabulate the changes observed in part 7.

9. Discuss briefly the experimental results.

References

Young, M. G., and Bueche, J. S., *Fundamentals of Electronics and Control* (New York: Harper and Brothers, Publishers, 1952).

Chance, B., *et al.*, *Waveforms* (New York: McGraw-Hill Book Co., Inc., 1949).

Gray, T. S., *Applied Electronics* (New York: John Wiley & Sons, Inc., 1954).

Ryder, J. D., *Electronic Fundamentals and Applications*, 2d ed. (Englewood Cliffs, N. J.: Prentice-Hall, Inc., 1959).

Materials required

Components	*Equipment*
1 6AL5 tube and socket	1 d-c cathode-ray oscillograph (both
1 1N34 diode	amplifiers capable of calibration)
1 germanium junction diode	1 variable temperature cabinet (it is
1 silicon point-contact diode	suggested that the diodes be
1 silicon junction diode	mounted in the cabinet and ter-
1 variable transformer	minals brought out to reduce per-
1 10 ohm resistor	formance time)
1 500 ohm potentiometer	1 100 volt d-c meter
1 10 K, 10 watt potentiometer	1 10 volt d-c meter
1 40 μf, paper capacitor	1 20 volt a-c meter
4 45 volt batteries	1 10 μa d-c meter
1 6.3 volt transformer	1 100 μa d-c meter
	1 1 ma d-c meter
	1 20 ma d-c meter
	1 d-c vacuum-tube voltmeter

EXPERIMENT

38-A

Transistor Characteristics

Purpose

The purpose of this experiment is to aid the understanding of transistor operation by plotting characteristics for a typical point-contact and junction transistors.

Information

Figure 1 illustrates the convention of positive voltage drops and positive currents for the transistor. Unlike vacuum tubes, the input impedance is low and is greatly affected by the load resistance (not shown). Likewise, the output impedance is affected by the internal impedance of the source. From Fig. 1, four variables are involved in transistor circuitry: V_e, I_e, V_c, and I_c. For a given transistor and corresponding circuit, setting values for any two of these variables fixes the other two. Out of the possible 24 different characteristic curves which may be drawn, usually two are sufficient for grounded-base operation; these are collector voltage plotted against collector current for several values of constant emitter current, and emitter

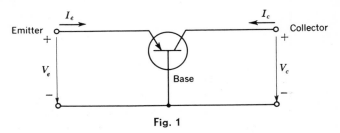

Fig. 1

voltage plotted against emitter current for several values of constant collector current. Because of the close coupling between input and output of a transistor, and because point-contact transistors are unstable, high impedance measuring devices must be used to obtain the static characteristic curves conveniently. This experiment utilizes two pentodes as approximate current sources. Whether the voltages and currents involved are positive or negative, according to the conventions of Fig. 1, depends on the impurity used in the germanium. Negative values are plotted as increasing downward and to the left.

Preliminary

1. Study the data given to you in the performance and draw the complete circuit diagram for obtaining the specified data for each set of characteristic curves. Also study carefully some transistor curves of the types to be plotted in the experiment.

Be sure to indicate how the transistor is to be connected in order to utilize the pentode current sources as shown in Fig. 2, and how the meters are to be connected.

Performance

2. Connect up the circuit as determined in the preliminary, using two power supplies set at about 170 volts. Protect the transistor by short circuiting emitter and collector to the base until you have tested the circuit and have become familiar with the operation. Do this when changing any part of the circuit. Construct your own voltmeter by using the micro-ammeter in series with a high resistance. Check the voltmeter against laboratory standard and adjust two series resistances to give full-scale reading of 1 volt and 50 volts for the emitter and collector voltages, respectively.

Typical point-contact transistor (type N germanium):

Maximum ratings

Collector voltage................	-50 volts
Collector current (d-c)..........	-20 ma
Collector dissipation............	120 mw
Emitter voltage.................	-50 to $+5$ volts
Emitter current.................	$+15$ ma
Emitter dissipation.............	50 mw
Ambient temperature...........	$55°$ C

Record the type, model number, and number of the transistor. Connect a 0.1 μf condenser from collector to base in order to avoid oscillations.

Tabulate and plot, as you go, emitter voltage versus emitter current for collector currents ranging from 0 to 5 ma in 1/2 ma steps. (When actually getting the data, it is recommended that emitter current be held constant and collector current varied in 1/2 ma steps.)

Tabulate data and plot, as you go, collector voltage versus collector current for emitter current ranging from 0 to 5 ma in 1/2 ma steps.

3. Junction transistors (N-P-N germanium):

Approximate maximum ratings
for
a typical junction transistor

Collector voltage............+50 volts
Collector current............+5 ma
Emitter current..............−5 ma
Collector dissipation.......... 50 mw
Ambient temperature......... 50° C

Record the type, model number, and number of the transistor. Removę the 0.1 μf condenser.

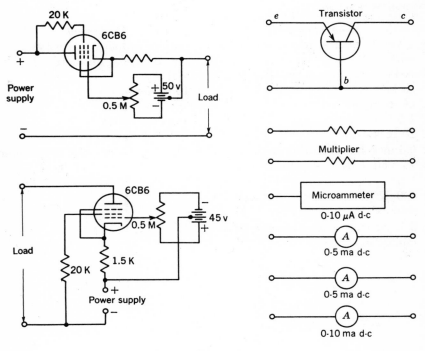

Fig. 2

Repeat as for the point-contact transistor. Attempt to reduce junction heating effects as much as possible by taking readings quickly and then reducing the current. Note that the dynamic collector resistance is extremely high and hence collector current may appear independent of collector voltage over a wide range.

Calculations and conclusions

4. Plot the characteristics for which data were taken.
5. Discuss any unusual experimental observations.

References

Ryder, J. D., *Electronic Fundamentals and Applications*, 2d ed. (Englewood Cliffs, N. J.: Prentice-Hall, Inc., 1959).

Shea, R. F., *Principles of Transistor Circuits* (New York: John Wiley & Sons, Inc., 1953).

Lo, A. W., Endres, R. O., Zawels, J., Waldhauer, F. D., and Cheng, C. C., *Transistor Electronics* (Englewood Cliffs, N. J.: Prentice-Hall, Inc., 1955).

Materials required

Components	*Equipment*
1 type N point-contact transistor with socket	2 power supplies (170–250 volts regulated, 20 ma and 6.3 volts, a-c)
1 N-P-N junction transistor with socket	1 10 μa d-c meter
2 6CB6 tubes and sockets	1 1 ma d-c meter
2 1.5 K resistors	2 5 ma d-c meter
2 20 K resistors	1 10 ma d-c meter
2 0.5 megohm potentiometers	1 20,000 ohms per volt multimeter
2 45 volt batteries with 22.5 volt taps	
1 100 K potentiometer (for multiplier)	
1 5 megohm potentiometer (for multiplier)	

38-B

Transistor Characteristics

Purpose

The purpose of this experiment is familiarization with transistor operation.

Information

From an engineering point of view, the fundamental information concerning any electronic component is given by its volt-ampere characteristics and maximum ratings. The ratings and parameters given here may be quite different from those of the transistors to be tested.

The student must become quite familiar with the type of curves to be drawn so that the experimental data will make sense.

Preliminary

1. Sketch the typical appearance of the following families of curves for a P-N-P junction transistor, and label with appropriate values of current and voltage:
   (a) Collector family
   (b) Emitter family
   (c) Transfer family (V_c vs I_e, I_c constant)

2. Define r_{11}, r_{22}, r_{12}, and r_{21}. How may these parameters be obtained graphically from the families of curves sketched in part 1? Illustrate.

3. Define r_e, r_b, r_c, r_m, and α in terms of the parameters of part 2.

Table 1

Electrical Ratings of a Typical P-N-P Transistor

Collector voltage	-22 volts	max.
Collector current	-10 ma	max.
Collector dissipation	33 mw	max.
Emitter current	10 ma	max.
Ambient temperature	50° C	max.

Performance

4. Record the laboratory number of the junction transistor which is supplied.

5. Connect the circuit of Fig. 1(a).

NOTE: Do not connect the emitter and collector terminals until it has been determined that both V_e and V_c are zero. In the following tests do not

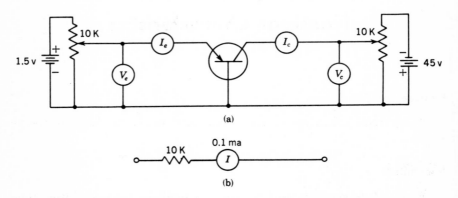

(a)

(b)

Fig. 1 P-N-P Junction transistor: **(a)** circuit for obtaining characteristic curves; **(b)** one volt voltmeter for emitter voltage measurements.

exceed any ratings equivalent to those given in Table 1, except that the collector voltage may be taken up to 50 per cent above rating if the collector dissipation rating is not exceeded. If the difference between I_e and I_c is difficult to measure, the base current may be measured with a very low resistance meter.

6. (a) Obtain data for the $V_c - I_c$ curve for the emitter circuit open. Note if there is any apparent drifting of the readings. Use a meter for I_c which is appropriate for the current being measured.

(b) Repeat part (a) for values of I_e up to 4.0 ma in 0.5 ma steps. Use care to obtain sufficient data for values of V_c less than 5 volts in absolute value. Currents and voltages must be set and readings taken with as much precision as possible.

7. Obtain data for $V_e - I_e$ curves for values of I_c ranging from -0.5 to -4.0 ma in 0.5 ma steps. These curves are segments only.

8. Obtain data for $V_c - I_e$ curves for values of I_c ranging from -0.5 to -4.0 ma in 0.5 ma steps.

Calculations and conclusions

9. Plot, on separate sheets, collector, emitter, and reverse transfer characteristics. Plot all voltages and currents which are negative in respect to the conventional direction as negative values.

10. Discuss the curves of part 9, and the techniques required to obtain satisfactory data.

11. In obtaining data for part 6(a) was any drifting noticed? Why might drift be expected in this case?

12. (a) From your data, in the region of the operating point $V_c = -10$ volts, $I_c = -2.0$ ma, compute and tabulate values for r_{11}, r_{22}, r_{12}, and r_{21}. Give, in each case, your estimate of the validity of the values which you computed.

(b) From the results of part 12(a) compute values for r_e, r_b, r_c, r_m, and α.

References

Ryder, J. D., *Electronic Fundamentals and Applications*, 2d ed. (Englewood Cliffs, N. J.: Prentice-Hall, Inc., 1959).

Shea, R. F., *Principles of Transistor Circuits* (New York: John Wiley & Sons, Inc., 1953).

Lo, A. W., Endres, R. O., Zawels, J., Waldhauer, F. E., and Cheng, C. C., *Transistor Electronics* (Englewood Cliffs, N. J.: Prentice-Hall, Inc., 1955).

Materials required

Components	Equipment
1 P-N-P junction transistor with socket	1 10 μa d-c meter
	2 100 μa d-c meters
1 10 K resistor	2 1 ma d-c meters
2 10 K, 2 watt potentiometers	2 10 ma d-c meters
1 1.5 volt battery	1 5 volt d-c meter
1 45 volt battery with 22.5 volt tap	1 10 volt d-c meter
	1 50 volt d-c meter

39-A

Transistor Parameters

Purpose

The purpose of this experiment is familiarization with methods of direct measurement of transistor parameters.

Information

The published transistor characteristics are quite reliable as to general shape and specified range of values of parameters. A good design method is to supply sufficient feedback to accommodate the variability present and still give the required results. On the other hand, if the exact parameters

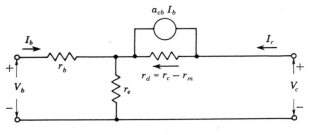

Fig. 1

are important, two methods suggest themselves. The first is to plot the characteristics and graphically compute the parameters. The second is direct measurement. Even with automatic plotting, the first is much less accurate than the second.

Direct measurements usually are made to determine the four parameters of Fig. 1, or their equivalents. Owing to the many possible equivalent circuits and their several four-terminal sets of parameters, the four quantities to measure can be chosen in endless ways. All choices work on paper, but few are practical with normal equipment. The most practical seems to be the common emitter hybrid or h parameters, and these will be used in this experiment.

Preliminary

1. Derive r_e, r_b, r_d, and α_{cb} in terms of the following common emitter hybrid parameters:

h_{11} = short-circuit input impedance
h_{12} = μ_{bc} reverse open-circuit amplification factor
h_{21} = α_{cb} forward short-circuit current amplification factor
h_{22} = output admittance with input open

2. Demonstrate from a representative set of emitter and collector characteristics how r_e, r_b, r_d, and α_{cb} may be found.

3. Give a brief description how h_{11} and α_{cb} may be found from Fig. 2(a), h_{22} from the bridge circuit of Fig. 2(b), and h_{12} from the circuit of Fig. 2(c).

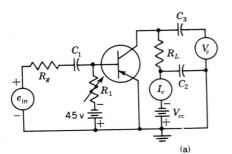

At 1 kc
$R_g \approx 100$ K
$R_1 \approx$ set to I_c desired
$R_L \approx 100\,\Omega$
$C_1 \approx 30\,\mu f$
C_2 and $C_3 \approx 10\,\mu f$

(a)

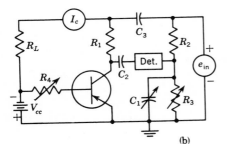
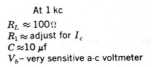

At 1 kc
R_1 and $R_2 \approx 100\,\Omega$
$R_3 \approx 100$ K decade
$R_L \approx 100\,\Omega$
$R_4 \approx$ adjust for I_c
$C_1 \approx 100\,\mu\mu f$ variable and calibrated
$C_2 \approx 1\,\mu f$
$C_3 \approx 30\,\mu f$

(b)

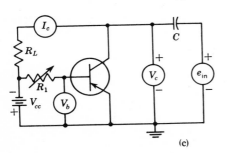

At 1 kc
$R_L \approx 100\,\Omega$
$R_1 \approx$ adjust for I_c
$C \approx 10\,\mu f$
$V_b -$ very sensitive a-c voltmeter

(c)

Fig. 2

Performance

4. Set up the circuit of Fig. 2(a) and determine α_{cb} and h_{11} for each of the transistors at $V_c = 10.5$ volts and $I_c = 2$ ma.

5. Connect the circuit of Fig. 2(b) and measure h_{22} and the output shunt capacitance of each transistor under the conditions of part 4.

6. Connect the circuit of Fig. 2(c) and measure the μ_{bc} for the transistors under the same conditions.

Calculations and conclusions

7. Tabulate r_b, r_e, r_d, and α_{cb} for the transistors. Do the transistors fulfill the manufacturers' specifications?

8. Discuss briefly the experimental results.

References

Lo, A. W., Endres, R. O., Zawels, J., Waldhauer, F. D., and Cheng, C. C., *Transistor Electronics* (Englewood Cliffs, N. J.: Prentice-Hall, Inc., 1955).

Ryder, J. D., *Electronic Fundamentals and Applications*, 2d ed. (Englewood Cliffs, N. J.: Prentice-Hall, Inc., 1959).

Bevitt, W. D., *Transistor Handbook* (Englewood Cliffs, N. J.: Prentice-Hall, Inc., 1956).

Materials required

Components	*Equipment*
several P-N-P transistors (suggest 2N369)	1 cathode-ray oscillograph
1 100 K decade resistor	1 audio frequency generator
1 1 megohm potentiometer	1 1000 cps null detector
3 100 ohm resistors (1%)	1 5 ma d-c meter
1 1 K resistor	2 a-c vacuum-tube voltmeters (one
1 100 K resistor	must have at least 1 millivolt,
1 1 μf capacitor	full-scale sensitivity)
2 10 μf capacitors	1 multimeter (high sensitivity)
1 30 μf capacitor	
1 100 μμf variable capacitor (calibrated)	
8 No. 6 dry cells	
1 10:1 transformer	

39-B

Transistor Parameters

Purpose

The purpose of this experiment is a study of measurement methods and the variation of transistor parameters with d-c biases.

Information

If the normal methods of measurement of transistor parameters are used (meaning the direct measurement of r_e, r_b, r_c, and α), results are usually marginal. If the hybrid parameters are measured, and the above ones derived, the measurements are relatively easy.

The assumption that emitter and collector currents are the independent variables leads to equation (1) for the grounded emitter connection.

$$I_b(r_b + r_e) + I_c r_e = V_b$$
$$I_b(r_e - r_m) + I_c(r_d + r_e) = V_c \tag{1}$$

To obtain the hybrid parameters, assume equations (2):

$$v_b = v_b(i_b, v_c)$$
$$i_c = i_c(i_b, v_c) \tag{2}$$

Then

$$\frac{\partial v_b}{\partial i_b} di_b + \frac{\partial v_b}{\partial v_c} dv_c = dv_b \tag{3}$$

$$\frac{\partial i_c}{\partial i_b} di_b + \frac{\partial i_c}{\partial v_c} dv_c = di_c$$

Replacing the differentials by rms values and the partial derivatives by parameter nomenclature, equations (4) obtain:

$$h_{11}I_b + h_{12}V_c = V_b$$
$$h_{21}I_b + h_{22}V_c = I_c \tag{4}$$

where h_{11} = input impedance with output short circuited

$h_{12} = \mu_{bc}$ = reverse open-circuit voltage amplification factor

$h_{21} = \alpha_{cb}$ = forward short-circuit amplification factor

h_{22} = output admittance with input open.

The parameters in equations (1) are most commonly used and they are easily obtained from those of (4).

The hybrid parameters are most easily measured and will be the only ones measured in this experiment.

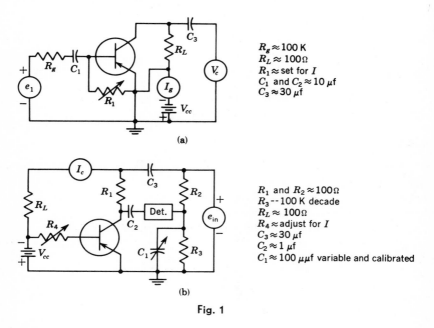

$R_g \approx 100$ K
$R_L \approx 100\,\Omega$
$R_1 \approx$ set for I
C_1 and $C_2 \approx 10\,\mu f$
$C_3 \approx 30\,\mu f$

(a)

R_1 and $R_2 \approx 100\,\Omega$
R_3 -- 100 K decade
$R_L \approx 100\,\Omega$
$R_4 \approx$ adjust for I
$C_3 \approx 30\,\mu f$
$C_2 \approx 1\,\mu f$
$C_1 \approx 100\,\mu\mu f$ variable and calibrated

(b)

Fig. 1

Preliminary

1. Derive r_e, r_b, r_c, and r_m from h_{11}, μ_{bc}, α_{cb}, and h_{22}.

2. Describe how the essentially shorted circuit of Fig. 1(a) and the bridge of Fig. 1(b) (when balanced) can be used to measure α_{cb}, h_{11} and h_{22}, μ_{bc}, respectively.

3. From the characteristic curves determine as many parameters as can be found for $V_c = 10.5$ volts and $I_c = 2$ ma, for the 2N369 transistor.

Performance

4. Set up the circuit of Fig. 1(a) with $V_c = 10.5$ volts and $I_c = 2$ ma. Measure α_{cb} and h_{11}. Repeat these measurements as I_c is varied from 0 to 10 ma, $V_c = 10.5$ volts. Repeat with $I_c = 2$ ma, as V_c is varied from 0 to

15 volts in approximately 1.5 volt steps. Use the CRO to assure linear operation.

5. Set up the circuit of Fig. 1(b) with $V_c = 10.5$ volts and $I_c = 2$ ma. Measure h_{22} and μ_{bc} over the same ranges as those in part 4. Record the output capacitance for each point.

Calculations and conclusions

6. Convert the data of parts 5 and 6 to the r_e, r_b, r_d, and α_{cb} form. Plot the variation of each of these with respect to I_c and V_c.

7. Discuss briefly the experimental results.

References

Lo, A. W., Endres, R. O., Zawels, J., Waldhauer, F. D., and Cheng, C. C., *Transistor Electronics* (Englewood Cliffs, N. J.: Prentice-Hall, Inc., 1955).

Ryder, J. D., *Electronic Fundamentals and Applications*, 2d ed. (Englewood Cliffs, N. J.: Prentice-Hall, Inc., 1959).

Bevitt, W. D., *Transistor Handbook* (Englewood Cliffs, N. J.: Prentice-Hall, Inc., 1956).

Materials required

Components	*Equipment*
1 2N369 transistor with socket	1 cathode-ray oscillograph
1 100 K decade resistor	1 audio frequency generator
1 1 megohm potentiometer	1 1000 cps null detector
3 100 ohm, 1% resistors	1 5 ma d-c meter
1 100 K resistor	1 10 ma d-c meter
1 100 $\mu\mu$f variable calibrated capacitor	2 a-c vacuum-tube voltmeters (one must have at least 1 mv, full-scale sensitivity)
1 1 μf capacitor	1 multimeter (high sensitivity)
2 10 μf capacitors	
1 30 μf capacitor	
10 No. 6 dry cells	
1 10:1 transformer	

40-A

Grounded Emitter Transistor Amplifiers

Purpose

The purpose of this experiment is to study the power gain of a grounded emitter N-P-N transistor. Special emphasis will be placed on matching.

Information

Only the junction transistor will be included in this experiment since point-contact units are seldom used as linear amplifiers. The unit to be tested may be quite different from the ones described by the data given.

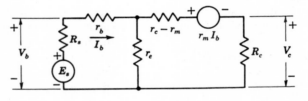

Fig. 1

Preliminary

1. Figure 1 shows the a-c equivalent circuit of a grounded emitter transistor stage. Show that the low-frequency input and output impedances are

$$R_{in} = r_e + r_b + \frac{r_e(r_m - r_e)}{r_e + r_c - r_m + R_c}$$

$$R_{out} = r_e + r_c - r_m + \frac{r_e(r_m - r_e)}{r_e + r_b + R_s}$$

2. Show that the system determinant is always positive for junction transistors and consequently the circuit is stable. (This is true for junction transistors in any type connection excluding transformers.)

3. Set $R_s = R_{in}$ and $R_c = R_{out}$ and show that the matched input and output impedances are

$$R_s = (r_e + r_b)\sqrt{1 + r_e(r_m - r_e)/(r_e + r_b)(r_e + r_c - r_m)}$$
$$R_c = (r_e + r_c - r_m)\sqrt{1 + r_e(r_m - r_e)/(r_e + r_b)(r_e + r_c - r_m)}$$

4. Prove that maximum power gain occurs when R_c has the value given in part 3. (Power input must be taken as $V_b I_b$.)

5. Calculate and plot power gain as a function of load resistance ranging from 0 to 100 K for the two transistors given below. Be sure to include the point of maximum power gain.

<table>
<tr><td>Transistor No. 1</td><td>Transistor No. 2</td></tr>
<tr><td>$r_e = 33.1$ ohms</td><td>$r_e = 31.6$ ohms</td></tr>
<tr><td>$r_b = 300$ ohms</td><td>$r_b = 44$ ohms</td></tr>
<tr><td>$r_c = 1.11$ megohms</td><td>$r_c = 0.626$ megohms</td></tr>
<tr><td>$r_c - r_m = 0.0168$ megohms</td><td>$r_c - r_m = 0.00387$ megohms</td></tr>
<tr><td>$\alpha = 0.9848$</td><td>$\alpha = 0.9936$</td></tr>
</table>

Performance

6. Set up the circuit of Fig. 2. Connect a scope on the output and make sure that the circuit is at a relatively low noise level.

Adjust bias for an emitter current of 1 ma and a collector to emitter voltage of 10 volts. Hold this constant during the experiment.

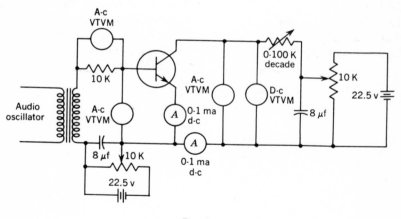

Fig. 2

Take data in order to plot voltage gain, current gain, and power gain as a function of R_c. Do not exceed approximately 4 mv a-c input voltage or 10 μ a a-c input current. Vary R_c over a range from 500 ohms to a value well beyond the point of maximum power gain.

7. Measure input impedance by use of an impedance bridge at 1000 cps.

Calculations and conclusions

8. Plot voltage gain, current gain, and power gain as a function of R_c.

9. How does the grounded emitter connection compare with the ground base connection?

References

Ryder, J. D., *Electronic Fundamentals and Applications*, 2d ed. (Englewood Cliffs, N. J.: Prentice-Hall, Inc., 1959).

Shea, R. F., *Principles of Transistor Circuits* (New York: John Wiley & Sons, Inc., 1953).

Lo, A. W., Endres, R. O., Zawels, J., Waldhauer, F. D., and Cheng, C. C., *Transistor Electronics* (Englewood Cliffs, N. J.: Prentice-Hall, Inc., 1955).

Materials required

Components	*Equipment*
1 junction transistor with socket	1 cathode-ray oscillograph
1 step-down transformer (at least 50/1)	1 audio oscillator
2 10 K, 2 watt potentiometers	1 impedance bridge (audio frequency)
1 10 K resistor	3 a-c vacuum-tube voltmeters (high impedance and sensitivity)
1 100 K decade resistor	1 d-c vacuum-tube voltmeter
2 8 μf capacitors	2 1 ma d-c meters
2 22.5 volt batteries	1 multimeter

40-B

Grounded Emitter Transistor Amplifiers

Purpose

This experiment is intended to further the familiarization of students with transistor circuits in general and the grounded emitter, junction transistor amplifier in particular.

Information

For most purposes the grounded emitter amplifier is considered superior to the grounded base and collector configurations. Its input impedance is reasonable and its power gain is the highest.

Historically the grounded base circuit was the first used. For this reason, rearrangements of this circuit, Fig. 1(a), are still occasionally used for the common emitter configuration. The circuit of Fig. 1(b) is more common, however.

To secure maximum power gain, impedances must be matched in transistor amplifiers. For the preceding reason, considerable attention will be given to input and output impedance of these amplifiers.

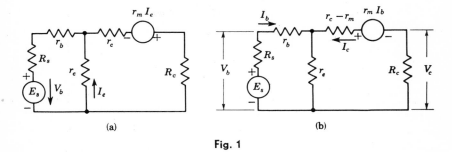

Fig. 1

Preliminary

1. Figure 1 shows two a-c equivalent circuits for the grounded emitter transistor stage. Draw the equivalent circuit from Fig. 1(b) where the

voltage generator is replaced by a current generator. The quantity $r_m/(r_c - r_m)$ defines $b \cong \beta$, and $(r_c - r_m)$ is commonly called r_d.

2. Derive expressions for voltage, current, and power gain of the circuit of Fig. 1.

3. Show that the low-frequency input and output impedances are given by the following expressions:

$$R_{in} = r_e + r_b + \frac{r_e(r_m - r_e)}{r_e + r_c - r_m + R_c} \tag{1}$$

$$R_{out} = r_e + r_c - r_m + \frac{r_e(r_m - r_e)}{r_e + r_b + R_s} \tag{2}$$

4. Set $R_s = R_{in}$ and $R_c = R_{out}$ and show that the matched input and output impedances are given by equations (3) and (4).

$$R_s = (r_e + r_b)\sqrt{1 + r_e(r_m - r_e)/(r_e + r_b)(r_e - r_m + r_c)} \tag{3}$$
$$R_c = (r_e + r_c - r_m)\sqrt{1 + r_e(r_m - r_e)/(r_e + r_b)(r_e + r_c - r_m)} \tag{4}$$

5. Calculate and plot power gain in decibels versus load resistance for a transistor with the following parameters. Take load resistances from zero to more than that for maximum power gain. Use semi-log paper.

$$r_e = \quad 25 \text{ ohms}$$
$$r_b = 120 \text{ ohms}$$
$$r_c - r_m = \quad 20 \text{ K}$$
$$r_m = 480 \text{ K}$$

Performance

6. Set up the circuit shown in Fig. 2. Connect an oscilloscope on the output. Adjust bias values for a collector current of -1 ma and collector voltage of -5 volts. Hold this constant during the experiment.

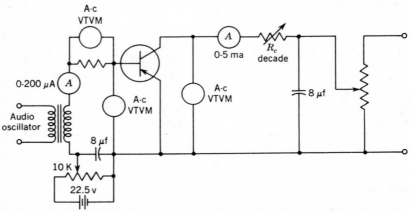

Fig. 2

Take data in order to plot voltage gain, current gain, and power gain as a function of R_c. Do not exceed approximately 5 mv a-c input voltage on 10 μa a-c input current. Vary R_c over a range from 500 ohms to a value well beyond the point of maximum power gain. Read all meters. Take into consideration the shunting effect of the vacuum-tube voltmeter and scope.

7. Increase input until distortion occurs with $R_c = 10$ K. Calculate voltage, current, and power gain.

8. Measure the input impedance at 1000 cps.

Calculations and conclusions

9. Plot voltage gain, current gain, and power gain as a function of R_c.

10. What is the output impedance for the source impedance used?

11. Discuss anything unusual observed.

References

Ryder, J. D., *Electronic Fundamentals and Applications*, 2d ed. (Englewood Cliffs, N. J.: Prentice-Hall, Inc., 1959).

Shea, R. F., *Principles of Transistor Circuits* (New York: John Wiley & Sons, Inc., 1953).

Lo, A. W., Endres, R. O., Zawels, J., Waldhauer, F. D., and Cheng, C. C., *Transistor Electronics* (Englewood Cliffs, N. J.: Prentice-Hall, Inc., 1955).

Materials required

Components	Equipment
1 junction transistor with socket	1 cathode-ray oscillograph
1 50:1 (or greater) step-down transformer	1 audio oscillator
	1 audio frequency impedance bridge
2 10 K, 2 watt potentiometers	3 a-c vacuum-tube voltmeters (high
1 10 K resistor	impedance and sensitivity and one
1 100 K decade resistor	battery operated, if possible)
2 8 μf capacitors	1 200 μa d-c meter
2 22.5 volt batteries	1 5 ma d-c meter
	1 10 volt d-c meter
	1 multimeter

41-A

Transistor Power Amplifiers

Purpose

The purpose of this experiment is a study of some of the principles of transistor power amplifiers.

Information

Some of the principles of vacuum-tube amplifiers do not apply to transistor power amplifiers, and some new ones become important. A short review may be advisable at this point.

Since power output is one of the prime considerations, impedance matching at the output is almost never used. An impedance much lower than the matching value is used. The supply voltage is usually chosen at about half the maximum rated value (transformer coupling) so that the maximum load can be used to give as much gain as possible. Approximately the same load resistance will be used with grounded emitter, base, or collector arrangements. The grounded emitter arrangement is generally preferred for its higher gain.

The two main sources of nonlinearity for the grounded emitter operation are the variations of current amplification factor and input resistance, of which the former is more serious.

Many power amplifier configurations are possible. Besides the three basic circuits for single-ended or push-pull operation, at least four push-pull variations are possible using similar or complementary transistors. Only the two circuits of Fig. 1 will be considered.

Preliminary

1. In Fig. 1(a) with $R_g = 1000$ ohms, R_1 set so that $I_c = 12$ ma, $(N_1/N_2)^2 R_L = 1$ K, find the maximum power output.

2. What is the distortion under the conditions of part 1? Assume only second harmonic distortion.

3. Repeat part 1 for Fig. 1(b), if $R_g = 2$ K, $R_e = 5$ ohms, and $(N_1/N_2)^2 R_L = 500$ ohms. Note that the operation is essentially Class B.

4. Compute the following under the conditions of part 3:
   (a) Power output
   (b) Efficiency [= (a-c output)/(d-c input) × 100%]
   (c) Third-harmonic distortion
   (d) Voltage, current, and power gain in db

5. What is "cross-over" distortion in Class B amplifiers? How is it eliminated or reduced?

6. How can the circuits of Fig. 1 be modified for high temperature operation?

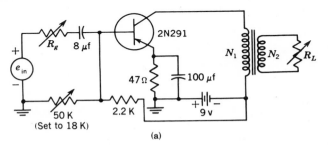

(a)

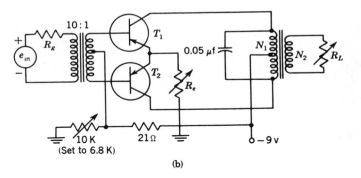

(b)

Fig. 1

Performance

7. Set up and test the circuit of Fig. 1(a). Meter the circuit to assure safe operation. Observe output with CRO and voltmeter. Vary R_g, R_e, and R_L and record results.

8. Repeat part 6 for the circuit of Fig. 1(b). The 0.05 μf capacitor may not be necessary unless excessive cross-over distortion or oscillation is present.

9. At some satisfactory operating point for the circuit of Fig. 1(b) near maximum power output, take data for a frequency response curve.

Calculations and conclusions

   10. Plot the frequency response curve of part 8.

   11. Discuss briefly the experimental results.

References

Lo, A. W., Endres, R. O., Zawels, J., Waldhauer, F. D., and Cheng, C. C., *Transistor Electronics* (Englewood Cliffs, N. J.: Prentice-Hall, Inc., 1955).

Shea, R. F., *Principles of Transistor Circuits* (New York: John Wiley & Sons, Inc., 1953).

Bevitt, W. E., *Transistor Handbook* (Englewood Cliffs, N. J.: Prentice-Hall, Inc., 1956).

Ryder, J. D., *Electronic Fundamentals and Applications*, 2d ed. (Englewood Cliffs, N. J.: Prentice-Hall, Inc., 1959).

Materials required

Components	*Equipment*
2 TI 2N291 transistors with sockets (matched for push-pull)	1 audio frequency generator
1 10 K decade resistor	1 cathode-ray oscillograph
1 100 K decade resistor	1 audio frequency power meter (variable input impedance, not required but convenient)
1 10 K potentiometer	
1 5 K potentiometer	1 10 ma d-c meter
1 1 K potentiometer	1 50 ma d-c meter
1 27 ohm resistor	2 a-c vacuum-tube voltmeters
1 2.2 K resistor	1 multimeter
1 0.05 μf capacitor	
1 8 μf capacitor	
1 100 μf capacitor	
1 10:1 transformer with secondary CT	
1 approximately 2:1 push-pull output transformer (primary for about 500 to 1000 ohms)	
6 No. 6 dry cells	

41-B

Transistor Power Amplifiers

Purpose

The purpose of this experiment is the study of Class B transistor power amplifiers.

Information

The wide power-output advantage available in Class B, push-pull operation over that of single-ended operation results in the almost universal use of the push-pull connection. With the availability of complementary symmetry the variety of push-pull transistor circuits is much larger than

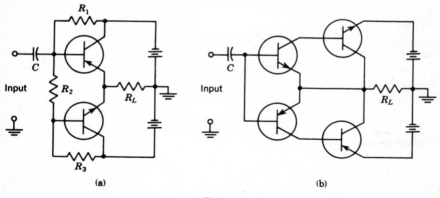

(a)   (b)

Fig. 1

for vacuum tubes. Figure 1 shows two examples of the desirable simplicity of the complementary amplifiers. Each has a single-ended load without direct current and unbalanced input. The circuit of Fig. 1(a) is a grounded collector connection and that of Fig. 1(b) is grounded emitter with 100% voltage feedback including the drivers. Owing to the difficulty of finding complementary transistors, matched both as to characteristics and frequency, this experiment will cover only the conventional type of circuits.

Preliminary

1. From the characteristics, with $N_1/N_2 = 1$, $R_L = 10$ K, and $R_e = 5$ ohms, calculate the maximum power output of the circuit of Fig. 1(a). Repeat for $R_L = 5$ K and 20 K.

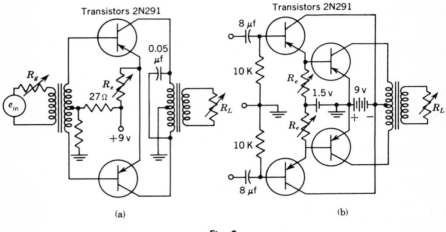

Fig. 2

2. Calculate the third-harmonic distortion under each set of conditions of part 1.

3. What is "cross-over" distortion in Class B amplifiers? How can it be prevented?

4. Why must the d-c emitter to base resistance be kept low in Class B transistor amplifiers?

5. Show a simple phase inverter to drive the circuit of Fig. 2(b).

Performance

6. Set up the circuit of Fig. 2(a). Meter the required currents to assure operation within ratings. With CRO across the load, adjust R_L, R_e, and R_g while recording the maximum output obtainable with acceptable distortion. Use the 0.05 μf capacitor only if necessary to reduce cross-over distortion or oscillation.

7. Take data for a frequency response curve under maximum power conditions obtained in part 6.

8. Connect a phase inverter and adjust for balanced output voltages.

9. Use the phase inverter to drive the circuit of Fig. 2(b). Adjust R_e for maximum undistorted output within transistor ratings. Record results.

Calculations and conclusions

10. Plot the frequency response curve of part 7; also plot power output versus R_L.

11. Discuss briefly the experiment and the results.

References

Lo, A. W., Endres, R. O., Zawels, J., Waldhauer, F. D., and Cheng, C. C., *Transistor Electronics* (Englewood Cliffs, N. J.: Prentice-Hall, Inc., 1955).

Shea, R. F., *Principles of Transistor Circuits* (New York: John Wiley & Sons, Inc., 1953).

Bevitt, W. D., *Transistor Handbook* (Englewood Cliffs, N. J.: Prentice-Hall, Inc., 1956).

Ryder, J. D., *Electronic Fundamentals and Applications*, 2d ed. (Englewood Cliffs, N. J.: Prentice-Hall, Inc., 1959).

Materials required

Components	*Equipment*
5 2N291 transistors with sockets and heat sinks (two pairs matched)	1 audio frequency generator
2 10 K decade resistors	1 cathode-ray oscillograph
2 1 K potentiometers	1 10 ma d-c meter
1 25 ohm variable resistor	1 50 ma d-c meter
1 27 ohm resistor	2 a-c vacuum-tube voltmeters
1 2.7 K resistor	1 multimeter
2 10 K resistors	
1 0.05 µf capacitor	
3 8 µf capacitors	
1 10:1 transformer with secondary CT	
1 approximately 2:1 push-pull output transformer (about 500 to 1000 ohms primary impedance)	
8 No. 6 dry cells	

42-A

Transistor Amplifier Configurations

Purpose

The purpose of this experiment is the comparison and testing of the various transistor amplifier configurations.

Information

The three common vacuum-tube connections are grounded cathode, grounded grid, and grounded plate or cathode follower. The equivalents of each of these circuits are in use with transistors. Their characteristics are essentially the same. The major differences are due to the lower input impedance of the transistor circuits in equivalent circuits.

In this experiment, the voltage, current, and power gain will be investigated. Although the P-N-P transistor is shown, N-P-N transistors will perform the same, with reversed bias.

Preliminary

1. Draw a practical circuit similar to the transistor circuit of Fig. 1(a), giving component values. The transistor is a 2N369. Draw an equivalent circuit, and derive literal voltage, current, and power gain expressions. Obtain numerical values for the circuit drawn. Assume quiescent values of $V_c = 10$ volts, $I_c = 2$ ma.

2. Repeat part 1 for the circuit of Fig. 1(b).

3. Repeat part 1 for the circuit of Fig. 1(c).

4. Compare the numerical values calculated in parts 1, 2, and 3 with results from the very approximate formulas given below. $\beta = \alpha/(1 - \alpha)$.

	Grounded emitter	Grounded base	Grounded collector
Current gain	$\beta/[1 + (R_L/r_d)]$	$-\alpha/[1 + (R_L/r_c)]$	$-1/[1 - \alpha + (R_L/r_c)]$
Voltage gain	$-\beta R_L/[r_p + (1 + \beta)r_e]$	$\alpha R_L/[r_e + (1 - \alpha)r_b]$	1 (very approx.)
Power gain	Product of above	Product of above	Product of above

5. (a) List some applications in which each of the above is preferable to the other two configurations. (b) Why is the common emitter connection usually considered the basic and most useful circuit?

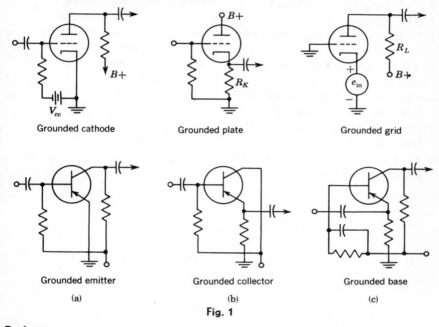

Grounded cathode   Grounded plate   Grounded grid

Grounded emitter   Grounded collector   Grounded base

(a)   (b)   (c)

Fig. 1

Performance

6. Set up the circuit of part 1. Check calculated values, amplitude before clipping, and frequency response to 20 kc.

7. Repeat part 6 for the circuit of part 2.

8. Repeat part 6 for the circuit of part 3.

Calculations and conclusions

9. Briefly discuss each of the circuits on a semicomparative basis.

10. Discuss any unexpected observations.

References

Shea, R. F., *Principles of Transistor Circuits* (New York: John Wiley & Sons, Inc., 1953).

Lo, A. W., Endres, R. O., Zawels, J., Waldhauer, F. D., and Cheng, C. C., *Transistor Electronics* (Englewood Cliffs, N. J.: Prentice-Hall, Inc., 1955).

Ryder, J. D., *Electronic Fundamentals and Applications*, 2d ed. (Englewood Cliffs, N. J.: Prentice-Hall, Inc., 1959).

Materials required

Components	*Equipment*

Components

1 2N369 transistor with socket
1 100 K decade resistor
1 10 K variable resistor (5% calibration)
1 500 K variable resistor (10% calibration)
3 10 μf, 50 volt capacitors (electrolytics are most instructive)
1 10:1 step-down transformer (for low input)
14 No. 6 dry cells (easier to use than higher voltage with divider)

Equipment

1 cathode-ray oscillograph
1 audio frequency generator
2 a-c vacuum-tube voltmeters
1 5 ma d-c meter
1 100 μa d-c meter
1 multimeter

EXPERIMENT

42-B

Transistor Amplifier Configurations

Purpose

This experiment is intended to make the various transistor amplifiers more familiar, and hence useful.

Information

Classically the grounded base transistor amplifier was used first, and was used extensively particularly with point-contact transistors. With junction transistors, the numerous advantages of the grounded emitter for most applications were recognized. Higher input impedances and higher power gain can be realized with the grounded emitter as compared with the grounded base.

In spite of the more general applicability of the grounded emitter, the other configurations have advantages in enough cases to make understanding of their operation desirable. The approximate voltage, current, and power gains are listed below. $\beta = \alpha/(1 - \alpha)$.

	Grounded emitter	Grounded base	Grounded collector
Current gain	$\beta/[1 + (R_L/r_d)]$	$-\alpha/[1 + (R_L/r_c)]$	$-1/[1 - \alpha + (R_L/r_c)]$
Voltage gain	$-\beta R_L/[r_b + (1 + \beta)r_e]$	$\alpha R_L/[r_e + (1 - \alpha)r_b]$	1 (very approx.)
Power gain	Product of above	Product of above	Product of above

This experiment will be devoted, mainly, to investigation of the input and output impedances of the three configurations. The equivalent circuits are given in Fig. 1.

Preliminary

1. For the 2N369 transistor with $V_c = 10$ volts and $I_c = 2$ ma, calculate the approximate voltage, current, and power gain for each of the circuits of Fig. 1, if $R_L = 10$ K and $R_g = 1$ K. (Note that the generator and load resistances are not optimum for any of the circuits.)

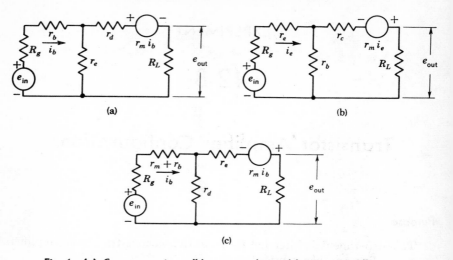

(a)   (b)

(c)

Fig. 1 **(a)** Common emitter; **(b)** common base; **(c)** common collector.

2. Calculate the "matched" input and output impedances of the circuit of Fig. 1(a), and draw a practical circuit using these values. Use d-c conditions of part 1.

3. Repeat part 2 for the circuit of Fig. 1(b).

4. Repeat part 2 for the circuit of Fig. 1(c).

5. For impedance matching, list some cases where each of the circuits would be most advantageous.

Performance

6. Set up the circuit of part 2. Check the input resistance (R_L = calculated value) by varying R_g until $v_b = \frac{1}{2}e_{in}$ and by impedance bridge. With $R_g = R_{input}$, measure the output impedance by varying R_L for maximum output and by impedance bridge. Use CRO to check for linear operation.

7. (a) Measure the input impedance of the circuit of part 6 as a function of the output impedance. (b) Measure output impedance as a function of input impedance. Maintain the d-c conditions of part 1, and check for linear conditions. Use any convenient impedance-measuring method.

8. Measure input and output impedance of the circuit of part 3.

9. Repeat part 8 for the circuit of part 4.

Calculations and conclusions

10. Plot the results of part 7.

11. Discuss briefly the experimental results, especially any difficulties.

References

Ryder, J. D., *Electronic Fundamentals and Applications*, 2d ed. (Englewood Cliffs, N. J.: Prentice-Hall, Inc., 1959).

Shea, R. F., *Principles of Transistor Circuits* (New York: John Wiley & Sons, Inc., 1953).

Lo, A. W., Endres, R. O., Zawels, J., Waldhauer, F. D., and Cheng, C. C., *Transistor Electronics* (Englewood Cliffs, N. J.: Prentice-Hall, Inc., 1955).

Materials required

Components

1 2N369 transistor and socket
2 100 K decade resistors
1 10 K variable resistor (10% calibration)
1 500 K variable resistor (10% calibration)
3 10 μf, 50 volt electrolytic capacitors
1 10:1 low-level transformer
14 No. 6 dry cells (more convenient than voltage dividers)

Equipment

1 cathode-ray oscillograph
1 audio frequency oscillator
1 audio frequency impedance bridge (should have tuned null detector for good low-level measurements)
2 a-c vacuum-tube voltmeters
1 5 ma d-c meter
1 100 μa d-c meter
1 multimeter

EXPERIMENT

43-A

Transistor Bias Stabilization

Purpose

The object of this experiment is familiarization with methods for temperature stabilization of transistor quiescent operating points.

Information

In this experiment the graphical approach to the reduction of Q-point drift in transistors will be emphasized. For example, in Fig. 1(a), a simple R-C amplifier with fixed bias (R_b) is shown. Figure 1(b) shows the characteristics of this transistor at 25° C, while (c) gives the characteristics of the same transistors at 40° C. With fixed bias the Q-point shifts from Q_1 to Q_2 over this temperature range. While with self-bias, as provided by R_b', the Q-point shifts only from Q_1' to Q_2'. This example is not particularly good since R_L is too small (changes in V_c are small) for good stabilization by this method.

Figure 1(d) shows a method by which the bias and stabilization may be established separately. The characteristics for the extremes of operating conditions must be available — such as Fig. 1(b) and (c). From the load line the selected limits of V_c (or I_c) variation are used to determine the corresponding changes in I_b. From V_c, I_b and V_c', I_b', and equation (1), the values of R_f and I_a are determined.

$$I_b = \frac{V_c}{R_f} - I_a \tag{1}$$

The values of R_a and E_a are then chosen conveniently to give I_a. The two approximations — V_b approximately equal to zero and neglect of I_f on V_c — are usually unimportant.

When very low resistance loads are used, as in transformer coupling, the only useful method is to include resistance in the emitter circuit to cause increasing base bias with increasing collector current. By-passing may be provided if a-c degeneration is not desired.

Other methods, such as the use of diodes, thermistors, and other non-linear elements, are quite useful in special cases but will not be covered in this experiment.

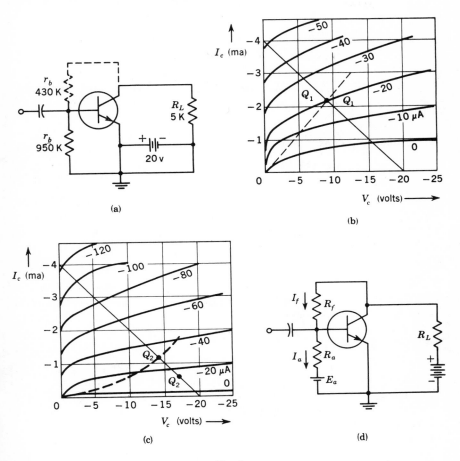

Fig. 1

Preliminary

1. Repeat the example outlined in Fig. 1 for the case where R_L is 10 K.

2. Assume that the characteristics of a 2N366 transistor change to those for the 2N364 over the range of 25° C to 50° C. Design a circuit of the type of Fig. 1(d) with $R_L = 10$ K, $V_{cc} = -20$ volts, $I_b = -10$ μa at 25° C. The variation of static collector voltage must not exceed 5 volts.

3. With a transformer-coupled stage and the same characteristic varia-tions as assumed in part 2, design an emitter bias arrangement to keep the

change in collector bias current to 0.5 ma. $V_{cc} = -15$ volts, $I_b = -15 \,\mu a$ at 25° C. Note that the emitter to base voltage is still assumed zero, and the base to V_{cc} resistor value must be specified.

Performance

4. Set up the circuit of part 1. Measure the change of I_c as the temperature is changed from 25° C to 60° C — or some rating is exceeded. Use both fixed and self bias.

5. Set up the circuit of part 2 and test over the same temperature range.

6. Set up the circuit of part 3 and test over the 25° C to 60° C range. A transformer is not required.

Calculations and conclusions

7. Discuss briefly the experiment and its anomalies.

References

Lo, A. W., Endres, R. O., Zawels, J., Waldhauer, F. D., and Cheng, C. C., *Transistor Electronics* (Englewood Cliffs, N. J.: Prentice-Hall, Inc., 1955).

Shea, R. F., *Principles of Transistor Circuits* (New York: John Wiley & Sons, Inc., 1953).

Bevitt, W. D., *Transistor Handbook* (Englewood Cliffs, N. J.: Prentice-Hall, Inc., 1956).

Materials required

Components	*Equipment*
1 2N366 transistor and socket	1 100 μa d-c meter
1 1 megohm decade resistor (calibrated potentiometers are satisfactory)	1 1 ma d-c meter
	1 10 ma d-c meter
2 100 K decade resistors	1 50 ma d-c meter
1 10 K decade resistor	1 25 volt d-c meter
1 10 K variable resistor	1 multimeter
13 No. 6 dry cells	1 variable temperature oven with thermometer and thermostat (a mercury thermometer beside the transistor and a heat lamp can be used; slow temperature changes and fast reading may be necessary)

43-B

Transistor Bias Stabilization

Purpose

The purpose of this experiment is the study of transistor bias stabilization methods.

Information

Reverse collector current and α_{cb} variation both cause temperature-induced Q-point drift. Procedures used to offset the effect of changing reverse collector current (the more important of the two processes) also compensate for α_{cb} variation. In addition, most procedures used to correct for Q-point drift will also improve the circuit tolerance for different transistors.

It can be shown that I_c is given by equation (1), as a first approximation. An improvement in the first approximation is all that is required to stabilize the Q-point. I_{co}' is the fictitious reverse collector junction current at zero

$$I_c = (1 + \alpha_{cb})I_{co}' + \alpha_{cb}I_b + \frac{V_c}{r_d} \tag{1}$$

collector voltage as illustrated by Fig. 1(a). The sensitivity of the collector current with respect to any quantity will be defined as in equation (2).

S_{cc} = derivative of I_c with respect to quantity in question

$$S_{cc} = \frac{dI_o}{dI_{co}'} \quad \text{(for example)} \tag{2}$$

To illustrate, S_{cc} for the circuit of Fig. 1(b) with R_b and then with R_b' will be derived.

$$S_{cc} = \frac{dI_c}{dI_{co}'} = (1 + \alpha_{cb}) + \alpha_{cb}\frac{dI_b}{dI_{co}'} + \frac{1}{r_d}\frac{dV_c}{dI_{co}'}$$

$$= 1 + \alpha_{cb} + \alpha_{cb}\frac{dI_b}{dI_c}\frac{dI_c}{dI_{co}'} + \frac{1}{r_d}\frac{dV_c}{dI_c} + \frac{1}{r_d}\frac{dV_c}{dI_c}\frac{dI_c}{dI_{co}'} \tag{3}$$

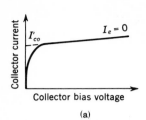

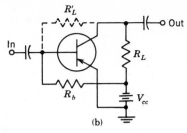

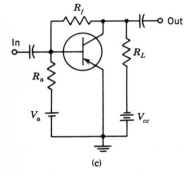

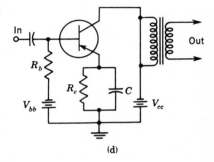

Fig. 1

Therefore

$$S_{cc} = \frac{dI_c}{dI'_{co}} = \frac{1 + \alpha_{cb}}{1 - \alpha_{cb}\dfrac{dI_b}{dI_c} - \dfrac{1}{r_d}\dfrac{dV_c}{dI_c}} \quad (4)$$

$V_c = V_{cc} - I_c R_L$, therefore $dV_c/dI_c = -R_L$ and

$$\frac{dI_b}{dI_c} = 0 \quad \text{(no connection from collector to base)}$$

Therefore

$$S_{cc} = \frac{1 + \alpha_{cb}}{1 + \dfrac{R_L}{r_d}} \quad \text{(for fixed bias)} \quad (5)$$

The following equations hold for self bias:

$$I_b = \frac{V_c}{R'_b}, \qquad V_c = V_{cc} - (I_b + I_c)R_L$$

therefore

$$V_c = \frac{V_{cc} - I_c R_L}{1 + R_L/R'_b} \quad \text{and} \quad \frac{\partial V_c}{\partial I_c} = -\frac{R_L R'_b}{R_L + R'_b} \quad (6)$$

$$I_b = \frac{V_{cc} - I_c R_L}{R'_b + R_L} \quad \text{and} \quad \frac{\partial I_b}{\partial I_c} = -\frac{R_L}{R'_b + R_L}$$

and

$$S'_{cc} = \frac{dI_c}{dI'_{co}} = \frac{1 + \alpha_{cb}}{1 + \alpha_{cb}R_L/(R_L + R'_b)} + \frac{1}{r_d}\left(\frac{R_L R'_b}{R_L + R'_b}\right) \quad (7)$$

Equation (7) indicates a decrease of I_c drift. Several approximations, including the nonvariance of all terms of the right side of equation (7), are used in deriving the results. In spite of these approximations, the results are quite indicative of the expected improvement.

The circuit of Fig. 1(c) allows independent establishment of bias and stabilization method when collector d-c potential does not change. These circuits will all be tested in the experiment.

Preliminary

1. For the circuit of Fig. 1(b), find S_{cc} and S'_{cc} under the following conditions: $\alpha_{cb} = 75$, $r_d = 20$ K, $R_L = 3$ K, $R'_b = 470$ K, $R_b = 1$ megohm.

2. Derive a value of S_{cc} for the circuit of Fig. 1(c).

3. Compare the results of part 2 with equation (7). What is the advantage of the latter circuit?

4. Derive S_{cc} for the circuit of Fig. 1(d). Assume a resistance r_e in the emitter circuit before R_e is added.

5. If $r_e = 25$ ohms, $R_c = 1$ K, $R_b = 1$ K, $\alpha_{cb} = 75$, and $r_d = 20$ K, calculate S_{cc} before and after the addition of R_e. What is optimum value of R_b? What is S_{cc} for this optimum value?

Performance

6. Set up both circuits of part 1 and the circuit of part 2 in such a fashion that you can change among them by moving only one or two wires. Meter base currents, collector current, and collector voltage. Be sure to connect the feedback resistors R_b and R_f to the collector side of the milliammeter, because the meter fuse may have a resistance of 200 to 400 ohms. Use a TI 2N366 transistor, with $V_{cc} = -18$ volts, $V_a = 1.5$ volts. If I_c is not in the range of 2.5 to 3.0 ma at room temperature, adjust R_b, R'_b, or R_f, as the case may be, until it is in this range. Check and record the variation of I_b, I_c, and V_c over the temperature range 25° to 55° C.

7. Set up the circuit of part 4 with the values of part 5. Use $V_{cc} = -9$ volts, $V_{bb} = -3$ volts. Measure the base and collector currents over the 25° to 55° C temperature range. No transformer is required.

Calculations and conclusions

8. Plot the I_c variations versus temperature for which data was taken on a single sheet.

9. Plot the V_c variations of part 6.

10. Plot the I_b variations of part 6.

11. Discuss the experiment briefly.

References

Lo, A. W., Endres, R. O., Zawels, J., Waldhauer, F. D., and Cheng, C. C., *Transistor Electronics* (Englewood Cliffs, N. J.: Prentice-Hall, Inc., 1955).

Shea, R. F., *Principles of Transistor Circuits* (New York: John Wiley & Sons, Inc., 1953).

Bevitt, W. D., *Transistor Handbook* (Englewood Cliffs, N. J.: Prentice-Hall, Inc., 1956).

Materials required

Components	Equipment
1 TI 2N366 transistor with socket	1 100 μa d-c meter
1 1 megohm resistor	1 5 ma d-c meter
1 470 K resistor	1 20,000 ohm per volt (or higher) multimeter
1 150 K resistor	1 variable temperature oven with thermometer and thermostat (or a substitute such as a heat lamp and mercury thermometer)
1 27 K resistor	
1 3 K resistor	
1 1 K resistor	
13 No. 6 dry cells	

44-A

Transistor Noise

Purpose

The purpose of this experiment is familiarization with the noise limitations of transistors.

Information

Since the point-contact transistor appears to generate 20 to 40 db more noise than the junction transistor, only the junction variety will be considered. In low-frequency applications, selected junction transistors are the most noise-free amplifying device available and give promise of continued improvement.

At least five sources of transistor noise have been identified. The first four are understood and mathematically derivable. The fifth is not well understood and seems to be associated with uncontrolled impurities and surface phenomena.

1. Base thermal noise
2. Emitter-base shot noise
3. Collector-base shot noise
4. Collector-base partition noise
5. Semiconductor excess noise

Workable emperical relations for excess noise are available. The important controllable parameters for noise improvement are generator resistance, collector current, and to some extent collector voltage.

In this experiment, the single-frequency noise figure will be determined for several conditions. Noise figure will be defined by equation (1).

$$F = 10 \log_{10} \frac{\text{actual noise power output}}{\text{noise input} \times \text{power gain}}$$

The accepted definition of noise figure is "the ratio of available signal-to-noise ratio at the input to the available signal-to-noise power ratio at the output." To avoid exact measurements of input impedance, equation (1) will be used. The decibel ratio is usually preferred.

Since the measurements are in terms of power and the signal is random instead of sinusoidal, rms reading meters should always be used. If average readings are taken, some error will be introduced.

Note: Noise measurements are extremely difficult to attain in some laboratories because of high ambient noise levels (electrical). Shielding and isolation from power lines are usually required. A shielded room or copper screen box with shielded input and output leads is the most satisfactory arrangement.

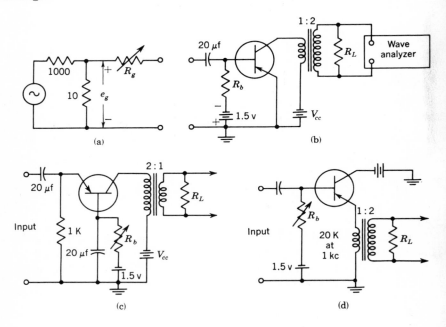

Fig. 1

Preliminary

1. Give the noise formula for a resistance R_1 and identify the terms.

2. Outline with block diagrams a method for obtaining the single-frequency noise figure of a transistor amplifier by means of a sine-wave generator and wave analyzer.

3. How is the bandwidth defined for noise measurements?

4. How is the integrated noise figure obtained from a complete knowledge of the single-frequency noise figure?

5. If two cascaded amplifiers have noise figures of F_1 and F_2, what is the total noise figure F?

Performance

6. Set up the circuit of Fig. 1(a) and (b) and test the noise figure of a P-N-P transistor from 100 cps to 20 kc. Set R_g to 1 K, R_b to $I_c = 0.25$ ma and $V_{cc} = 3$ volts. Observe output with CRO, but do not leave connected during measurements.

7. Compare three other transistors at 100, 1000, and 10,000 cps.

8. Repeat part 6 for the ground base circuit of Fig. 1(c). Also check F at 1000 cps with $R_g = 40$ ohms, making the generator resistance 50 ohms.

9. Repeat part 7 for the circuit of part 8.

10. Repeat part 6 for the grounded collector circuit of Fig. 1(a). Also check F at 1000 cps with $R_g = 50$ K.

11. Repeat part 7 for the circuit of part 10.

Calculations and conclusions

12. Plot the noise figure versus frequency for parts 6, 8, and 10.

13. Tabulate F for the various transistors in the three configurations.

14. Discuss briefly any experimental difficulties.

References

Lo, A. W., Endres, R. O., Zawels, J., Waldhauer, F. D., and Cheng, C. C., *Transistor Electronics* (Englewood Cliffs, N. J.: Prentice-Hall, Inc., 1955).

Terman, F. E., and Pettit, J. M., *Electronic Measurements* (New York: McGraw-Hill Book Co., Inc., 1952).

Shea, R. F., *Principles of Transistor Circuits* (New York: John Wiley & Sons, Inc., 1954).

Materials required

Components	*Equipment*
4 2N369 transistors with sockets	1 cathode-ray oscillograph
1 1:2 transformer (primary approximately 20 K)	1 audio frequency generator
	1 wave analyzer with capacitive
1 1 K decade resistor	damping on meter
2 100 K decade resistors	1 1 ma d-c meter
1 1 megohm resistor	1 multimeter
2 10 ohm resistors	
2 1 K resistors	
2 20 µf capacitors	
3 No. 6 dry cells	

44-B

Transistor Noise

Purpose

This experiment is designed to show the variability of transistor noise figure from sample to sample and the influence of the circuit design.

Information

Several sources of transistor noise have been recognized and thoroughly investigated. A complete theory accounting for the low-frequency excess noise is not available, even though a strong connection with semiconductor surface states has been shown. The general shape of the single-frequency noise figure versus frequency for all transistors is shown in Fig. 1(a). For selected units f_1 may be as low as a few hundred cycles, f_2 as high as a few hundred kilocycles, and F_m perhaps as low as 5 db.

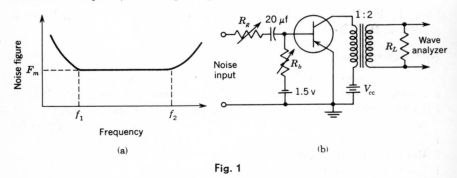

Fig. 1

Since the noise figure for transistors is not a constant, the single-frequency noise figure is more useful in determining application suitability than the integrated noise figure. Commercial units are usually specified at 1 kc. In this experiment noise figure will be checked at several audio frequencies.

The most convenient noise measurement scheme utilizes a noise source, since no knowledge of amplifier gain or the bandwidth of the detector (as long as it is small for single-frequency measurements) is necessary. This method will be assumed, but if sufficient noise power is not available the signal generator method may be substituted.

Since the noise figures of the various transistor configurations are approximately the same, and the grounded emitter has higher gain, only this will be tested for noise figure. All noise figures will be expressed in decibels.

Preliminary

1. Outline, with a block diagram, the method of finding single-frequency noise figures with a noise generator and narrow-band detector.

2. Show the modifications of the method of part 1, if a signal generator (sine wave) is used instead of the noise source.

3. Define and identify the following terms:

(a) resistor (or Johnson noise)

(b) amplifier noise figure

(c) noise figure, F, of two cascaded amplifiers of undivided noise figures F_1 and F_2

(d) integrated noise figure.

4. If the first of two cascaded amplifiers has a noise figure of 10 db and a gain of 10 db, what is the noise figure of the second if the overall figure is 11 db?

Performance

5. Set up the circuit of Fig. 1(b) with input, output, and metering devices. Set I_c to 250 μa by means of R_b, V_{cc} to 3 volts, R_g to 1000 ohms, and determine the noise figures of the four transistors provided at 100, 1000, and 20,000 cps.

6. With the circuit of part 5 and the lowest noise transistor, vary R_g from 100 to 10 K (higher if possible) and take data of F vs R_g.

7. With the circuit of part 5, vary V_{cc} from 1.5 to 15 volts in 1.5 volt steps. Record F vs V_c. I_d is to be kept constant at 1 ma, by adjustment of R_b.

8. With the circuit of part 5 vary I_c from 100 μa to 10 ma. Record results.

Calculations and conclusions

9. Plot the data of parts 6, 7, and 8.

10. Discuss briefly the experimental results.

References

Lo, A. W., Endres, R. O., Zawels, J., Waldhauer, F. D., and Cheng, C. C., *Transistor Electronics* (Englewood Cliffs, N. J.: Prentice-Hall, Inc., 1955).

Terman, F. E., and Pettit, J. M., *Electronic Measurements* (New York: McGraw-Hill Book Co., Inc., 1952).

Shea, R. F., *Principles of Transistor Circuits* (New York: John Wiley & Sons, Inc., 1953).

Materials required

Components

4 P-N-P transistors and socket (same general ratings as 2N369)

1 1 K decade resistor

2 100 K decade resistors

1 1 megohm variable resistor (or potentiometer)

1 20 μf capacitor

1 1:2 transformer (approximately 20 K primary with good frequency response)

11 No. 6 dry cells

Equipment

1 low-frequency noise generator

1 cathode-ray oscillograph

1 wave analyzer (100 cps or more bandwidth may be needed)

1 1 ma d-c meter

1 10 ma d-c meter

1 multimeter

45-A

Transistor Feedback Amplifiers

Purpose

The purpose of this experiment is familiarization with feedback technique and its effects in transistor amplifiers.

Information

The theory of feedback amplifiers, as usually developed, applies to all amplifiers. For this reason the only purpose of a special experiment with transistor feedback amplifiers is to present their few peculiarities and to provide more circuit experience in general. In this experiment, attention will be focused on the common emitter circuit with the common base and common collector circuits considered as feedback modifications. The base current (or voltage with respect to the emitter) is considered to be the transistor control medium.

Preliminary

1. Derive the voltage gain, current gain, input impedance, and output impedance of the circuit of Fig. 1(a). Include R_L in the input expression in this and following sections.

2. What transistor parameter is an apparent feedback element in the grounded emitter circuit? Does it provide voltage or current feedback? Note: The terms "voltage" and "current" feedback are unimportant to general feedback theory. Current feedback here refers to a reduction of current gain by feedback and similarly for voltage feedback.

3. Write the gain and impedance expressions for the circuit of Fig. 1(b) Considering the grounded collector as a feedback arrangement of the grounded emitter circuit, what type of feedback is present? What general trends of the gain and impedance expressions are caused by this feedback?

4. Write the gain and impedance expressions for the grounded collector of Fig. 1(c). In Fig. 1(a), what type of feedback is present? What trends are caused in the gain and impedance expressions by this feedback?

5. Draw circuits, with component values, for the connections of Fig. 1. Collector current should be 2 ma and collector supply voltage should not exceed 15 volts. The transistor is a TI 2N369.

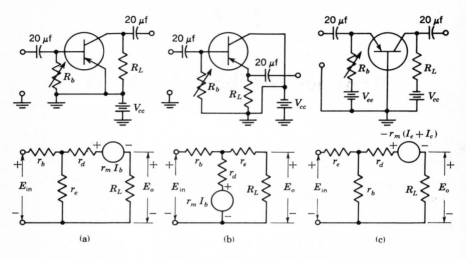

Note: Circuits are drawn to emphasize feedback features of (b) and (c).

Fig. 1

Performance

6. Using the input circuit of Fig. 2 with $R_g = 1$ K, set up the circuit of Fig. 1(a). $V_{cc} = 15$ volts, $R_L = 5$ K. Adjust R_b for $I_c = 2$ ma. Check the maximum output with small distortion at 1 kc. Measure the voltage-gain frequency response, with E_g considered to be the input voltage.

Measure input impedance at 1 kc and 20 kc by adjusting R_g until $E_2 = \frac{1}{2}E_g$. It will probably be necessary to keep E_2 below 5 millivolts in this part of the experiment, to prevent distortion. If oscillograph preamplifiers are available, observe Lissajous patterns of E_g and E_2 so that the complex input impedance can be computed.

7. Insert 470 ohms in the emitter lead and repeat part 6. Larger input voltages can be used so that Lissajous patterns can be observed without preamplifiers.

8. Repeat part 6 for Fig. 1(b) with $R_L = 5$ K, $V_{cc} = 15$ volts, and R_b adjusted for $I_c = 2$ ma. Repeat with $R_L = 470$ ohms and $V_{cc} = 6$ volts. Larger input voltages can again be used; in fact, it will be necessary to replace the 20 ohm resistor in the input circuit by a 470 ohm resistor when checking for maximum undistorted output.

9. Repeat part 6 for Fig. 1(c) with $R_L = 5$ K, $V_{cc} = 15$ volts, $V_{ee} = 4.5$ volts, and R_e adjusted for $I_c = 2$ ma.

Calculations and conclusions

10. Plot the frequency response curves from the data given. Why is a comparison of the voltage gains of the different amplifiers somewhat unfair?

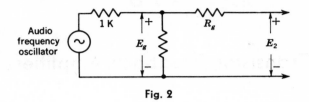

Fig. 2

11. Compute input impedances and current gains and tabulate along with maximum output voltages.

12. Rank the amplifiers as to increasing voltage gain, current gain, input impedance, and output impedance.

13. Briefly discuss the experimental results.

References

Ryder, J. D., *Electronic Fundamentals and Applications*, 2d ed. (Englewood Cliffs, N. J.: Prentice-Hall, Inc., 1959).

Shea, R. F., and Wallman, H., *Principles of Transistor Circuits* (New York: John Wiley & Sons, Inc., 1953).

Lo, A. W., Endres, R. O., Zawels, J., Waldhauer, F. D., and Cheng, C. C., *Transistor Electronics* (Englewood Cliffs, N. J.: Prentice-Hall, Inc., 1955).

Materials required

Components	*Equipment*
1 TI 2N369 transistor with socket	1 cathode-ray oscillograph
1 100 K decade resistor	1 audio frequency generator
1 1 K decade resistor	2 a-c vacuum-tube voltmeters, pref-
1 1 megohm variable resistor (or	erably with provision for use as
potentiometer)	amplifiers
1 20 ohm resistor	1 5 ma d-c meter
1 1000 ohm resistor	
1 5 K resistor	
2 100 K resistors	
1 5000 ohm potentiometer	
1 20 μf capacitor (or larger)	
13 No. 6 dry cells	

45-B

Transistor Feedback Amplifiers

Purpose

The object of this experiment is a study of some simple transistor feedback arrangements.

Information

Since feedback theory is quite general, its application to transistor circuits presents no new problems. Some familiarization is useful, however, so the two very basic circuits of Fig. 1 will be investigated. More complicated arrangements of feedback over several stages follow the same lines as vacuum-tube circuits.

Preliminary

1. Calculate the voltage gain, current gain, input impedance, and output impedance of Fig. 1(a), neglecting R_b. Simplify as much as possible and calculate numerical values when $I_c = -1$ ma, $V_c = -5$ volts, $R_g = 1$ K, and $R_f = 0$.

2. Calculate voltage gain, current gain, input impedance, and output impedance of Fig. 1(b). Use the input circuit of Fig. 1(c), and neglect R_b. Other conditions are as in part 1.

3. Resistor R_f in Fig. 1(a) is useful in both a-c and d-c stabilization. How could the a-c feedback be eliminated? the d-c stabilization?

4. Resistor R_f in Fig. 1(b) also provides both a-c and d-c stabilization. How could either one or the other be eliminated?

Performance

5. Set up the circuit of Fig. 1(a) with input circuit of (c), metering, and an oscillograph. Replace the load resistor with an output transformer. (Reduce V_{cc} to 4.5 volts whenever a transformer output is used, 1:1.) Measure the output impedance by maximum power transfer. Adjust I_c to -1 ma in each case and set R_g to 1 K. With the 10 K load resistor in place,

check voltage gain and input impedance. $E_{out} = \frac{1}{2}E_g$. Check frequency response data.

6. Set up as in part 5, with transformer output and 10 K reflected load, and take data of voltage gain versus R_f. $I_c = -1$ ma.

7. Repeat part 5 for the circuit of Fig. 1(b).

8. Repeat part 6 for the circuit of Fig. 1(b).

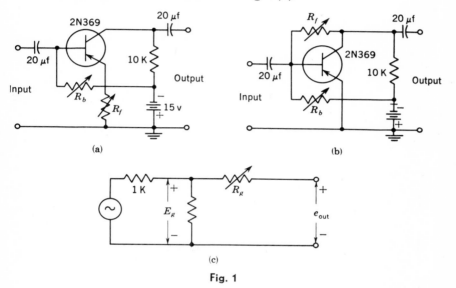

Fig. 1

Calculations and conclusions

9. Plot the curves for which data was taken.

10. Was the feedback of the "voltage" or "current" feedback type?

11. Discuss briefly any experimental difficulties.

References

Shea, R. F., *Principles of Transistor Circuits* (New York: John Wiley & Sons, Inc., 1953).

Lo, A. W., Endres, R. O., Zawels, J., Waldhauer, F. D., and Cheng, C. C., *Transistor Electronics* (Englewood Cliffs, N. J.: Prentice-Hall, Inc., 1955).

Ryder, J. D., *Electronic Fundamentals and Applications*, 2d ed. (Englewood Cliffs, N. J.: Prentice-Hall, Inc., 1959).

Materials required

Components

1 2N369 transistor with socket
2 100 K decade resistors
1 10 K decade resistor
1 1 K, 1% resistor
1 10 ohm, 1% resistor
2 20 μf capacitors
1 1:1 transformer (about 10 K impedance
10 No. 6 dry cells

Equipment

1 cathode-ray oscillograph
1 audio frequency generator
2 a-c vacuum-tube voltmeters
1 5 ma d-c meter
1 multimeter

EXPERIMENT

46-A

Transistor Multivibrators

Purpose

The purpose of this experiment is the study of the transistor astable trigger circuit or multivibrator.

Information

The junction transistor in the grounded emitter configuration is closely analogous to the grounded cathode, low input resistance triode. Analogs of all the normal vacuum-tube multivibrators can therefore be drawn, and most will operate satisfactorily.

All the multivibrator (or trigger) circuits, whether astable, monostable, or bistable, have two stable regions of operation separated by an unstable one. If the input impedance between any two points of a circuit indicates a negative resistance, this obviously represents the unstable region separating the two stable regions.

The analysis is quite similar to that of vacuum-tube circuits. Ordinarily an accurate and detailed analysis is not required to give the needed design information.

Preliminary

1. Assume T_1 conducting and T_2 nonconducting, and find the steady-state voltages and currents for each transistor. (The base to emitter voltage is usually taken initially as zero and corrected slightly, if necessary.) Check results on characteristic curves.

2. Plot the results of part 1 for T_1 and T_2 on separate graphs. Assume the base of T_2 arrives at conduction (initially assume zero volts) at $t = 0$ and switches in zero time. Plot the switched voltages. Note that the base of T_2 is driven into heavy conduction but quickly returns toward zero as its coupling capacitor charges through the few hundred ohms base-emitter resistance. Sketch both base and collector voltages on the graph for both T_1 and T_2 for a complete cycle.

303

3. The base of T_1, in the switching process of part 2, was driven to what negative voltage? As the base of T_1 relaxes, what voltage *would* it approach asymptotically? As the base of T_1 crosses the cut-off voltage, about 0.2 volts from characteristics, a second switching operation takes place. Find the time between the first and second switching operation. This time is 1/2 period. What is the frequency?

4. Explain briefly the effect of minority carrier storage in the base region under collector saturation conditions.

5. What other transistor phenomena can influence the waveforms sketched for the multivibrator? Indicate these approximately on your sketches.

6. Show how the circuit of Fig. 1 can be modified for "single-shot" or monostable operation.

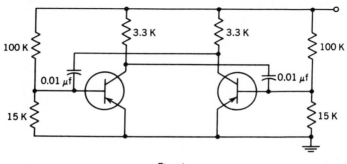

Fig. 1

7. Show modifications for emitter-coupled (corresponding to cathode-coupled) astable and monostable circuits.

Performance

8. Set up the circuit of Fig. 1. Record waveforms, voltages, and time intervals.

9. Vary the coupling capacitors over the operable range and record waveforms, voltage, and intervals.

10. With the values of Fig. 1, vary the base to ground resistance. Record results.

11. Modify the circuit for single-shot operation. Drive with a differential square wave or pulse on one base. Record results.

Calculations and conclusions

12. Compare calculated and measured waveforms. Explain the discrepancies in the waveforms.

13. Plot the frequency variations observed in parts 9 and 10.
14. Briefly discuss experimental results.

References

Lo, A. W., Endres, R. O., Zawels, J. ,Waldhauer, F. D., and Cheng, C. C., *Transistor Electronics* (Englewood Cliffs, N. J.: Prentice-Hall, Inc., 1955).

Von Tersch, L. W., and Swago, A. W., *Recurrent Electrical Transients* (Englewood Cliffs, N. J.: Prentice-Hall, Inc., 1953).

Shea, R. F., *Principles of Transistor Circuits* (New York: John Wiley & Sons, Inc., 1953).

Materials required

Components	*Equipment*
1 TI 2N366 transistor with socket	1 d-c cathode-ray oscillograph
2 470 ohm resistors	1 square-wave generator (or pulse generator)
2 1.5 K resistors	
2 4.7 K resistors	1 10 ma d-c meter
2 15 K resistors	1 d-c vacuum-tube voltmeter
2 47 K resistors	1 multimeter
2 100 K resistors	
2 150 K resistors	
1 10 K potentiometer (or variable resistor)	
2 250 $\mu\mu$f capacitors	
2 0.001 μf capacitors	
2 0.0025 μf capacitors	
2 0.01 μf capacitors	
2 0.025 μf capacitors	
2 0.1 μf capacitors	
2 0.25 μf capacitors	
7 No. 6 dry cells	

46-B

Transistor Multivibrators

Purpose

The purpose of this experiment is the introduction to and familiarization with the experimental behavior of monostable multivibrators.

Information

Because of the greater stability and predictability of junction transistors, these will be studied rather than the variety of point-contact multivibrator-type devices. The junction circuits, in general, have vacuum-tube counterparts. This fact makes the analysis of transistor circuits much easier, if their low base input resistance (grounded emitter configuration) is kept in mind. In addition, the tendency of base emitter voltages to be almost zero during conduction and that of collector voltages to be only a few tenths of a volt, if sufficient base current is present, are both useful approximations.

Owing to the much greater possible swing on the collector characteristics, the approximate calculations are actually much easier than with vacuum-tube circuits. The extra factors of capacitances, parameter variation, and minority carrier storage limit switching speeds and repetition rates. These will not be included in the circuit analysis.

Preliminary

1. Calculate the waveforms at point V_1, V_2, V_3, V_4, and V_5 of the single-shot multivibrator of the circuit of Fig. 1. Calculate also the bias currents while T_1 is conducting and while T_2 is conducting.

2. Calculate the "on" time of T_1. This is also called the multivibrator "delay" time.

3. What is the major factor limiting the repetition rate? How can the circuit be modified to accommodate faster repetition rates?

4. How can the circuit of Fig. 1 be made free-running? Draw such a circuit with pertinent waveforms.

5. What is meant by "minority carrier storage?"

6. What factors have been neglected that will affect the calculated waveforms?

Performance

7. Set up the circuit of Fig. 1 and record all voltages and waveforms.

8. Vary C from 1 μf down to the minimum operable value. Record all values, time intervals, and waveforms of V_3.

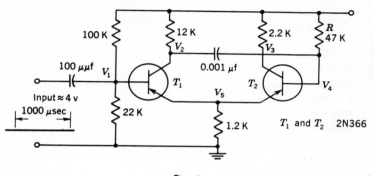

Fig. 1

9. Vary R (with $C = 0.01$ μf) from 10 K to the maximum operable value. Record the values, time intervals, and waveforms of V_3.

10. Modify the circuit for free-running operation by substituting a 100 K potentiometer for the 100 K plus 22 K base divider. Record waveforms and time intervals.

Calculations and conclusions

11. Plot delay time versus R and C.

12. Discuss briefly the experimental results.

References

Ryder, J. D., *Electronic Fundamentals and Applications*, 2d ed. (Englewood Cliffs, N. J.: Prentice-Hall, Inc., 1959).

Lo, A. W., Endres, R. O., Zawels, J., Waldhauer, F. D., and Cheng, C. C., *Transistor Electronics* (Englewood Cliffs, N. J.: Prentice-Hall, Inc., 1955).

Chance, B., *et al.*, *Waveforms* (New York: McGraw-Hill Book Co., Inc., 1949).

Von Tersch, L. W., and Swago, A. W., *Recurrent Electrical Transients* (Englewood Cliffs, N. J.: Prentice-Hall, Inc., 1953).

Materials required

Components

2 TI 2N366 transistors with sockets
1 100 K potentiometer
2 100 K decade resistors
1 220 ohm resistor
1 1 K resistor
1 1.2 K resistor
1 2.2 K resistor
1 10 K resistor
1 12 K resistor
1 22 K resistor
1 47 K resistor
1 100 K resistor
1 220 K resistor
1 470 K resistor
1 1 megohm resistor
1 4.7 megohm resistor
2 100 $\mu\mu$f capacitors
1 300 $\mu\mu$f capacitor
1 0.001 μf capacitor
1 0.003 μf capacitor
1 0.01 μf capacitor
1 0.03 μf capacitor
1 0.1 μf capacitor
1 1.0 μf capacitor
7 No. 6 dry cells

Equipment

1 d-c cathode-ray oscillograph (with time and voltage calibration)
1 pulse generator (with care, a square-wave generator may be substituted)
1 d-c vacuum-tube voltmeter
1 multimeter

47-A

Transistor Flip-flops

Purpose

This experiment is designed to introduce the experimental aspects of transistor bistable circuits.

Information

The analysis of junction transistor pulse circuits follows closely that for vacuum-tube circuits. In general, only their very low resistance in the saturation region and low base to emitter resistance in their regeneration region are major differences.

In Fig. 1(a), assuming the fictitious characteristics of (b) and that T_1 is "on" and T_2 is "off," the collector of T_1 is only a few tenths of a volt and its base is also very close to ground potential. This makes the calculations of potentials and currents rather easy for both transistors.

In Fig. 1(c) the circuit has been simplified for analysis. The circuit is stable for zero collector current, hence $V_{A'A} = I_A R$. This is the first stable region. Zero collector voltage, $V_c = 0$, represents the second unstable region. The intervening unstable is found as follows:

$$I_A = I_1 + I_2 \qquad I_3 = I_5 + I_4$$
$$I_2 = \alpha_{cb}^2 I_5 \qquad I_4 = \alpha_{cb} I_1$$
$$I_1 = V_{A'A}/R \qquad V_{cc} = I_3 R_L + I_5 R$$

giving
$$I_A = \frac{V_{A'A}}{R}\left(1 - \frac{\alpha_{cb}^2 R_L}{R + R_L}\right) + \frac{\alpha_{cb} V_{cc}}{R + R_L} \qquad (1)$$

Equation (1) is meaningful only for linear parameters, which is the case over most of the range. The combination of these three regions is shown in Fig. 1(d). With a good choice of α_{cb}, this curve can be experimentally checked except for some rounding of the corner. If the load line is caused to intersect the characteristic in all three regions, the desired flip-flop action will result.

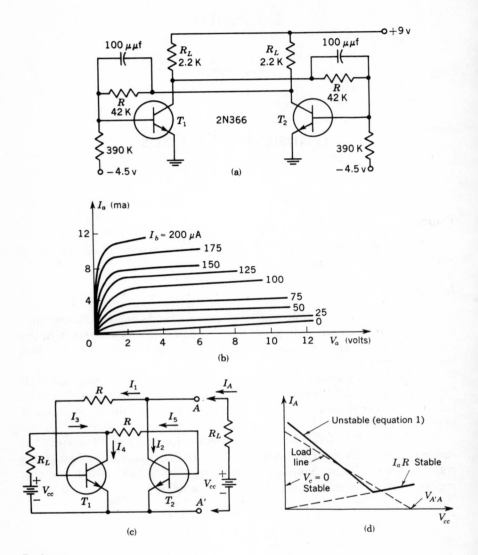

(a)

(b)

(c)

(d)

Preliminary

1. From the circuit of Fig. 1(a), and the transistor characteristics, calculate the "on" and "off" potentials and currents of the two transistors.

2. Calculate and draw the volt-ampere characteristic for the circuit of Fig. 1(a) similar to (d). Design a circuit to plot this curve on an oscillograph, being careful to exceed neither the voltage nor the current ratings of the transistors.

3. Illustrate some possible methods for triggering the circuit of Fig. 1. Give polarities, approximate amplitudes, and any other requirement for the triggering signals.

4. What factors having an influence on the switching times and repetition rates have been omitted? What will be their effect?

5. Draw a modified circuit to eliminate the need for the negative supply of Fig. 1. Calculate voltages and currents.

Performance

6. Set up and check the potentials of the circuit of Fig. 1(a). Switching should at least be possible by the momentary interruption of the bias supply.

7. Set up the required equipment and plot the curve of Fig. 1(d) on an oscillograph. Is hysteresis present? What would the presence of hysteresis mean in this case?

8. Try several triggering arrangements. Test for maximum repetition rates with each. Vary circuit component sizes, trigger amplitude, and duration while noting results on operation. Record all waveforms.

Calculations and conclusions

9. Discuss experimental results briefly, especially difficulties and anomalies.

References

Lo, A. W., Endres, R. O., Zawels, J., Waldhauer, F. D., and Cheng, C. C., *Transistor Electronics* (Englewood Cliffs, N. J.: Prentice-Hall, Inc., 1955).

Von Tersch, L. W., and Swago, A. W., *Recurrent Electrical Transients* (Englewood Cliffs, N. J.: Prentice-Hall, Inc., 1953).

Chance, B., *et al.*, *Waveforms* (New York: McGraw-Hill Book Co., Inc., 1949).

Materials required

Components	*Equipment*
2 TI 2N366 transistors with sockets	1 d-c cathode-ray oscillograph
2 1N34 diodes with mountings	1 pulse generator
2 100 K decade resistors	1 audio frequency generator
1 10 ohm resistor	1 10 ma d-c meter
2 1 K resistors	1 sensitive multimeter
2 2.2 K resistors	
2 4.7 K resistors	
2 10 K resistors	
2 22 K resistors	

Components

2 42 K resistors
2 100 K resistors
2 310 K resistors
2 1 megohm resistors
2 30 $\mu\mu$f capacitors
2 100 $\mu\mu$f capacitors
2 300 $\mu\mu$f capacitors
2 1000 $\mu\mu$f capacitors
2 3000 $\mu\mu$f capacitors
2 0.1 μf capacitors
2 0.01 μf capacitors
9 No. 6 dry cells

47-B

Transistor Flip-flops

Purpose

Familiarization with laboratory operations of bistable transistor circuits and modifications is the object of this experiment.

Information

The flip-flop circuits of Fig. 1 are quite analogous to their comparable vacuum-tube counterparts. They will be analyzed and modified on this basis.

Preliminary

1. Calculate the potentials and currents for T_1 "on" and T_2 "off" in the circuit of Fig. 1(a).
2. Repeat part 1 for Fig. 1(b).
3. Show a modification of Fig. 1(b) in which the "high collector resistance to low base resistance" problem is solved by including two grounded collector coupling stages.
4. Show a modification of Fig. 1(b) using 4 1N34 collector "catching" diodes to increase switching speeds by eliminating collector saturation and shortening recovery time. Note that in this case some emitter resistance must be included to protect the transistors.
5. Show several triggering methods and discuss briefly.

Performance

6. Set up the circuit of Fig. 1(a). Test for repetition rate, trigger amplitude, and record waveforms.
7. Repeat part 6 for the circuit of Fig. 1(b).
8. Modify the circuit of Fig. 1(b) as discussed in part 3. Repeat the tests of part 6.
9. Modify the circuit of Fig. 1(b) as discussed in part 4. Repeat the test of part 6.

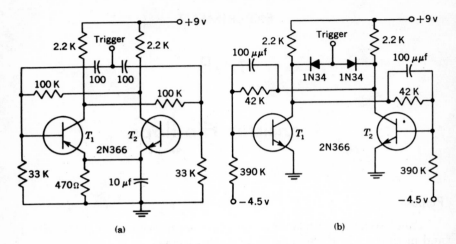

Fig. 1

Calculations and conclusions

10. Discuss any unexpected experimental results and difficulties.

References

Lo, A. W., Endres, R. O., Zawels, J., Waldhauer, F. D., and Cheng, C. C., *Transistor Electronics* (Englewood Cliffs, N. J.: Prentice-Hall, Inc., 1955).

Von Tersch, L. W., and Swago, A. W., *Recurrent Electrical Transients* (Englewood Cliffs, N. J.: Prentice-Hall, Inc., 1953).

Chance, B., *et al.*, *Waveforms* (New York: McGraw-Hill Book Co., Inc., 1949).

Materials required

Components	*Equipment*
4 TI 2N366 transistors with sockets	1 d-c cathode-ray oscillograph
4 1N34 diodes with mounts	1 pulse generator
2 100 K decade resistors	1 10 ma d-c meter
1 470 ohm resistor	1 sensitivity multimeter
2 1 K resistors	
2 2.2 K resistors	
2 4.7 K resistors	
2 10 K resistors	
2 22 K resistors	
2 42 K resistors	

Components

2 100 K resistors
2 390 K resistors
2 1 megohm resistors
2 30 $\mu\mu$f capacitors
2 100 $\mu\mu$f capacitors
2 300 $\mu\mu$f capacitors
2 1000 $\mu\mu$f capacitors
2 3000 $\mu\mu$f capacitors
2 0.01 μf capacitors
1 10 μf capacitor
9 No. 6 dry cells

48-A

Transistor Blocking Oscillators

Purpose

This experiment is designed to introduce applications of the blocking oscillator.

Information

In essence the blocking oscillator is just the same circuit as a sine-wave oscillator, but with as much feedback as can be obtained. The feedback is so violent that only one cycle of operation occurs before sufficient bias is generated to drive the transistor far beyond cutoff.

The transformer is the most important item in the oscillator design. For short pulses with fast rising and falling edges, the high-frequency response must be good, resulting in low leakage inductance, distributed capacitance, and core losses. Longer pulses require good low-frequency response determined mainly by primary and secondary inductances.

Free-running, synchronized, and triggered operation are all possible. Feedback may be from collector to base, collector to emitter, or from emitter to base. As with vacuum-tube circuits, many triggering methods are possible.

Preliminary

1. The blocking oscillator shown is free-running. Assume good high- and low-frequency response and the diodes disconnected. Sketch typical waveforms for the potentials at V_1, V_2, and V_3.

2. Draw modifications of the given circuit having feedback from collector to emitter and emitter to base.

3. Describe in detail the reasons diodes D_1 and D_2 are included.

4. Draw a modification that will permit external synchronization of the free-running oscillator.

5. Modify the given circuit for driven operation. Connect the shunt trigger transistor and estimate the characteristics of the trigger signal necessary for proper operation.

6. What other trigger methods are available?

7. Why is a sharp trigger pulse preferable?

Performance

8. Set up the circuit of Fig. 1, without D_2, with $R = 50$ K, and $C = 0.01$ μf. Record the potentials and waveshapes at V_1, V_2, and V_3.

9. Synchronize the oscillator with an audio oscillator. See how many of the blocking oscillator harmonic frequencies can be used for synchronization.

10. Connect the driven oscillator and its trigger transistor with a pulse generator. Observe and record V_3 as the input is increased to the maximum operable value.

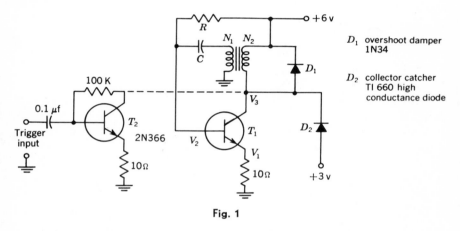

Fig. 1

11. Connect D_2 and recheck the operable range.

12. Change N_1/N_2 over all possible values and note changes in waveshapes and operating range.

13. Vary C and note waveshapes and range.

14. Check the other configurations of part 2.

Calculations and conclusions

15. Discuss briefly the experimental results.

References

Lo, A. W., Endres, R. O., Zawels, J., Waldhauer, F. D., and Cheng, C. C., *Transistor Electronics* (Englewood Cliffs, N. J.: Prentice-Hall, Inc., 1955).

Von Tersch, L. W., and Swago, A. W., *Recurrent Electrical Transients* (Englewood Cliffs, N. J.: Prentice-Hall, Inc., 1953).

Chance, B., *et al.*, *Waveforms* (New York: McGraw-Hill Book Co., Inc., 1949).

Materials required

Components	*Equipment*
2 TI 2N366 transistors with sockets	1 d-c cathode-ray oscillograph (high frequency)
1 1N34 diode with mount	1 audio frequency generator
1 TI 660 silicon diode	1 pulse generator
1 pulse transformer (with possible turns ratios up to 6/1 and low resistance)	1 10 ma d-c meter
1 100 K decade resistor	1 multimeter
1 1 megohm potentiometer	
2 10 ohm resistors	
1 1 K resistor	
1 10 K resistor	
2 100 K resistors	
1 1 μf capacitor	
1 0.001 μf capacitor	
1 0.1 μf capacitor	
6 No. 6 dry cells	

48-B

Transistor Blocking Oscillators

Purpose

The object of this experiment is a study of the effects of parameter variation on blocking oscillator performance.

Information

The usual application of blocking oscillators calls for a fast falling and rising, flat-bottom collector voltage pulse. Many effects contribute to these results, but maximum instantaneous current, distributed capacitance, trigger pulse, and transformer response, both high and low frequency, are the major factors.

The blocking oscillator is the limiting case of feedback when applied to linear oscillators. Only those linear oscillator circuits allowing maximum regeneration (transformer coupled) are used.

In this experiment, triggering methods, feedback methods, control of repetition rate, and pulse length will be investigated.

Preliminary

1. In Fig. 1 the 10 and 50 ohm resistors are added to study waveshapes. Some by-passed emitter resistance might be added for temperature stabilization. The voltage and current waveshapes are representative only. This circuit is free-running. Draw a modification for synchronized operation and explain how synchronization takes place.

2. Draw a modification for triggered or driven operation.

3. Since the sharpness of the leading edge depends somewhat on rapidity of change from no current to maximum regeneration, what are the desirable characteristics of trigger pulses?

4. Illustrate two other possible trigger methods.

5. Will both R_b and C_b have the same effect when changed to control pulse repetition rate?

6. What effect will the low base impedance (compared to a vacuum tube) have on the optimum turns ratio of the transformer?

7. Why is the inclusion of the overshoot damping more important in transistor circuits?

Performance

8. Set up the circuit of Fig. 1 with $C_b = 0.01$ µf, $R_b = 100$ K, and N_1/N_2 approximately 3/1. Record the waveshapes at points 1, 2, 3, and 4.

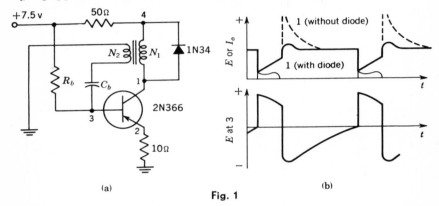

Fig. 1

9. Synchronize the oscillator with a sine-wave generator, at three times the blocking frequency. Observe and record the grid waveform for various amplitudes of sync signal. Check the frequency range over which synchronization can be held for various signal amplitudes.

10. Vary R_b and note changes in waveshapes and repetition rate. Do not exceed 0.05 µf.

11. Vary R_b and note changes in waveshapes and repetition rate. Do not decrease below 5 K.

12. Vary N_1/N_2 from 1/1 to maximum available. Observe changes.

13. Reduce the supply voltage to 3 volts, remove damping diode, and record changes in waveshapes. Use circuit values of part 8.

Calculations and conclusions

14. Plot the results of part 11.

15. Discuss briefly the experimental results and difficulties.

References

Chance, B., *et al.*, *Waveforms* (New York: McGraw-Hill Book Co., Inc., 1949).

Von Tersch, L. W., and Swago, A. W., *Recurrent Electrical Transients* (Englewood Cliffs, N. J.: Prentice-Hall, Inc., 1953).

Lo, A. W., Endres, R. O., Zawels, J., Waldhauer, F. D., and Cheng, C. C., *Transistor Electronics* (Englewood Cliffs, N. J.: Prentice-Hall, Inc., 1955).

Ryder, J. D., *Electronic Fundamentals and Applications*, 2d ed. (Englewood Cliffs, N. J.: Prentice-Hall, Inc., 1959).

Materials required

Components	*Equipment*
1 TI 2N366 transistor and socket	1 high-frequency cathode-ray oscillograph
2 1N34 diodes with mounts (any low capacitance diodes will be satisfactory)	1 sine-wave generator
	1 10 ma d-c meter
1 multiple ratio, low resistance pulse transformer	1 multimeter
1 10 ohm resistor	
1 50 ohm resistor	
1 5.6 K resistor	
1 10 K resistor	
1 56 K resistor	
1 100 K resistor	
1 560 K resistor	
1 1 megohm resistor	
1 100 $\mu\mu$f capacitor	
1 300 $\mu\mu$f capacitor	
1 1000 $\mu\mu$f capacitor	
1 3000 $\mu\mu$f capacitor	
1 0.01 μf capacitor	
1 0.03 μf capacitor	
5 No. 6 dry cells	

49-A

Transistor Radio Frequency and

Intermediate Frequency Amplifiers

Purpose

The purpose of this experiment is a study of transistors in the low radio frequency range.

Information

Junction transistors have, in some cases, useful amplification up to 15 megacycles, and newer special units to several times this value. The peculiarities of the reactive components of their parameters must be taken into account in order to secure the maximum or even useful gains. Figure 1 illustrates a common low-frequency equivalent and a general equivalent circuit, for the grounded emitter circuit.

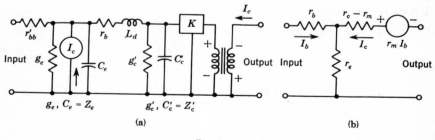

(a) (b)

Fig. 1

Figure 1(a) is used only to illustrate the difficulty to be expected in calculating high-frequency performance when manufacturers do not supply complete parameter information. With all data available, the given general circuit is not excessively difficult to use.

From experimentation the procedure is more straightforward. Only the resistive portions of input and output impedance (experimentally determined) are matched, and the reactive portions are combined with the coupling networks. The matching of impedances (at least approximately) is much more important in transistor amplifiers, where low input impedances are found.

In addition to maximization of gain, selectivity, automatic gain control, and neutralization are important considerations. Selectivity is primarily a problem of fixing the loaded Q of the coupling circuit. Automatic gain control may be accomplished by variation of any of the bias voltages or currents. The base or emitter currents are usually selected. Neutralization is used to reduce the net power fed from output to input to zero. This not only reduces the oscillation hazard but also makes independent circuit adjustment possible.

In this experiment examples of each important method will be illustrated and tested by means of the circuit of Fig. 2 and modifications.

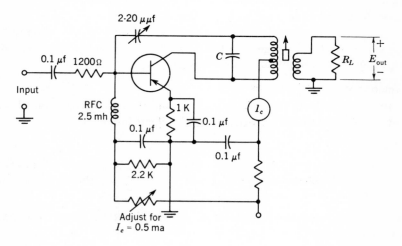

Fig. 2

Preliminary

1. The single-tuned coupling circuit shown in Fig. 2 should ideally tune to the required frequency, provide a given selectivity, and match transistor output to load both in magnitude and phase. Can all of these requirements be fulfilled simultaneously? If not, what ones would normally be left mismatched?

2. Show a selection of single- and double-tuned circuits for radio frequency interstage coupling. What are some advantages of the double-tuned circuits?

3. Design a single-tuned circuit to match 100,000 ohms to 1000 ohms at 455 kc and with a 10 kc bandwidth. Assume an infinite unloaded Q.

4. Either base or emitter current variation may be used for automatic gain control. Show modifications of the given circuit to accomplish gain control by each method.

Performance

5. Set up the given circuit and tune for maximum gain with both an oscilloscope and a vacuum-tube voltmeter across the load. For a small usable signal take data of power gain versus load resistance. When optimum R_L is found use this for the remainder of the experiment.

6. Connect the r-f generator across the load and the vacuum-tube voltmeter across the input. Adjust the neutralization capacitor for minimum reading.

7. Apply 50 per cent modulation to the input signal and take data of output voltage versus input voltage. Note from the oscilloscope when either the r-f signal or the envelope becomes distorted.

8. Take data for a frequency response curve.

9. Modify the given circuit for automatic gain control. Take data of gain versus control voltage or current. Note any detuning by checking for frequency of maximum gain at each setting.

Calculations and conclusions

10. Plot the data taken in parts 7, 8, and 9. Discuss each plot briefly.

11. Briefly discuss any experimental difficulties encountered.

References

Lo, A. W., Endres, R. O., Zawels, J., Waldhauer, F. D., and Cheng, C. C., *Transistor Electronics* (Englewood Cliffs, N. J.: Prentice-Hall, Inc., 1955).

Ryder, J. D., *Electronic Fundamentals and Applications*, 2d ed. (Englewood Cliffs, N. J.: Prentice-Hall, Inc., 1959).

Valley, G. E., and Wallman, H., *Vacuum Tube Amplifiers*, vol. 18, Rad. Lab. Series (New York: McGraw-Hill Book Co., Inc., 1948).

Terman, F. E., *Radio Engineers' Handbook* (New York: McGraw-Hill Book Co., Inc., 1943).

Materials required

Components	*Equipment*
1 TI 2N146 transistor with socket	1 cathode-ray oscillograph
1 transistor i-f transformer (single-tuned with center-tapped primary)	1 r-f generator with modulation
	1 200 μa d-c meter
	2 1 ma d-c meters
1 2–20 $\mu\mu$f variable capacitor	1 a-c vacuum-tube voltmeter
1 100 K potentiometer	1 multimeter

Components

2 10 K potentiometers (composition)
1 r-f choke (2.5 mh)
1 330 ohm resistor
2 1 K resistors
1 1.2 K resistor
1 2.2 K resistor
1 4.7 K resistor
2 10 K resistors
1 0.01 μf capacitor
4 0.1 μf capacitors
7 No. 6 dry cells

49-B

Transistor Radio Frequency and
Intermediate Frequency Amplifiers

Purpose

The object of this experiment is familiarization with transistorized radio frequency circuits.

Information

The actual application of transistors in higher frequency amplifiers is experimentally straightforward — at frequencies at which gain is realizable. For analysis, if the low-frequency equivalent circuit is taken as a starting point, several modifications must be made to match derived and experimental results. A simple set of modifications consists of adding reactive part of X_{cb}, r_b, r_e, and r_d, and realizing that each real and imaginary part may be independently frequency dependent in some complex manner. The modifications are simple but analysis from the resulting circuit is almost impossible.

Quite acceptable circuits are available containing only linear parameters of R, L, and C and a single generator. The application of these excellent circuits is made quite difficult only because manufacturers do not supply data from which the parameters may be determined.

For the above reasons, the analysis in this experiment will be purely qualitative. However, considerable valuable insight can still be obtained. The factors to be experimentally investigated are impedance matching, selectivity, and gain control.

A typical transistor intermediate frequency amplifier is shown in Fig. 1, along with some of the many single- and double-tuned coupling networks available.

Preliminary

1. In Fig. 1(a), the combination R_N and C_N is often found in transistor radio frequency amplifiers. What are some possible uses of such a network?

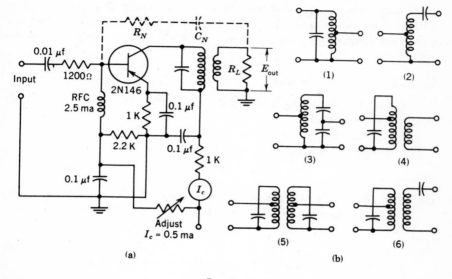

Fig. 1

2. The commonly employed variational quantity for automatic gain control is the emitter current. This changes the collector current but does not appreciably affect the collector voltage. Draw a modification of the given circuit to accommodate automatic gain control.

3. The networks shown in Fig. 1 are ordinarily designable to match input resistance R_i, output resistance R_o, frequency f_o, and bandwidth $\Delta f = f_o/Q$. How can the reactive components of amplifier input and output impedances be accommodated?

4. Design a network of the type of (2) in Fig. 1 to accommodate the following conditions: transistor output resistance is 20 K, input resistance is 1 K, frequency is 455 kc, and the bandwidth is 15 kc. Assume an unloaded coil Q of 120.

Performance

5. Set up the circuit of Fig. 1. Adjust for maximum gain at 455 kc. Adjust R_L for maximum power transfer. Take data for a frequency response curve to 20 db down points on either side of 455 kc.

6. Insert the variable R_N and C_N units. If increased gain occurs, reverse the secondary coil. By successive approximations pick values that minimize the voltage at the input when the signal generator is placed across R_L. Record the values of R_N and C_N. Substitute other transistors of the same type and record each new R_N and C_N.

7. Remove the 2.2 K and adjustable base bias resistors. Substitute a 10 K potentiometer, 1.5 volt battery, and 1 ma meter all in series in place of the 1 K emitter resistor. Take data of gain versus emitter current to 1 ma. Check the frequency of maximum gain for each setting to estimate the detuning caused.

Calculations and conclusions

8. Plot the curves for which data was taken. Discuss the important characteristics of each.

9. Discuss the significance of part 6.

10. Briefly discuss any experimental difficulties.

References

Lo, A. W., Endres, R. O., Zawels, J., Waldhauer, F. D., and Cheng, C. C., *Transistor Electronics* (Englewood Cliffs, N. J.: Prentice-Hall, Inc., 1955).

Valley, G. E., and Wallman, H., *Vacuum Tube Amplifiers*, vol. 18, Rad. Lab. Series (New York: McGraw-Hill Book Co., Inc., 1948).

Terman, F. E., *Radio Engineers' Handbook* (New York: McGraw-Hill Book Co., Inc., 1943).

Bulletin No. DL-5 568, Texas Instrument Company.

Materials required

Components	*Equipment*
3 TI 2N146 transistors with sockets	1 radio frequency generator
1 transistor, single-tuned, i-f transformer	1 r-f vacuum-tube voltmeter
2 10 K potentiometers	2 1 ma d-c meters
1 100 K potentiometer	1 multimeter
1 1 megohm potentiometer	
2 1 K resistors	
1 1.2 K resistor	
1 2.2 K resistor	
1 465 $\mu\mu$f variable capacitor	
4 500 $\mu\mu$f capacitors	
1 0.01 μf capacitor	
3 0.1 μf capacitors	
1 2.5 mh r-f choke	

50-A

Transistor Clipping, Clamping, and

Waveshaping Circuits

Purpose

The object of this experiment is a study of the junction transistor characteristics applicable in some of the circuit's switching applications, in particular those of clipping, clamping, and waveshaping.

Information

Most of the switching circuits using vacuum tubes have analogs in junction transistors and diodes. The impedance levels are different, the potentials are lower, and most transistor circuits will neither switch nor recover as

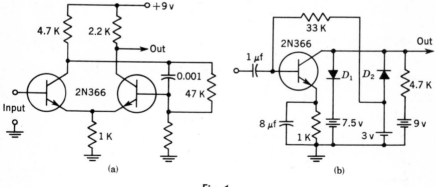

Fig. 1

fast. Switching speeds, as with vacuum tubes, can be improved by "catching" diodes.

The only useful transistor phenomena not observed in vacuum tubes is the Zener breakdown which is nondestructive. This can be observed at either the emitter or the collector junction.

In this experiment the four-quadrant transistor characteristics will be observed and an analog of a Schmitt trigger circuit will be tested. The latter is much used in pulse forming and standardization.

Preliminary

1. Design a circuit to display the input volt-ampere characteristics with variable collector to emitter voltage. Include meters and protection resistors. Sketch the expected result.

2. Repeat part 1, except that base to collector voltage will be used as a parameter.

3. Design a circuit to display the collector to emitter volt-ampere characteristic with emitter to base voltage as a parameter. Include meters and protective resistors. Sketch the expected results.

4. The circuit of Fig. 1(a) is a transistor version of the Schmitt trigger circuit. Explain its operation. Calculate the potentials and currents for T_2 conducting and repeat for T_1 conducting.

5. The circuit of Fig. 1(b) has "catching" diodes to improve the pulse rise and fall time. Assume a large sinusoidal input. Calculate and sketch the output with and without diodes.

Performance

6. Set up and check the circuit of part 1. Record potentials and waveforms.

7. Set up and check the circuit of part 2. Record potentials and waveforms.

8. Set up and check the circuit of part 3. Record potentials and waveforms.

9. Connect the Schmitt circuit. Record the output waveforms as a sine input is increased from zero to 5 volts.

10. Check the results sketched for the circuit of Fig. 1(b).

Calculations and conclusions

11. Briefly discuss the results of parts 6, 7, and 8.

12. What are some uses for the Schmitt trigger circuit?

13. Discuss briefly any experimental difficulties.

References

Lo, A. W., Endres, R. O., Zawels, J., Waldhauer, F. E., and Cheng, C. C., *Transistor Electronics* (Englewood Cliffs, N. J.: Prentice-Hall, Inc., 1955).

Ryder, J. D., *Electronic Fundamentals and Applications*, 2d ed. (Englewood Cliffs, N. J.: Prentice-Hall, Inc., 1959).

Von Tersch, L. W., and Swago, A. W., *Recurrent Electrical Transients* (Englewood Cliffs, N. J.: Prentice-Hall, Inc., 1953).

Materials required

Components	*Equipment*
2 TI 2N366 transistors with sockets	1 d-c cathode-ray oscillograph
2 TI 660 silicon diodes	1 audio frequency generator
2 10 K decade boxes	1 a-c vacuum-tube voltmeter
2 100 K decade boxes	1 1 ma d-c meter
1 1 K resistor	2 10 ma d-c meters
1 2.2 K resistor	1 multimeter
1 4.7 K resistor	
1 33 K resistor	
1 47 K resistor	
1 100 K resistor	
1 1 megohm potentiometer	
1 8 μf capacitor	
1 0.001 μf capacitor	
8 No. 6 dry cells	

50-B

Transistor Clipping, Clamping, and Waveshaping Circuits

Purpose

The purpose of this experiment is familiarization with the peculiarities of transistors in clipping, clamping, and waveshaping circuits.

Information

While this experiment deals primarily with transistors, it is important to mention some of the properties of solid-state diodes — in particular, junction diodes. The junction diode circuits do not differ from those using vacuum diodes, but some characteristics are radically different.

In Fig. 1, the approximate characteristics of a 6AL5 vacuum diode, a high conductance silicon junction diode, and a silicon junction Zener

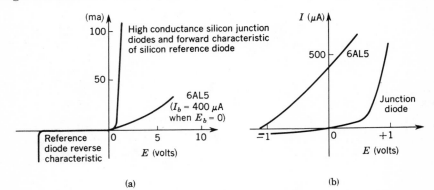

Fig. 1

reference diode are shown. The d-c conductance for junction diodes may be as low as 8 to 10 ohms, and the dynamic resistance as low as 1 ohm.

These parameters are available from the low values to values equivalent to those of vacuum diodes. Since the capacitances are roughly equivalent, the peculiar advantages of junction diodes may greatly improve the operation of some clipping, clamping, and waveshaping circuits.

The junction triode as a voltage- or current-controlled switch can be understood from the static characteristics in a manner similar to vacuum tubes. The transistor, however, has at least two peculiarities besides its high-frequency limitation. The resistance of a transistor under saturation (high current) conditions is only a few ohms, and both emitter and collector junctions will have Zener breakdown (nondestructive) voltages.

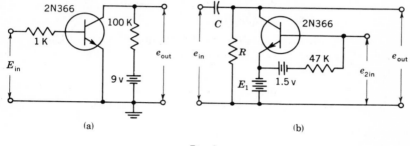

Fig. 2

Although not covered in this experiment, the "catching" of transistor potentials with diodes should be considered in improving switching speeds.

Preliminary

1. Sketch the output voltage of the circuit of Fig. 2(a) for 1 kc sinusoidal input voltages from zero to 10 volts.

Note: The 1 K base resistor is for transistor protection when driven from a low impedance source.

2. The circuit of Fig. 2(a) clips large output signals outside the levels of zero and 9 volts. How could it be modified to clip between other levels?

3. Show how the circuit of Fig. 2(a) can be modified to clamp the input signal at emitter potential. Where is the output signal clamped?

4. The circuit of Fig. 2(b) may be used for synchronized clamping at emitter potential E_1 by inserting positive pulses at $e_{2\,in}$. With a large sine wave at $e_{1\,in}$ and positive pulses occurring at the sine-wave peaks, at $e_{2\,in}$, show the output for large and small RC products.

Performance

5. Set up and check the results of part 1. Record the results.

6. Modify the circuit of part 1 to clip the output at plus and minus 4.5 volts. Record the results.

7. Modify the circuit of Fig. 2(a) to clamp the input at emitter potential. Record potentials and waveforms.

8. Set up the circuit of Fig. 2(b) and check the results of part 4. Record data and waveforms. Set E_1 to zero.

Calculations and conclusions

9. Discuss the experimental results briefly, along with difficulties encountered.

References

Ryder, J. D., *Electronic Fundamentals and Applications*, 2d ed. (Englewood Cliffs, N. J.: Prentice-Hall, Inc., 1959).

Lo, A. W., Endres, R. O., Zawels, J., Waldhauer, F. D., and Cheng, C. C., *Transistor Electronics* (Englewood Cliffs, N. J.: Prentice-Hall, Inc., 1955).

Von Tersch, L. W., and Swago, A. W., *Recurrent Electrical Transients* (Englewood Cliffs, N. J.: Prentice-Hall, Inc., 1953).

Materials required

Components	*Equipment*
1 TI 2N366 transistor with socket	1 d-c cathode-ray oscillograph
2 100 K decade resistors	1 audio frequency generator
2 100 K resistors	1 pulse generator
2 47 K resistors	2 10 ma d-c meters
2 10 K resistors	1 multimeter
2 1 K resistors	
2 0.1 μf capacitors	
1 0.01 μf capacitor	
1 0.001 μf capacitor	
7 No. 6 dry cells	

APPENDIX

Transistor and Vacuum Tube Characteristics

12AU7-A — 12AU7 — 6SN7*

AVERAGE PLATE CHARACTERISTICS
EACH SECTION

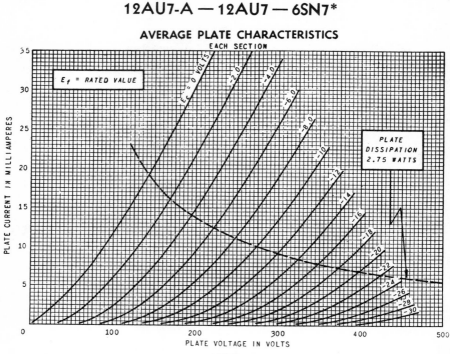

E_f = RATED VALUE

PLATE DISSIPATION 2.75 WATTS

PLATE CURRENT IN MILLIAMPERES

PLATE VOLTAGE IN VOLTS

6SN7

Maximum Ratings (Design-Center Values Unless Otherwise Indicated, Each Section):

Class A amplifier:

D-c plate voltage...	450 v
Peak positive pulse plate voltage............................	
Peak negative grid voltage...................................	
Plate dissipation, each plate................................	5.0 w
Total plate dissipation, both plates.........................	7.5 w
D-c cathode current..	20 ma
Peak cathode current...	
Heater-cathode voltage	
Heater positive with respect to Cathode	
D-c component..	100 v
Total d-c and peak..................................	200 v
Heater negative with respect to cathode	
Total d-c and peak..................................	200 v
Grid circuit resistance	
With fixed bias..	1.0 meg
With cathode bias...	1.0 meg

*Courtesy of The General Electric Company.

AVERAGE PLATE CHARACTERISTICS
EACH SECTION

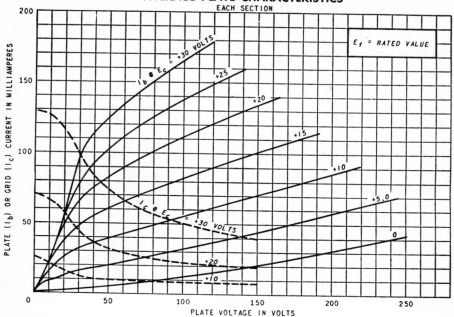

Terminal Connections:

Pin 1: Grid (Section 2)
Pin 2: Plate (Section 2)
Pin 3: Cathode (Section 2)
Pin 4: Grid (Section 1)

Pin 5: Plate (Section 1)
Pin 6: Cathode (Section 1)
Pin 7: Heater
Pin 8: Heater

12AU7

Maximum Ratings (Design-Center Values Unless Otherwise Indicated, Each Section):

Class A_1 amplifier:

D-c plate voltage..	300 v
Peak positive pulse plate voltage.............................	
Peak negative grid voltage.......................................	
Plate dissipation...	2.75 w
D-c cathode current..	20 ma
Peak cathode current..	
Heater-cathode voltage	
Heater positive with respect to cathode	
D-c component..............................	100 v
Total d-c and peak........................	200 v
Heater negative with respect to cathode	
Total d-c and peak........................	200 v

Grid circuit resistance
    With fixed bias. . . . .   0.25 meg
    With Cathode bias. . . . .   1.0 meg

Terminal Connections:

Pin 1: Plate (Section 2)
Pin 2: Grid (Section 2)
Pin 3: Cathode (Section 2)
Pin 4: Heater
Pin 5: Heater

Pin 6: Plate (Section 1)
Pin 7: Grid (Section 1)
Pin 8: Cathode (Section 1)
Pin 9: Heater center-tap

Note:

These tubes are not electrically identical, but are similar enough for graphical solutions.

6S4-A TRIODE*

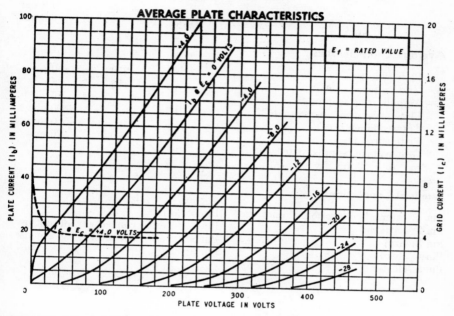

Maximum Ratings (Design-Center Values Unless Otherwise Indicated):

Vertical-Deflection amplifier:

D-c plate voltage	500 v
Peak positive pulse plate voltage	2200 v
Peak negative grid voltage	250 v
Plate dissipation	7.5 w
D-c cathode current	30 ma
Peak cathode current	105 ma
Heater-cathode voltage	
Heater positive with respect to cathode	
D-c component	100 v
Total d-c and peak	200 v
Heater negative with respect to cathode	
Total d-c and peak	200 v
Grid circuit resistance	
With cathode bias	2.2 meg

Electrical Data:

Cathode — coated unipotential	
Heater voltage, a-c or d-c	6.3 v
Heater current	0.6 amp
Heater warm-up time	11 sec

*Courtesy of The General Electric Company.

Direct interelectrode capacitances, approximate

Grid to plate... 2.6 $\mu\mu$f

Input... 4.2 $\mu\mu$f

Output.. 0.9 $\mu\mu$f

Average Characteristics:

Plate voltage	250	250 v
Grid voltage	−15	−8 v
Amplification factor		16
Plate resistance, approximate		3600 ohms
Transconductance		4500 μmhos
Plate current	4.5	26 ma
Grid voltage, approximate		
$I_b = 50$ ma		−23 v

Terminal Connections:

Pin 1: Internal connection (do not use)

Pin 2: Cathode

Pin 3: Grid

Pin 4: Heater

Pin 5: Heater

Pin 6: Grid

Pin 7: Internal connection (do not use)

Pin 8: Internal connection (do not use)

Pin 9: Plate

2A3 POWER-AMPLIFIER TRIODE*

AVERAGE PLATE CHARACTERISTICS

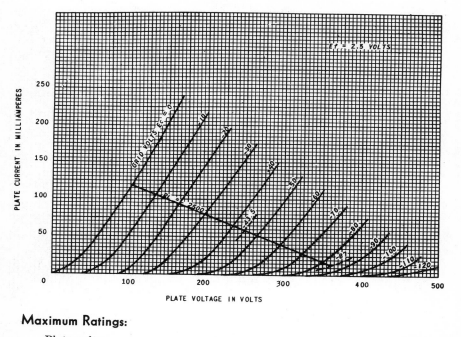

Maximum Ratings:

Plate voltage..................................... 330 v
Plate dissipation................................ 17 w

Terminal Connections:

Pin 1: Filament   Pin 3: Grid
Pin 2: Plate   Pin 4: Filament

Characteristics and Typical Operation

Class A_1 amplifier:

Plate voltage................................. 250 v
Grid voltage................................. −45 v
Plate current................................ 60 ma
Amplification factor......................... 4.2
Plate resistance............................. 800 ohms
Transconductance............................. 5250 μmhos
Load resistance.............................. 2500 ohms
Second harmonic distortion................... 5 per cent
Power output................................. 3.5 w

*Courtesy of The General Electric Company.

12AX7 TWIN TRIODE*

AVERAGE PLATE CHARACTERISTICS
EACH SECTION

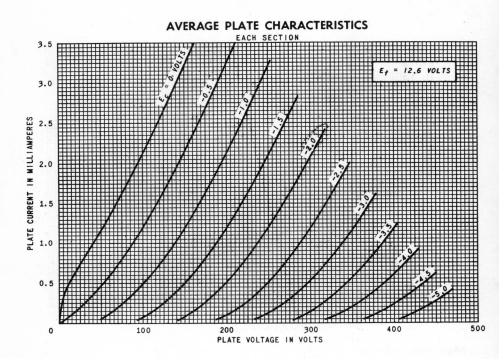

Direct Interelectrode Capacitances:

	With Shield	*Without Shield*
Grid to plate, each section...............	1.7	1.7 μμf
Input, each section......................	1.8	1.6 μμf
Output, Section 1........................	1.9	0.46 μμf
Output, Section 2........................	1.9	0.34 μμf

Maximum Ratings (Design-Center Values, Each Section):

Plate voltage..	300 v
Positive d-c grid voltage..	0 v
Negative d-c grid voltage.......................................	50 v
Plate dissipation...	1.0 w
Heater-cathode voltage	
Heater positive with respect to cathode.................	180 v
Heater negative with respect to cathode................	180 v

*Courtesy of The General Electric Company.

Terminal Connections:

Pin 1: Plate (Section 2)
Pin 2: Grid (Section 2)
Pin 3: Cathode (Section 2)
Pin 4: Heater
Pin 5: Heater
Pin 6: Plate (Section 1)
Pin 7: Grid (Section 1)
Pin 8: Cathode (Section 1)
Pin 9: Heater center-tap

PHYSICAL DIMENSIONS

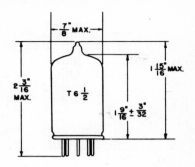

Characteristics and Typical Operation:

Class A_1 amplifier, each section:

Plate voltage	100	250 v
Grid voltage	−1	−2 v
Amplification factor	100	100
Plate resistance, approximate	80000	62500 ohms
Transconductance	1250	1600 μmhos
Plate current	0.5	1.2 ma

6AQ5 BEAM PENTODE*

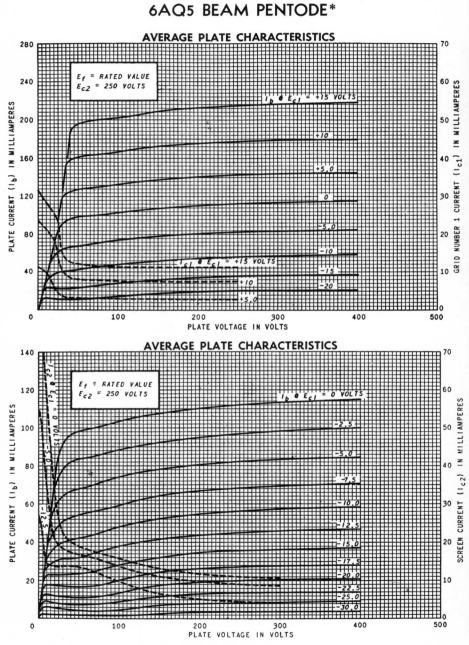

AVERAGE PLATE CHARACTERISTICS

E_f = RATED VALUE
E_{c2} = 250 VOLTS

I_b @ E_{c1} = +15 VOLTS
+10
+5.0
0
-5.0
-10
I_{c1} @ E_{c1} = +15 VOLTS
-15
+10
-20
+5.0

PLATE CURRENT (I_b) IN MILLIAMPERES
GRID NUMBER 1 CURRENT (I_{c1}) IN MILLIAMPERES
PLATE VOLTAGE IN VOLTS

AVERAGE PLATE CHARACTERISTICS

E_f = RATED VALUE
E_{c2} = 250 VOLTS

I_b @ E_{c1} = 0 VOLTS
-2.5
-5.0
-7.5
-10.0
-12.5
-15.0
-17.5
-20.0
-22.5
-25.0
-30.0

PLATE CURRENT (I_b) IN MILLIAMPERES
SCREEN CURRENT (I_{c2}) IN MILLIAMPERES
PLATE VOLTAGE IN VOLTS

*Courtesy of The General Electric Company.

Electrical Data:

6AQ5

Cathode — coated unipotential
    Heater voltage, a-c or d-c............................ 6.3 v
    Heater current................................. 0.45 amp
    Heater warm-up time............................... sec
Direct interelectrode capacitances, approximate
    Grid number 1 to plate............................ 0.4 $\mu\mu$f
    Input... 8.0 $\mu\mu$f
    Output.. 8.5 $\mu\mu$f

Maximum Ratings (Design-Center Values Unless Otherwise Indicated):

Class A_1 amplifier:

D-c plate voltage.. 250 v
Peak positive pulse plate voltage............................ v
Screen voltage.. 250 v
Peak negative grid number 1 voltage........................ v
Plate dissipation.. 12 w
Screen dissipation... 2.0 w
D-c cathode current.. ma
Peak cathode current....................................... ma
Heater-cathode voltage
    Heater positive with respect to cathode
        D-c component.................................. 100 v
        Total d-c and peak............................. 200 v
    Heater negative with respect to cathode
        Total d-c and peak............................. 200 v
Grid number 1 circuit resistance
    With fixed bias................................... 0.1 meg
    With cathode bias................................. 0.5 meg
Bulb temperature at hottest point........................... 250 °C

Terminal Connections:

Pin 1: Grid number 1
Pin 2: Cathode and beam plates
Pin 3: Heater
Pin 4: Heater
Pin 5: Plate
Pin 6: Grid number 2 (screen)
Pin 7: Grid number 1

BASING DIAGRAM

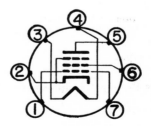

RETMA 7BZ

6V6 BEAM POWER AMPLIFIER*

AVERAGE PLATE CHARACTERISTICS

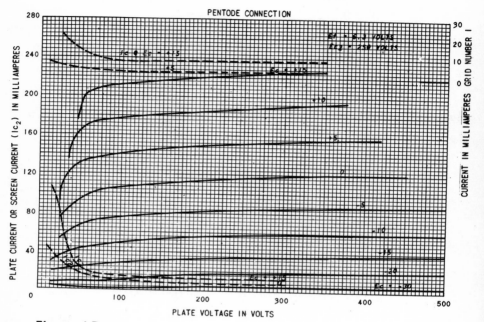

PENTODE CONNECTION

Electrical Data:

6V6-GT

Cathode — coated unipotential
Heater voltage, a-c or d-c .... 6.3 v
Heater current .... 0.45 amp
Heater warm-up time .... sec
Direct interelectrode capacitances, approximate
Grid number 1 to plate .... 0.7 μμf
Input .... 9.0 μμf
Output .... 7.5 μμf

Maximum Ratings (Design-Center Values Unless Otherwise Indicated):

Class A_1 amplifier:

D-c plate voltage .... 315 v
Peak positive pulse plate voltage v
Screen-supply voltage .... 315 v
Screen voltage .... 285 v
Peak negative grid number 1 voltage v

*Courtesy of The General Electric Company.

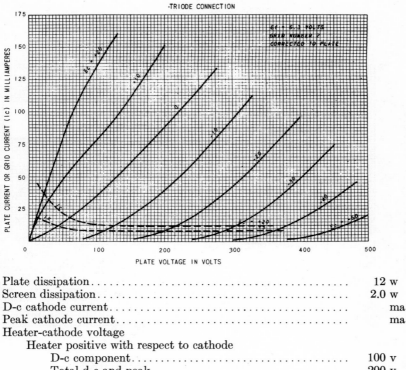

TRIODE CONNECTION

Ef = 5.3 VOLTS
GRID NUMBER 2
CONNECTED TO PLATE

Plate dissipation	12 w
Screen dissipation	2.0 w
D-c cathode current	ma
Peak cathode current	ma

Heater-cathode voltage
    Heater positive with respect to cathode

| D-c component | 100 v |
| Total d-c and peak | 200 v |

    Heater negative with respect to cathode

| Total d-c and peak | 200 v |

Grid number 1 circuit resistance

| With fixed bias | 0.1 meg |
| With cathode bias | 0.5 meg |

Terminal Connections:

Pin 1: No connection
Pin 2: Heater
Pin 3: Plate
Pin 4: Grid number 2 (screen)
Pin 5: Grid number 1
Pin 7: Heater
Pin 8: Cathode and beam plates

BASING DIAGRAM

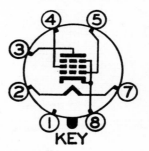

2E26 BEAM PENTODE*

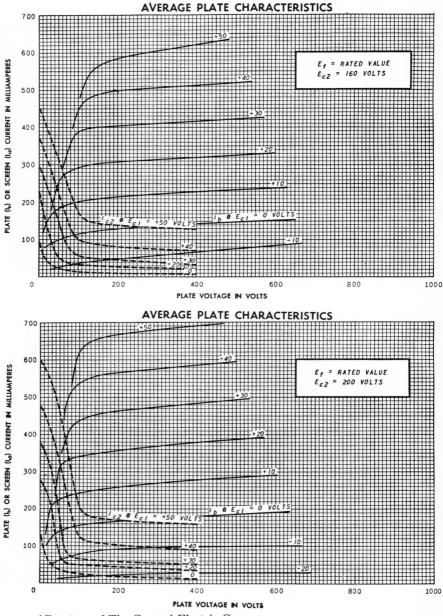

AVERAGE PLATE CHARACTERISTICS

E_f = RATED VALUE
E_{c2} = 160 VOLTS

AVERAGE PLATE CHARACTERISTICS

E_f = RATED VALUE
E_{c2} = 200 VOLTS

*Courtesy of The General Electric Company.

Electrical Data:

Cathode — coated unipotential
    Heater voltage, a-c or d-c........................ 6.3 ± 10% v
    Heater current................................. 0.8 amp
Direct interelectrode capacitances, without external shield
    Grid number 1 to plate, maximum................ 0.2 $\mu\mu$f
    Input... 12.5 $\mu\mu$f
    Output.. 7.0 $\mu\mu$f

Average Characteristics:

Plate voltage	200	500 v
Screen voltage	200	200 v
Plate current	20	20 ma
Transconductance		3500 μmhos
Amplification factor, grid number 1 to grid number 2.	6.5	

Terminal Connections:

Pin 1: Cathode, beam plates, and internal shield
Pin 2: Heater
Pin 3: Grid number 2 (screen)
Pin 4: Cathode, beam plates, and internal shield
Pin 5: Grid number 1
Pin 6: Cathode, beam plates, and internal shield
Pin 7: Heater
Pin 8: Base Sleeve
Cap: Plate

BASING DIAGRAM

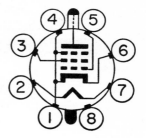

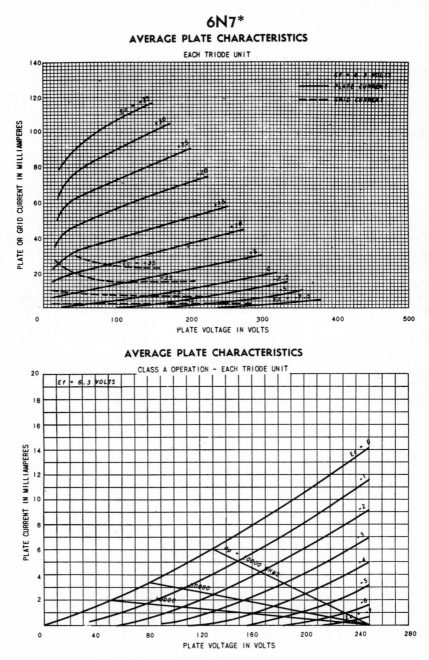

6N7*

AVERAGE PLATE CHARACTERISTICS

EACH TRIODE UNIT

PLATE OR GRID CURRENT IN MILLIAMPERES

PLATE VOLTAGE IN VOLTS

AVERAGE PLATE CHARACTERISTICS

CLASS A OPERATION - EACH TRIODE UNIT

Ef = 6.3 VOLTS

PLATE CURRENT IN MILLIAMPERES

PLATE VOLTAGE IN VOLTS

*Courtesy of The General Electric Company.

Maximum Ratings (Each unit):

Class B power amplifier:

	Design Center	Absolute
Plate voltage...........................	300	330 v
Peak plate current.....................	125	140 ma
Average plate dissipation................	5.50	6.05 w
D-c heater-cathode voltage..............	90	100 v

Class A amplifier:

Plate voltage...........................	300	330 v
Plate dissipation.......................	1.0	1.1 w
D-c heater-cathode voltage..............	90	100 v

Terminal Connections:

Pin 1: Shell
Pin 2: Heater
Pin 3: Plate (Unit number 2)
Pin 4: Grid (Unit number 2)
Pin 5: Grid (Unit number 1)
Pin 6: Plate (Unit number 1)
Pin 7: Heater
Pin 8: Cathode

BASING DIAGRAM

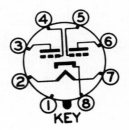

KEY

Characteristics and Typical Operation:

Class B power amplifier:

	Ideal	Typical
Heater voltage..........................	6.3	6.3 v
Zero-signal plate voltage................	300	300 v
D-c grid bias voltage....................	0	0 v
Peak a-f grid-to-grid voltage	58	82 v
Grid-circuit impedance per unit..........	0	516 ohms
Plate supply impedance..................	0	1000 ohms
Zero-signal d-c plate current.............	35	35 ma
Maximum-signal d-c plate current........	70	70 ma
Peak grid current per unit...............	20	22 ma
Effective plate to plate load resistance.....	8000	8000 ohms
Third harmonic distortion...............	3.5	7.5 per cent
Fifth harmonic distortion...............	1.5	2.5 per cent
Total harmonic distortion...............	4	8 per cent
Maximum-signal power output...........	10	10 w

884*

AVERAGE CONTROL CHARACTERISTICS

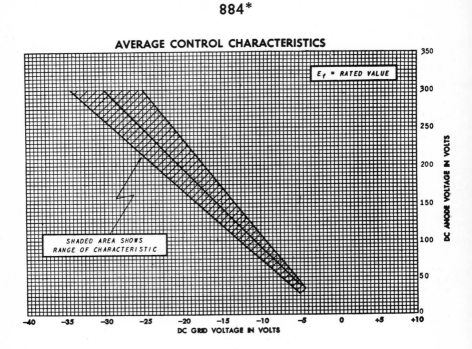

Ratings — Absolute Maximum Values:

	Relaxation Oscillator	Grid-Controlled Rectifier
Peak anode voltage	300	350 v
Peak voltage between any two electrodes	350	350 v
Peak cathode current	300	300 ma
Average cathode current†		75 ma
Peak grid current	1.0	ma
Heater-cathode voltage rating		
Heater positive with respect to cathode	25	25 v
Heater negative with respect to cathode	100	100 v
Grid-circuit resistance‡	0.5	meg
Ambient temperature limits	−75 to +90	−75 to +90 °C

Terminal Connections:

Pin 1: No connection
Pin 2: Heater
Pin 3: Anode

Pin 5: Grid
Pin 7: Heater
Pin 8: Cathode

*Courtesy of The General Electric Company.
†Average over period of not more than 30 seconds.
‡Grid resistor should not be smaller than 1000 ohms per maximum instantaneous volt applied to grid.

Characteristics and Typical Operation:

Anode voltage drop, approximate........................... 16 v
Control characteristics, approximate
    Anode voltage... 300 v
    Grid voltage.. −30 v

2D21 THYRATRON*

CONTROL CHARACTERISTICS

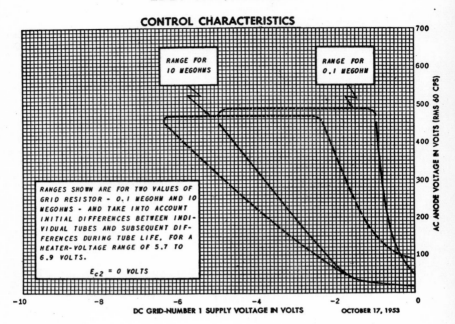

RANGE FOR
10 MEGOHMS

RANGE FOR
0.1 MEGOHM

RANGES SHOWN ARE FOR TWO VALUES OF
GRID RESISTOR - 0.1 MEGOHM AND 10
MEGOHMS - AND TAKE INTO ACCOUNT
INITIAL DIFFERENCES BETWEEN INDI-
VIDUAL TUBES AND SUBSEQUENT DIF-
FERENCES DURING TUBE LIFE, FOR A
HEATER-VOLTAGE RANGE OF 5.7 TO
6.9 VOLTS.

$E_{c2} = 0$ VOLTS

AC ANODE VOLTAGE IN VOLTS (RMS 60 CPS)

DC GRID-NUMBER 1 SUPPLY VOLTAGE IN VOLTS   OCTOBER 17, 1953

Terminal Connections:

Pin 1: Grid number 1 (control grid)
Pin 2: Cathode
Pin 3: Heater
Pin 4: Heater
Pin 5: Grid number 2 (shield grid)
Pin 6: Anode
Pin 7: Grid number 2 (shield grid)

BASING DIAGRAM

Ratings — Absolute Maximum Values:

Maximum peak anode voltage
    Inverse... 1300 v
    Forward... 650 v
Maximum cathode current
    Peak.. 0.5 amp
    Average... 0.1 amp

*Courtesy of The General Electric Company.

354

Surge (maximum duration 0.1 sec).................... 10 amp
Maximum averaging time............................ 30 sec
Maximum negative control-grid voltage
  Before conduction.................................... −100 v
  During conduction.................................... −10 v
Maximum positive control-grid current
  Anode positive....................................... 0.01 amp
  Anode negative....................................... 0.01 amp
Maximum negative shield-grid voltage
  Before conduction.................................... −100 v
  During conduction.................................... −10 v
Maximum positive shield-grid current
  Anode positive....................................... 0.01 amp
  Anode negative....................................... 0.01 amp
Maximum heater-cathode voltage
  Heater negative...................................... −100 v
  Heater positive...................................... 25 v
Ambient temperature limits........................ −75 to +90 °C

Electrical Data:

	$Minimum$	$Bogey$	$Maximum$
Heater voltage......................	5.7	6.3	6.9 v
Heater current (E_f = 6.3 v).................		0.60	0.66 amp
Cathode heating time required.......	10		sec
Anode-to-control-grid capacitance, typical......		0.026	$\mu\mu$f
Control-grid-to-cathode and shield-grid capacitance, typical..............		2.4	$\mu\mu$f
Deionization time, approximate E_{bb} = 125 v d-c, I_b = 0.1 amp d-c			
(a) E_{cl} = −100 v d-c....		35	microseconds
R_g = 1000 ohms (b) E_{cl} = − 11 v d-c....		75	microseconds
Ionization time, approximate.................		0.5	microsecond
Anode voltage drop, typical..................		8	v
Critical grid current, E_{bb} = 460 v rms.................			0.5 μa

Mechanical Data:

Type of cooling — Air
Mounting position — Any
Net weight, maximum........................ 0.3   oz

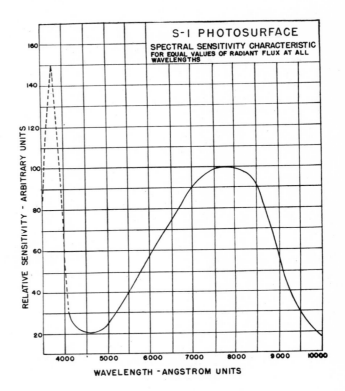

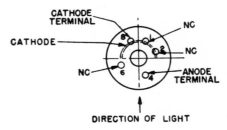

DIRECTION OF LIGHT

929—930

*Courtesy of The General Electric Company.

S-4 PHOTOSURFACE
SPECTRAL SENSITIVITY CHARACTERISTIC

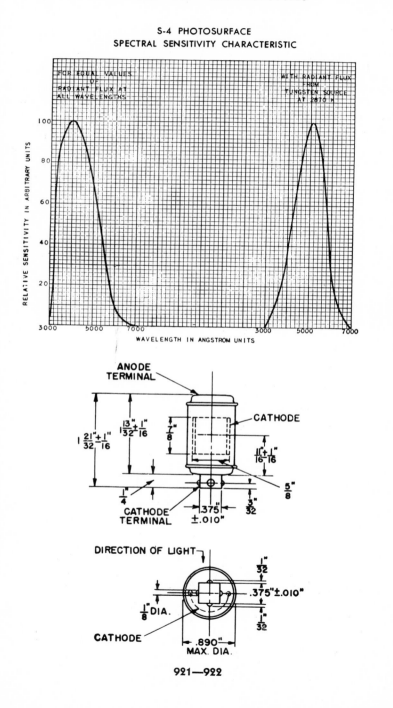

921—922

921

Maximum Ratings:

Anode voltage, d-c or peak a-c...................... 90 v
Cathode current density............................ 152 μa per sq in.

Electrical Data:

Spectral response.................................. S-1
Luminous sensitivity at 90 v, 0 cycles................. 135 μa per lm
Maximum gas amplification.......................... 10
Interelectrode capacitance.......................... 1.0 μμf
Maximum dark current at 90 v....................... 0.1 μa
Wavelength of maximum response..................... 8000 A
Sensitivity at maximum response..................... 0.013 μa per μw

922

Maximum Ratings:

Anode voltage, d-c or peak a-c...................... 500 v
Cathode current density............................ 152 μa per sq in.

Electrical Data:

Spectral response.................................. S-1
Luminous sensitivity at 250 v, 0 cycles............... 20 μa per lm
Interelectrode capacitance.......................... 0.5 μμf
Wavelength of maximum response..................... 8000 A
Sensitivity at maximum response..................... 0.0020 μa per μw

929

Maximum Ratings:

Anode voltage (d-c or peak a-c).................... 250 max v
Averaging time.................................... 30 max sec
Peak cathode — current density.................... 100 max μa per sq in.
Average cathode current........................... 5 max μa
    Averaging time 30 sec, maximum
Peak cathode current.............................. 20 max μa
Ambient temperature.............................. 75 max °C

Electrical Data:

	Minimum	Bogey	Maximum
Spectral response...			S-4
Luminous sensitivity at 250 v, 0 cycles..	25	45	70 μa per lm

Relative luminous sensitivity at 250 v			
10,000 cycles..................		100	per cent
Wavelength of maximum response.....	3500	4000	4500 A
Sensitivity at maximum response......		0.037	μa per μf
Leakage resistance...................	20000		meg
Gas amplification factor..............		1.25	
Interelectrode capacitance...........		2.6	$\mu\mu$f

930

Maximum Ratings:

Anode voltage (d-c or peak a-c)	
Average cathode current 3 μa..............	90 max v
Average cathode 6 μa.....................	70 max v
Averaging time...............................	30 max sec
Average cathode — current density	
Below 70 v...............................	10.0 max μa per sq in.
Above 70 v...............................	5 max μa per sq in.
Peak cathode current.........................	20 max μa

Electrical Data:

	Minimum	*Bogey*	*Maximum*
Spectral response..			S-1
Luminous sensitivity at 90 v, 0 cycles...	90	135	205 μa per lm
Relative luminous sensitivity at 90 v			
10,000 cycles..................		75	per cent
Wavelength of maximum response.....	7000	8000	9000 A
Sensitivity at maximum response......		0.0135	μa per μw
Leakage resistance...................	900		meg
Gas amplification factor..............			10
Interelectrode capacitance...........		2.4	$\mu\mu$f

2N146 N-P-N GROWN JUNCTION GERMANIUM TRANSISTOR*

Absolute Maximum Ratings at 25°C Ambient:

Collector voltage referred to emitter........................ 20 v
Collector current... 5 ma
Collector dissipation..................................... 65 mw
Junction temperature rise/mw............................. 0.7 °C/mw
Maximum operating temperature........................... 75 °C

Typical Design Characteristics (V_c = 9v, I_c = 0.5ma:

		Design Center
Collector cutoff current	I_{co}	0.2 μa
Common emitter input impedance	Z_{in}	1200 ohms
Common emitter output impedance	Z_{out}	100,000 ohms
Output cap. referred to base at 1mc	C_{ob}	1 $\mu\mu$f
Output cap. referred to emitter at 455kc	C_{oe}	6 $\mu\mu$f
Input cap. referred to emitter at 455kc	C_{ie}	200 $\mu\mu$f
Power cain at 455kc (in test circuit)	A_p	35 db

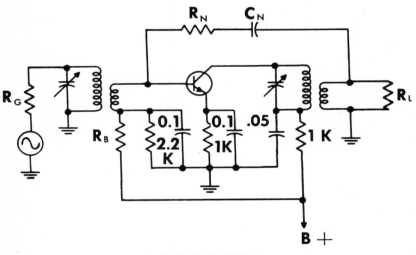

R₈ ADJUSTED FOR PROPER I𝒸

*Courtesy of Texas Instruments, Inc.

Notes:

1. C_N and R_N are determined by circuit configuration and transformer design. Their values should be chosen to minimize the internal feedback of the transistor.   For any particular circuit, fixed values may be used.

2. Generator impedance, R_G, must reflect an impedance of 1200 ohms at the transistor input (base to ground).

3. Load impedance, R_L, must reflect an impedance of 100,000 ohms at the transistor output (collector to ground).

4. Power gain is transistor gain only and is equal to: (power delivered to 100,000 ohms collector load)/(maximum available power from 1200 ohms source).

5. Base bias resistor, R_B, is chosen to give proper range of I_c.   Typical value is 15,000 ohms.

2N291 P-N-P ALLOYED JUNCTION GERMANIUM TRANSISTOR*

Class A Output:

Collector supply... −9 v
Power output.. 50 mw
Frequency.. 1000 cps
R_L, collector load.................................... 500 ohms
Driving impedance...................................... 400 ohms
Average distortion...................................... 6 per cent
Power gain — Minimum................................. 31 db
            — Design center............................ 33 db

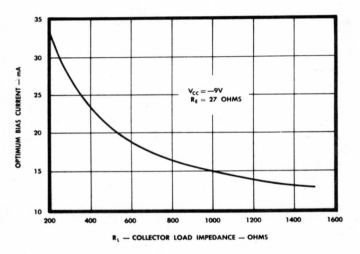

OPTIMUM BIAS CURRENT FOR MINIMUM DISTORTION VS. COLLECTOR LOAD

Class B Output:

Collector supply... −12 v
Power output.. 0.5 w
Frequency.. 1000 cps
R_L, load — collector to collector..................... 500 ohms
Input impedance.. 1000 ohms
Average distortion...................................... 5 per cent
Power gain — Minimum................................. 22 db
            — Design center............................ 24 db

*Courtesy of Texas Instruments, Inc.

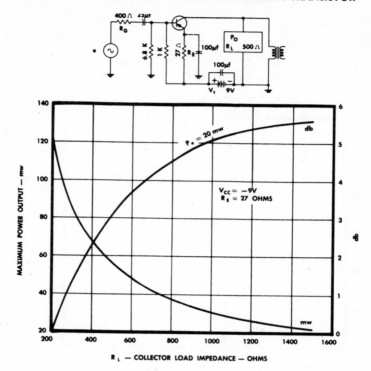

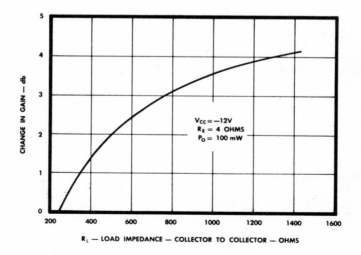

MAXIMUM POWER AND CHANGE IN GAIN VS. COLLECTOR LOAD IMPEDANCE
(BIAS OPTIMIZED FOR LOW DISTORTION)

$V_{CC} = -12V$
$R_E = 4$ OHMS
$P_O = 100$ mW

R_L — LOAD IMPEDANCE — COLLECTOR TO COLLECTOR — OHMS

CHANGE IN GAIN VS. LOAD IMPEDANCE

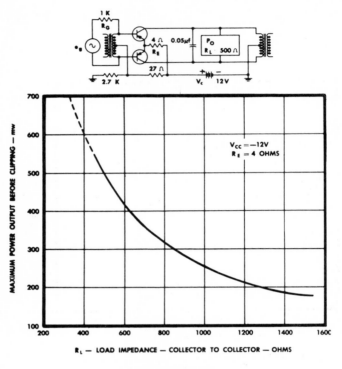

MAXIMUM POWER OUTPUT BEFORE CLIPPING VS. LOAD IMPEDANCE

Absolute Maximum Ratings at 25°C Ambient:

Collector voltage......................................	-25 v
D-c supply voltage (for inductive load)..................	-12 v
Collector current......................................	-200 ma
Device dissipation (free air)...........................	180 mw
Junction temp rise/mw (free air)........................	0.25 °C/mw
Device dissipation (infinite heat sink)..................	300 mw
Junction temp rise/mw (infinite heat sink)..............	0.125 °C/mw
Maximum operating temperature.........................	50 °C

Typical Design Characteristics at 25°C Ambient:

Collector cutoff current	I_{co}	$(V_{cb} = -25\text{v},\ I_E = 0)$	$-10\ \mu\text{a}$
Beta at 60 cps	h_{fe}	$(V_{ce} = -0.5\text{v},\ I_C = -100\ \text{ma})$	45

2N364 N-P-N GROWN JUNCTION GERMANIUM TRANSISTOR*

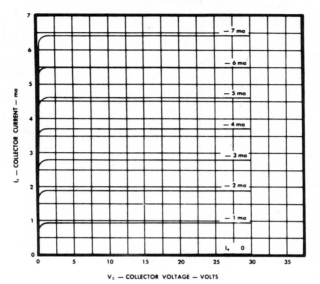

COMMON BASE OUTPUT CHARACTERISTICS

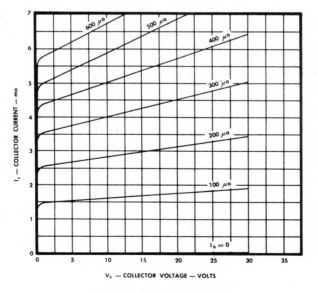

COMMON EMITTER OUTPUT CHARACTERISTICS

*Courtesy of Texas Instruments, Inc.

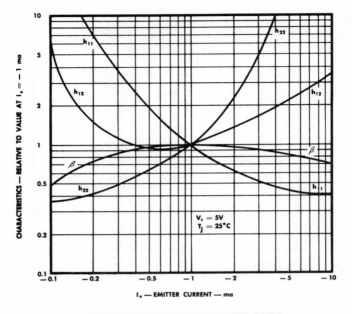

COMMON EMITTER CHARACTERISTICS VS. EMITTER CURRENT

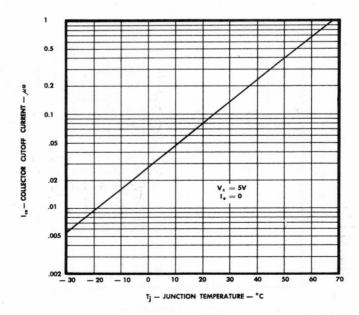

COLLECTOR CUTOFF CURRENT VS. JUNCTION TEMPERATURE

Absolute Maximum Ratings at 25°C Ambient:

Collector voltage referred to base.........................	30 v
Emitter voltage referred to base..........................	2 v
Collector current..	50 ma
Emitter current...	−50 ma
Device dissipation (free air).............................	150 mw
Junction temperature rise/mw (free air)...................	0.5 °C/mw

Common Base Design Characteristics at $T_j = 25°C$:

				Design Center
Collector cutoff current	I_{co}	$V_c = 30v$	$I_e = 0$	1 μa
Collector cutoff current	I_{co}	$V_c = 5v$	$I_e = 0$	0.1 μa
Input impedance	h_{ib}	$V_c = 5v$	$I_e = -1$ma	55 ohms
Output admittance	h_{ob}	$V_c = 5v$	$I_e = -1$ma	0.1 μmhos
Feedback voltage ratio	h_{rb}	$V_c = 5v$	$I_e = -1$ma	90 X10^{-6}
Current transfer ratio	h_{fb}	$V_c = 5v$	$I_e = -1$ma	0.925
Beta, common emitter	β	$V_c = 5v$	$I_e = -1$ma	12
Noise figure, common emitter	NF	$V_c = 5v$	$I_e = -1$ma	12 db
Frequency cutoff	F_{co}	$V_c = 5v$	$I_e = -1$ma	2.5 mc
Output capacitance	C_{ob}	$f = 1$mc	$I_e = -1$ma	4.5 $\mu\mu$f

2N366 N-P-N GROWN JUNCTION GERMANIUM TRANSISTOR*

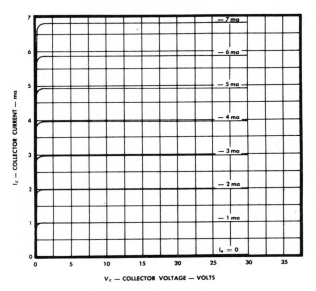

COMMON BASE OUTPUT CHARACTERISTICS

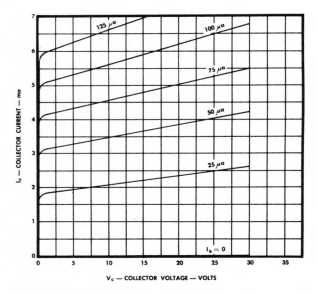

COMMON EMITTER OUTPUT CHARACTERISTICS

*Courtesy of Texas Instruments, Inc.

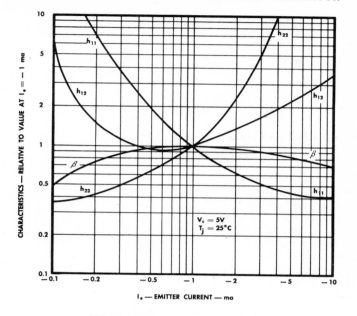

COMMON EMITTER CHARACTERISTICS VS. EMITTER CURRENT

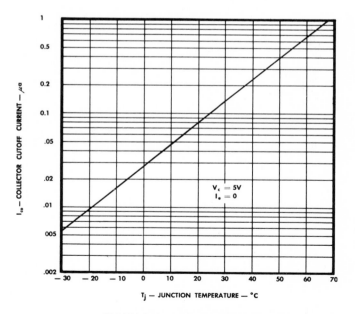

COLLECTOR CUTOFF CURRENT VS. JUNCTION TEMPERATURE

Absolute Maximum Ratings at 25°C Ambient:

Collector voltage referred to base............................	30 v
Emitter voltage referred to base............................	2 v
Collector current..	50 ma
Emitter current...	−50 ma
Device dissipation (free air)...............................	150 mw
Junction temperature rise/mw (free air)...................	0.5 °C/mw

Common Base Design Characteristics at T_j = 25°C:

				Design Center
Collector cutoff current	I_{co}	$V_c = 30v$	$I_e = 0$	1 μa
Collector cutoff current	I_{co}	$V_c = 5v$	$I_e = 0$	0.1 μa
Input impedance	h_{ib}	$V_c = 5v$	$I_e = -1$ma	55 ohms
Output admittance	h_{ob}	$V_c = 5v$	$I_e = -1$ma	0.1 μmhos
Feedback voltage ratio	h_{rb}	$V_c = 5v$	$I_e = -1$ma	90 X10^{-6}
Current transfer ratio	h_{fb}	$V_c = 5v$	$I_e = -1$ma	0.985
Beta, common emitter	β	$V_c = 5v$	$I_e = -1$ma	65
Noise fig., common emitter	NF	$V_c = 5v$	$I_e = -1$ma	9 db
Frequency cutoff	F_{co}	$V_c = 5v$	$I_e = -1$ma	3.5 mc
Output capacitance	C_{ob}	$f = 1$mc	$I_e = -1$ma	4.5 $\mu\mu$f

2N369 P-N-P ALLOYED JUNCTION GERMANIUM TRANSISTOR*

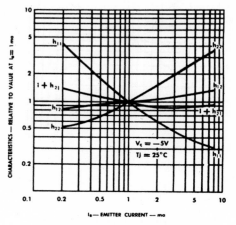

COMMON BASE CHARACTERISTICS VS EMITTER CURRENT

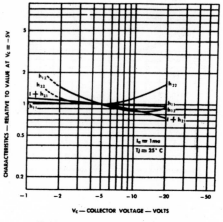

COMMON BASE CHARACTERISTICS VS COLLECTOR VOLTAGE

*Courtesy of Texas Instruments, Inc.

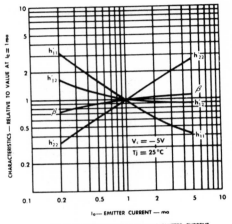

COMMON EMITTER CHARACTERISTICS VS EMITTER CURRENT

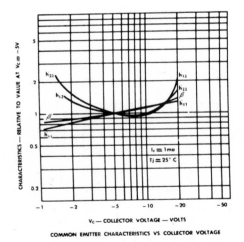

COMMON EMITTER CHARACTERISTICS VS COLLECTOR VOLTAGE

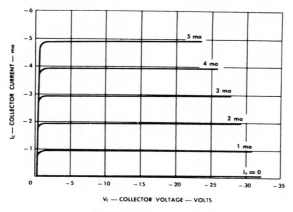

COMMON BASE OUTPUT CHARACTERISTICS

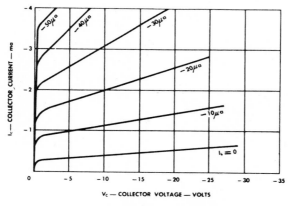

COMMON EMITTER OUTPUT CHARACTERISTICS

Absolute Maximum Ratings at 25°C Ambient:

Collector voltage referred to base	-30 v
Emitter voltage referred to base	-10 v
Collector current	-50 ma
Emitter current	50 ma
Device dissipation (free air)	100 mw
Junction temp rise/mw (free air)	0.5 °C/mw
Device dissipation (infinite heat sink)	150 mw
Junction temp rise/mw (infinite heat sink)	0.33 °C/mw

Common Base Design Characteristics at $T_j = 25$°C:

				Design Center
Collector cutoff current	I_{co}	$V_c = -30$v	$I_e = 0$	8 μa
Collector cutoff current	I_{co}	$V_c = -5$v	$I_e = 0$	5 μa
Input impedance	h_{ib}	$V_c = -5$v	$I_e = 1$ma	30 ohms
Output admittance	h_{ob}	$V_c = -5$v	$I_e = 1$ma	0.47 μmhos
Feedback voltage ratio	h_{rb}	$V_c = -5$v	$I_e = 1$ma	830 X10^{-6}
Current transfer ratio	h_{fb}	$V_c = -5$v	$I_e = 1$ma	0.982
Beta, common emitter	β	$V_c = -5$v	$I_e = 1$ma	55
Noise fig., common emitter	NF	$V_c = -2.5$v	$I_e = 0.5$ma	20 db
Frequency cutoff	F_{co}	$V_c = -5$v	$I_e = 1$ma	1.3 mc
Output capacitance	C_{ob}	$f = 10$kc		33 $\mu\mu$f